FUNCTIONS OF A
COMPLEX VARIABLE
and some of their applications

Volume I

ADDIWES INTERNATIONAL SERIES

IN MATHEMATICS

A. J. Lohwater, Consulting Editor

FUNCTIONS OF A
COMPLEX VARIABLE
and some of their applications

Volume I

by

B. A. FUCHS   and   B. V. SHABAT

Original translation by
J. BERRY

Revised and Expanded by
J. W. REED
Mathematics Department,
Royal Holloway College,
University of London

PERGAMON PRESS
OXFORD · LONDON · NEW YORK · PARIS

1964

ADDISON-WESLEY PUBLISHING COMPANY, INC.
Reading, Massachusetts

517.8
F961
v.1

Sole distributors in the U.S.A.

ADDISON-WESLEY PUBLISHING COMPANY, INC.

Reading, Massachusetts · Palo Alto · London

PERGAMON PRESS
International Series of Monographs on
Pure and Applied Mathematics

Volume
51

This translation has been made from the Russian 2nd Edition
*Funktsii kompleksnogo peremennogo i ngkotoryye ikh prilozheniya
Spetsial'nyye glavy*

Published in the U.S.S.R. by Fizmatgiz, Moscow, 1959

Library of Congress Catalog No. 61–14931

Set in Modern No. 7, 10 on 12 pt. and printed in Great Britain by
J. W. ARROWSMITH LTD., Bristol

CONTENTS

FROM THE FOREWORD TO THE FIRST EDITION

THIS book is intended for undergraduate and postgraduate students of higher technical institutes and for engineers wishing to increase their knowledge of theory. The aim influenced the manner of presentation: the authors decided against a "theorem-proof" sequence, but at the same time considered it inadvisable to transform the book into a work of reference.

Considerable attention is paid to the fundamental ideas of the theory of functions of a complex variable; on those occasions when the proof of a theorem is omitted the authors have tried to illustrate, by means of examples, the significance of the assumptions and the conclusion. The authors also attach great importance to the development of skill in the practical application of the methods described; for this reason many examples are included in the text and a set of exercises appears at the end of each chapter. These exercises are provided with answers, and hints for solution are given for some. The authors stress that the independent solution of these problems is essential if a real mastery of the methods of function theory is to be attained (exercises marked * may be regarded as optional).

For readers who cannot study the book in its entirety the authors indicate the following three ways of making a partial study. The first method (giving an introduction to the theory of functions) includes the Introduction, Chapter I (omitting Art. 9), Chapter II (omitting Art. 17), Arts. 24–25 and 29–31 of Chapter III, Arts. 46–53 of Chapter V, and Arts. 58–61, 64–67, and 69 of Chapter VI; attention may also be directed to selected illustrative examples from Chapters IV and VII.

A second course (for students interested in the analytical theory only—for example, those wishing to proceed to a study of the operational calculus) would consist of Chapter II (omitting Arts. 18–23), the definitions of the elementary functions in Chapter III (Arts. 29–31), Arts. 34–37 of Chapter IV, Chapter V (omitting Arts. 55–57), and Chapter VI (omitting Art. 70); Chapter VII should be studied in its entirety, Chapter VIII may be omitted.

The third variant would suit those interested only in conformal transformations and their applications; here it would be possible to omit Arts. 54–57 of Chapter V, Arts. 66–68 of Chapter VI, and the whole of Chapter VII.

We shall dwell on certain peculiarities in our treatment (here we are addressing ourselves primarily to teachers who might recommend this book to their pupils). The Introduction surveys arithmetical operations with complex numbers; the authors have abandoned the method of introducing complex numbers usually adopted in the middle school since that method leads the pupil to regard complex numbers as being literally "imaginary"; in this book, complex numbers are defined as vectors, or points of a plane, on which certain defined operations can be performed. The authors recognize the imperfections of this approach; however, they consider it the most appropriate for the purposes of this book since it would make considerable demands on the reader if these numbers were introduced as the elements of an abstract algebraic field having certain properties.

Chapter I expounds the fundamentals of complex analysis. As the authors desire to impart concrete ideas to their readers the function concept is introduced simultaneously with that of the corresponding transformation. Other basic concepts are also treated geometrically. The treatment emphasizes that the point at infinity on the sphere of complex numbers plays a part which is of equal importance to that played by the finite points.

In view of its special importance, the concept of conformal transformations is made the subject of a complete chapter (Chapter II). An account of fundamental definitions and theorems is followed by a detailed study of the bilinear transformation. Acquaintance with the properties of these transformations should prepare the reader for the account, given in the final article of this chapter, of the general principles of the theory of conformal transformations.

Chapter III introduces the most important of the elementary functions. Here the authors have tried to explain geometrically the procedures for separating the regular (single-valued) branches of many-valued functions. The discussion is, naturally, restricted to particular functions; the idea of the general many-valued analytic function and its regular branches is introduced in Chapter VI. An important aim of this chapter (and the Exercises following it) is the development of the reader's skill in selecting elementary functions which accomplish the required conformal mappings of given domains.

Chapter IV is concerned with the complex potential for a plane vector field and with the application of the simplest methods of function theory to the analysis of such a field. As this is the stage at which problems of an applied character make their first appearance the authors have thought it advisable to give an introductory account of the theory of plane fields before proceeding to the solution of these problems; also, the authors feel that a unified treatment of the complex potentials of the most important plane fields will assist the reader in applying function–theoretic methods to technical problems. In later chapters applied problems usually appear as illustrative examples following the exposition of mathematical methods.

An account of the fundamental apparatus of the theory of regular functions is given in Chapters V and VI: Chapter V deals with basic integral theorems, Chapter VI with expansions in series. Chapter VI also introduces the general concept of an analytic function as the set of all possible analytic continuations of a given regular function-element.

Chapters VII and VIII are devoted to applications of the theory—analytic applications in Chapter VII and geometric in Chapter VIII. The first of these chapters depends mainly on the theory of residues and contains numerous worked examples illustrating general methods for evaluating definite integrals; the authors considered it inadvisable to set up special lemmas for the evaluation of particular types of integral (a procedure which might well be followed in certain other courses) and recommend that the student base each evaluation on general principles. The same chapter contains examples illustrating the representation of functions by contour integrals; it is hoped that these will assist the reader when he proceeds to the study of the operational calculus.

B. A. FUCHS
B. V. SHABAT

FOREWORD TO THE ENGLISH EDITION

THIS book results from a complete rewriting and revision of a translation of the second (1957) Russian edition. The original was often rather condensed in presentation and contained a large number of errors and misprints. Accordingly, I have made numerous changes and additions, both in the text and in the solutions of the Exercises. It would be difficult to indicate all these additions since nearly every article has been extended in some measure; typical of the changes made are the expanded account of the complex curvilinear integral in Art. 46, the alternative proof of the maximum-modulus principle sketched in Art. 53, the counter-example at the end of Art. 56 and the tightening of the argument in Arts. 77 to 80. My main contribution, perhaps, has been the provision of a rigorous proof, in Art. 85, of the extension of the Schwarz–Christoffel formula covering the important cases of zero and non-zero angles at a vertex at infinity (the heuristic discussion given in the Russian edition was incomplete and could not easily be made into a strict proof); it is hoped that this will fill a gap in the literature: most of the standard texts give examples concerning these cases, but none, it appears, gives general proofs of the required extensions. References to standard texts in English have been added at appropriate points. This said, it must be remarked that the book remains essentially that written by Fuchs and Shabat.

The authors have produced an unusual and skilful synthesis of topics from pure and applied mathematics. A sound, useful account of analytic function theory is given in Chapters V, VI and VII, the field covered corresponding roughly with the content of the usual honours degree course; features of interest are the introductory account of harmonic functions and Dirichlet's problem in Arts. 54–57 and the excellent collection of worked examples in Arts. 72–75. As an introduction to the theory *and* application of conformal mappings the book is outstanding: I know of no other text which can match the account of elementary mappings given in Chapters II and III, and the discussion of the four main types of plane potential problem in Chapter IV. To anyone who has lectured on the topics discussed in Chapter VIII, it will be clear that in, Arts. 82 to 88, the authors have made a valuable contribution to the teaching

literature; here, again, it is fair to claim that no other text to
date can match the combination of theory and application appearing in the accounts of the Schwarz reflection principle and the
Schwarz–Christoffel formula. The wealth of worked examples
makes the book specially useful to the student who must work on
his own.

Certain standard notational conventions have been adopted:
square brackets are used to denote closed intervals, round brackets
to denote open intervals; and e^z denotes $\exp(z)$. Brackets have also
been used to represent line segments in the complex plane: for
example, $[-i, 1+i]$ denotes the *closed* line segment joining the
points $-i$ and $1+i$. It should be noted that symbols such as Arg z,
Log z are used to denote, not only the corresponding multi-valued
functions, but also, on occasion, particular branches of these functions differing (usually) from the corresponding principal branches.

In conclusion I wish to thank two of my pupils, Miss M. Lewis
and Miss P. Tayler, for considerable help in checking text and
solutions.

J. W. REED

INTRODUCTION

1. Complex numbers

The reader will have met complex numbers in his course on elementary algebra. Usually, in such courses, complex numbers are introduced through the equation $x^2+1 = 0$: first it is shown that no real number satisfies this equation; then a new "imaginary" number $i = \sqrt{(-1)}$ is introduced, and the equation becomes solvable, its roots being $+i$ and $-i$; "complex" numbers $x+iy$ then appear as the sums of real numbers x and "imaginary" numbers iy. The rules given for manipulating these new numbers express the possibility of performing arithmetical operations with them in the same way as for real numbers, i^2 being replaced by -1 in the final results. After these new numbers have been introduced it is shown that all quadratic equations

$$x^2+px+q = 0$$

and, more generally, all equations of the form

$$x^n+p_1x^{n-1}+p_2x^{n-2}+ \ldots +p_n = 0,$$

the coefficients being arbitrary, can be solved.

This method of introducing complex numbers is unsatisfactory because it presents them as entities having no real existence, entities which are literally "imaginary". Accordingly, we shall follow a different path.

We consider a system of free vectors lying in a plane. (A system of vectors is said to be *free* when any two vectors are considered *identical* if it is possible to bring one into complete coincidence with the other by means of a parallel translation.) In the following sections (Arts. 2, 3 and 4) we introduce certain operations on the vectors of our system. These operations fall into two groups. The first group (Art. 2) contains addition, subtraction, and multiplication by real numbers (scalars), operations which are carried out just as in ordinary vector algebra. On the other hand, the operations of the second group draw a sharp distinction between our new algebra and ordinary vector algebra. In the latter, two distinct products (scalar product and vector product) are introduced, but neither completely satisfies the laws of arithmetic of real numbers. For example, neither of these operations permits inversion: "scalar division" and "vector division" are not defined. In the following articles, however, the reader will see that for plane systems of vectors it is possible to introduce products and quotients (Art. 3) and powers and roots (Art. 4) in such a way as to preserve the fundamental laws of arithmetic of real numbers; the corresponding operations form the second group mentioned above. On the basis of the two groups of operations described, a plane system of vectors can be considered as a new kind of number system, the numbers being called complex numbers.

Thus, *by a set of complex numbers we shall understand a plane system of free vectors on which operations are performed according to the rules indicated in Arts. 2, 3 and 4.*

The proposed method of introducing complex numbers is free of the defects mentioned at the beginning of this article. Another point in its favour is that vector quantities are often considered in applied problems; the adaptability of our new algebra to the solution of such problems will be seen in Art. 9, in Chapter IV, and in other parts of the book.

We call the plane containing our free vectors the plane of complex numbers. As our vectors are free we take a given point O in the plane as their common base point. Then, any vector (complex number) $z = \overline{OP}$ is defined by the position of its end point P; conversely, any point P of the plane is uniquely determined by the vector (complex number) $z = \overline{OP}$. Thus we establish a one–one correspondence between complex numbers and the points of the plane. (The point O itself corresponds with the null vector; that is, with the complex number 0.) This justifies the dual representation of a complex number as a *vector* and as a *point of the plane*. In what follows we speak of the "point" z as often as of the "vector" z.

2. The simplest operations

Definition. The *sum* and *difference* of the complex numbers z_1 and z_2 are given, as shown in Fig. 1, by the diagonals of the parallelogram having the vectors z_1, z_2 as adjacent sides.

In other words, the sum $z_1 + z_2$ is represented by the line segment closing the two-bar linkage formed by drawing the vectors z_1 and

z_2 consecutively, and the difference $z_1 - z_2$ is equal to the vector joining the point z_2 to the point z_1. The idea of a sum is extended in the obvious way to the case of n terms $(n > 2)$.

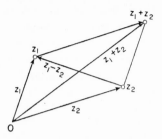

FIG. 1

Definition. The *product* kz of the real number k and the complex number z ($z \neq 0$, $k \neq 0$) is defined as the vector whose length is $|k|$ times the length of z and whose direction is parallel or antiparallel to that of z according as $k > 0$ or $k < 0$; if either $k = 0$ or $z = 0$, kz is defined as the null vector (complex number 0). (See Fig. 2, where the numbers z, $2z$, $\frac{1}{2}z$ and $-z$ are represented.)

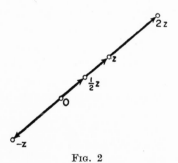

FIG. 2

It is shown in any textbook on vector algebra that the operations introduced here have the ordinary arithmetical properties.

We take rectangular Cartesian axes Oxy in the complex number plane, with origin at the point O (see Art. 1), and denote by 1 and i the unit vectors along the coordinate axes Ox and Oy. The representaion of an arbitrary vector (complex number) z in terms of its (signed) projections x, y (see Fig. 3) follows from our definitions as in ordinary vector analysis: $z = x1 + yi$. This relation is written

$$z = x + iy \qquad (1)$$

and expresses the *Cartesian form* of the complex number z. We call 1 and i the *real* and *imaginary units*; correspondingly, Ox, Oy are the *real* and *imaginary axes*. The projections x and y are called the *real* and *imaginary parts* of the complex number z and we write

$$x = \operatorname{Re} z, \qquad y = \operatorname{Im} z. \qquad (2)$$

If the end point of the vector z (with base point at 0) lies on the real axis, we identify the corresponding complex number $z = x + 0i$ with the real number x giving the abscissa of the end point. In this way the set of complex numbers is made to include all real numbers. If the end point lies on the imaginary axis we say the corresponding complex number $z = 0 + iy$ is *imaginary* and write $z = iy$.

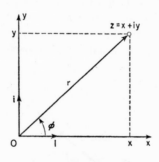

FIG. 3

By the *equality* of complex numbers is understood equality of the corresponding vectors (see Art. 1). It is easy to express equality in terms of coordinates: two complex numbers $z_1 = x_1 + iy_1$ and $z_2 = x_2 + iy_2$ are equal to one another if, and only if,

$$x_1 = x_2, \qquad y_1 = y_2. \qquad (3)$$

Thus, *one* equality between complex numbers implies *two* equalities between real numbers.

We shall also speak of *conjugate* complex numbers: $z_2 = x_2 + iy_2$ is said to be conjugate to $z_1 = x_1 + iy_1$ if

$$x_2 = x_1, \qquad y_2 = -y_1, \qquad (4)$$

and we then write $z_2 = \bar{z}_1$ or $\bar{z}_2 = z_1$. The number $\bar{z}_1$ is represented by the point symmetrical with the point z_1 with respect to the real axis Ox.

Addition (subtraction) of complex numbers clearly reduces to the addition (subtraction) of their real and imaginary parts: if $z_1 = x_1 + iy_1$, $z_2 = x_2 + iy_2$ then

$$z = z_1 \pm z_2 = (x_1 \pm x_2) + i(y_1 \pm y_2). \tag{5}$$

The product $kz \,(= zk)$ of the complex number $z = x + iy$ and the real number k is obtained by multiplying the real and imaginary parts of z by k:

$$z_1 = kz = kx + iky. \tag{6}$$

An alternative to the Cartesian form (1), the representation in *polar* coordinates, is often useful. We take the pole at the origin O of the Cartesian axes and the polar axis along the positive Ox axis. Let r, ϕ denote the polar coordinates of the point $z = x + iy$ ($\neq 0$) (see Fig. 3). The positive sense of rotation of the radius vector is chosen so that points of the positive Oy axis correspond with the value $\frac{1}{2}\pi$ of ϕ. (As usual, our diagrams are drawn so that this positive sense of rotation is *counter-clockwise*.) Then,

$$x = r\cos\phi, \qquad y = r\sin\phi, \tag{7}$$

and (1) becomes

$$z = x + iy = r(\cos\phi + i\sin\phi). \tag{8}$$

The relation (8) gives what is called the *trigonometrical form* of the complex number z. The quantities r and ϕ are called the *modulus* and *argument* of z and are denoted by

$$r = |z|, \qquad \phi = \text{Arg } z. \tag{9}$$

It will be clear that the point z coincides with O (that is, $z = 0$) if, and only if, $r = |z| = 0$. In this case the angle coordinate ϕ is not defined. However, $r(\cos\phi + i\sin\phi) = 0$ for *all* values of ϕ when $r = 0$. To avoid special discussion of trivial degenerate cases in the definition of a product in Art. 3 we may suppose that a zero factor is expressed in the form $z = 0(\cos\phi + i\sin\phi)$, where ϕ is an arbitrary real number.

We note that, while the Cartesian coordinates of a complex number are determined uniquely, there is a certain ambiguity for polar coordinates. Although

$$r = |z| = \sqrt{(x^2+y^2)} \tag{10}$$

(where $\sqrt{}$ denotes the non-negative root) is a single-valued function of x and y, the function $\phi = \text{Arg } z$ $(z \neq 0)$ is many-valued and has an infinite number of values differing from one another by arbitrary (integral) multiples of 2π. For example, the point $z = i$ on the positive Oy axis corresponds not only with the value $\phi = \pi/2$ but also with the value $\phi = -3\pi/2$ obtained by supposing the radius vector to have rotated in the negative sense from an initial position along the polar axis. The general value of $\text{Arg } i$ is $\frac{1}{2}\pi + 2k\pi$, where k is any integer; the set of these values corresponds with the angles obtained from the angle $\frac{1}{2}\pi$ by the addition of complete rotations, in either sense, about the point 0. We repeat that $\text{Arg } z$ is not defined for $z = 0$.

For given $z \neq 0$ there is *exactly one* value (θ, say) of $\text{Arg } z$ in the interval $(-\pi, \pi]$; that is, such that $-\pi < \theta \leqslant \pi$. We denote this value by arg z. The single-valued function of z thus defined is called the *principal branch of the argument of z*. (Subsequently we sometimes use a different notation; on each such occasion we specify the particular branch of the argument under consideration.)

From the definition,

$$-\pi < \arg z \leqslant \pi. \tag{11}$$

By (7), $\tan(\arg z) = y/x$ for $x \neq 0$. It follows from (11) that

$$\left.\begin{aligned}
\arg z &= \text{arc tan}(y/x) \quad \text{for } x > 0, \\
\arg z &= \pi + \text{arc tan}(y/x) \quad \text{for } x < 0, y \geqslant 0, \\
\arg z &= -\pi + \text{arc tan}(y/x) \text{ for } x < 0, y < 0.
\end{aligned}\right\} \tag{12}$$

The results

$$\left.\begin{aligned}
\arg z &= \tfrac{1}{2}\pi \quad \text{for } x = 0, y > 0, \\
\arg z &= -\tfrac{1}{2}\pi \quad \text{for } x = 0, y < 0
\end{aligned}\right\} \tag{13}$$

are immediate consequences of the definition of arg z.

We note that the principal branch of $\text{Arg } z$ is discontinuous along the negative real axis: as z approaches a point of this semi-axis from above, arg z tends to π; as z approaches the same point from below, arg z tends to $-\pi$. At the remaining points of the plane (excluding $z = 0$) arg z is continuous. (Continuity and limits are discussed in Art. 8.)

From the definitions of the functions Arg z and arg z we have

$$\text{Arg } z = \arg z + 2k\pi, \tag{14}$$

where k is an arbitrary integer.

Expressed in polar coordinates, the conditions for the equality of two non-zero complex numbers z_1 and z_2 are

$$|z_1| = |z_2|, \quad \arg z_1 = \arg z_2. \tag{15}$$

If $z_1 = z_2 \ (\neq 0)$ the difference of any two particular values of Arg z_1 and Arg z_2 must be of the form $2k\pi$ where k is an integer. Accordingly the second equation (15) can be replaced by

$$\text{Arg } z_1 = \text{Arg } z_2 + 2k\pi, \tag{15'}$$

k denoting an arbitrary integer.

The corresponding relations between conjugate numbers z, $\bar{z}$ are

$$|z| = |\bar{z}|, \quad \arg z = -\arg \bar{z} \quad (z \neq 0, \arg z \neq \pi). \tag{16}$$

If z lies on the negative real axis it coincides with $\bar{z}$ and we then have $\arg z = \arg \bar{z} = \pi$. For *all* real values of r and ϕ the conjugate of $z = r(\cos\phi + i\sin\phi)$ is

$$\bar{z} = r[\cos(-\phi) + i\sin(-\phi)] = r(\cos\phi - i\sin\phi).$$

The Cartesian form of $z_1 + z_2$ follows immediately from the Cartesian forms of z_1 and z_2; in general, however, the polar forms of z_1, z_2 do not lead readily to the polar form of $z_1 \pm z_2$. By the elementary triangle inequality it follows from Fig. 1 that

$$|z_1 + z_2| \leqslant |z_1| + |z_2|, \quad |z_1 - z_2| \geqslant \big||z_1| - |z_2|\big|, \tag{17}$$

the signs of equality holding if $\arg z_1 = \arg z_2$ or if either (or each) of the numbers z_1, z_2 is zero.

We conclude this article with examples showing how complex numbers can be used to express certain geometrical loci in the plane.

Examples: 1. It is easy to find the conditions which are necessary and sufficient in order that a point z should be inside, on, or outside the circle with radius r and centre at a given point a of the plane; these are, respectively,

$$|z-a| < r, \quad |z-a| = r, \quad |z-a| > r.$$

The corresponding loci are represented by these relations. In the same way the inequalities

$$r \leqslant |z-a| < R$$

represent the annulus between concentric circles of radii r and R centred at the point a, the inner boundary being included, the outer excluded.

2. The equation

$$\arg z = \alpha$$

represents the ray drawn from the origin at an angle α to the positive real axis; the inequalities

$$\alpha < \arg z < \beta$$

represent the infinite sector between the rays $\arg z = \alpha$, $\arg z = \beta$, the rays themselves being excluded.

3. Each of the equations

$$\operatorname{Re} z = \alpha, \qquad \operatorname{Im} z = \beta$$

represents a line parallel to one of the axes; the inequalities

$$\alpha \leqslant \operatorname{Re} z \leqslant \beta$$

represent a vertical strip, including its boundary lines; the inequalities

$$\alpha \leqslant \operatorname{Re} z \leqslant \beta, \qquad |\operatorname{Im} z| \leqslant \gamma$$

represent the set of points inside and on a rectangle.

3. Multiplication, division, integral powers and roots

Definition. The *product* $z_1 z_2$ of complex numbers

$$z_1 = r_1(\cos \phi_1 + i \sin \phi_1), \qquad z_2 = r_2(\cos \phi_2 + i \sin \phi_2)$$

is

$$z = z_1 z_2 = r_1 r_2 [\cos(\phi_1 + \phi_2) + i \sin(\phi_1 + \phi_2)]. \tag{18}$$

(We recall that if, say, $z_2 = 0$ then $r_2 = 0$ and ϕ_2 may be chosen arbitrarily. Clearly, the product vanishes if either factor vanishes.)

The product of two complex numbers is thus given by multiplying their moduli and adding their arguments. For the latter step any particular values (ϕ_1, ϕ_2, say) of $\operatorname{Arg} z_1$ and $\operatorname{Arg} z_2$ may be chosen; the particular value of $\operatorname{Arg} z$ then obtained is $\phi_1 + \phi_2$. These arguments will all be principal values only if ϕ_1, ϕ_2 and $\phi_1 + \phi_2$ all lie in the interval $(-\pi, \pi)$.

It is clear that if z_1 and z_2 are real, the definition (18) is equivalent to the ordinary rule for multiplication of real numbers.

Geometrically, the multiplication of a complex number z_1 by z_2 (z_1, $z_2 \neq 0$) is equivalent to a *magnification* of the vector z_1 by the factor $|z_2|$ followed by a *rotation* through an angle $\phi_2 = \mathrm{Arg}\, z_2$. (See Fig. 4: the triangles $O1z_1$, Oz_2z are similar.)

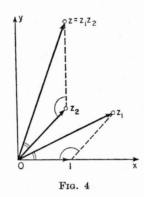

Fɪɢ. 4

It follows from our definition that the multiplication of complex numbers obeys the *commutative* and *associative* laws:

$$z_1 z_2 = z_2 z_1, \qquad z_1(z_2 z_3) = (z_1 z_2)z_3. \tag{19}$$

Examples: 1. If $z = r(\cos\phi + i \sin\phi)$ then

$$\bar{z} = r[\cos(-\phi) + i \sin(-\phi)]$$

and

$$z\bar{z} = r^2(\cos 0 + i \sin 0) = r^2.$$

Thus, the product of a complex number and its conjugate is the square of its modulus.

2. If $z_1 = z_2 = \cos(\pi/2) + i \sin(\pi/2) = i$, then

$$z_1 z_2 = ii = \cos\pi + i\sin\pi = -1; \tag{20}$$

that is, the product of the imaginary unit i with itself is -1.

We now express the product $z_1 z_2$ in terms of the Cartesian coordinates of z_1 and z_2. From the definition (18),

$$z_1 z_2 = r_1 r_2 \{\cos(\phi_1 + \phi_2) + i \sin(\phi_1 + \phi_2)\}$$
$$= r_1 r_2(\cos\phi_1 \cos\phi_2 - \sin\phi_1 \sin\phi_2) + ir_1 r_2(\sin\phi_1 \cos\phi_2 + \cos\phi_1 \sin\phi_2).$$

Recalling the relations (7) ($x_1 = r_1 \cos \phi_1$, $y_1 = r_1 \sin \phi_1$, etc.), we have

$$z_1 z_2 = (x_1 + iy_1)(x_2 + iy_2) = (x_1 x_2 - y_1 y_2) + i(x_1 y_2 + x_2 y_1). \qquad (21)$$

The second equality in (21) can be obtained by formally multiplying the bracketed terms on the left according to the rules of elementary algebra and then substituting -1 for ii (in accord with (20)). Using the form for product given by (21) it is easy to establish the distributive law

$$(z_1 + z_2)z = z_1 z + z_2 z. \qquad (22)$$

The idea of a product is extended in an obvious fashion to the case of n factors ($n > 2$).

As mentioned earlier, the product defined above is essentially different from the vector and scalar products of ordinary vector analysis; and therein lies the main difference between the algebra described here and ordinary vector algebra.

Definition. The *quotient* z_1/z_2 of the complex numbers

$$z_1 = r_1(\cos \phi_1 + i \sin \phi_1), \qquad z_2 = r_2(\cos \phi_2 + i \sin \phi_2) \neq 0$$

is

$$z = \frac{z_1}{z_2} = \frac{r_1}{r_2}[\cos(\phi_1 - \phi_2) + i \sin(\phi_1 - \phi_2)]. \qquad (23)$$

(As before, if $z_1 = 0$ then $r_1 = 0$ and ϕ_1 may be chosen arbitrarily; in this case, as $z_2 \neq 0$, the quotient vanishes.)

Thus, in dividing complex numbers we divide the modulus of the numerator by that of the denominator and subtract the argument of the denominator from that of the numerator. As before, any particular values ϕ_1, ϕ_2 of Arg z_1, Arg z_2 may be chosen. From the definition it follows that the operation of division is inverse to that of multiplication: if $z = z_1/z_2$ ($z_2 \neq 0$) then $zz_2 = z_1$. Division of z_1 by z_2 reduces to multiplication of z_1 by $1/z_2$.

We now give a geometrical construction for the reciprocal

$$w = 1/z \qquad (24)$$

of any given non-zero complex number z (see Fig. 5). Suppose first that $|z| \leqslant 1$. From the point z draw a perpendicular to the ray Oz to intersect the unit circle $|z| = 1$ at the point ω, and from ω draw the tangent to this circle to intersect the ray Oz at the point ζ.

(The points z, ω, ζ *coincide* if $|z| = 1$.) If $|z| > 1$ these steps are taken in reverse order. Suppose $|z| \neq 1$: the triangles $Oz\omega$, $O\omega\zeta$ are similar (they are right-angled and have a common angle), whence $Oz/O\omega = O\omega/O\zeta$; that is, $|z|/1 = 1/|\zeta|$. This last result also

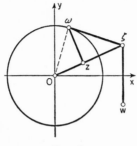

holds when $|z| = 1$. Thus, in all cases, $|\zeta| = 1/|z|$; as the arguments of z and ζ are equal,

$$\zeta = 1/\bar{z}. \qquad (25)$$

The passage from the point z to the point $\zeta = 1/\bar{z}$ is called *inversion* with respect to the unit circle, and each of the points z and ζ is called the *inverse*, or *image*, or *conjugate* of the other with respect to this circle. The required point w is the point symmetrical with ζ with respect to the axis Ox. For, then, $|w| = |\zeta| = 1/|z|$; and, in general, $\arg w = -\arg \zeta = -\arg z$. In the exceptional case, z and ζ lie on the negative real axis and each is its own conjugate; it then follows from (25) that $w = \zeta = 1/\bar{z} = 1/z$. Thus, in all cases, $w = 1/z$.

If

$$z_1 = r_1(\cos\phi + i\sin\phi_1), \quad z_2 = r_2(\cos\phi_2 + i\sin\phi_2) \neq 0,$$

it follows from definition (23) and formulae (11) and (7) that

$$z = \frac{z_1}{z_2} = \frac{r_1}{r_2}\{\cos(\phi_1 - \phi_2) + i\sin(\phi_1 - \phi_2)\}$$

$$= \frac{r_1}{r_2}(\cos\phi_1\cos\phi_2 + \sin\phi_1\sin\phi_2) + i\,\frac{r_1}{r_2}(\sin\phi_1\cos\phi_2 - \sin\phi_2\cos\phi_1)$$

$$= \frac{(x_1x_2 + y_1y_2) + i(y_1x_2 - y_2x_1)}{r_2{}^2} = \frac{(x_1 + iy_1)(x_2 - iy_2)}{r_2{}^2}.$$

In this last expression the numerator is $z_1 \bar{z}_2$ and the denominator is $|z_2|^2$. Thus,

$$z = \frac{z_1}{z_2} = \frac{z_1 \bar{z}_2}{|z_2|^2}.$$

Examples.

1. $\quad \dfrac{1}{i} = -\dfrac{1 \cdot i}{|i|^2} = -i.$

2. $\quad \dfrac{1+i}{1-i} = \dfrac{(1+i)(1+i)}{|1-i|^2} = \dfrac{2i}{2} = i.$

3. $\quad \dfrac{1}{1+i} = \dfrac{1-i}{|1+i|^2} = \dfrac{1}{2} - \dfrac{i}{2}.$

Definition. The *n*th *power* of the number z is the product

$$z^n = \underbrace{z \, z \dots z}_{(n \text{ factors})}.$$

If $z = r(\cos \phi + i \sin \phi)$ it follows from our definition of a product that

$$z^n = r^n(\cos n\phi + i \sin n\phi). \tag{26}$$

Examples: 1. Taking $z = i$ we find

$$i^2 = ii = -1, \qquad i^3 = i^2 i = -i, \qquad i^4 = i^3 i = 1,$$

and, in general,

$$i^{4k} = 1, \qquad i^{4k+1} = i, \qquad i^{4k+2} = -1, \qquad i^{4k+3} = -i,$$

where k is any integer.

2. Taking $z = \cos \phi + i \sin \phi$ we obtain de Moivre's formula:

$$(\cos \phi + i \sin \phi)^n = \cos n\phi + i \sin n\phi.$$

Separating real and imaginary parts, we find, for example, taking $n = 3$,

$$\cos 3\phi = \cos^3 \phi - 3 \cos \phi \sin^2 \phi, \qquad \sin 3\phi = -\sin^3 \phi + 3 \cos^2 \phi \sin \phi.$$

Definition. If $w^n = z$ we call w *a root of degree n* of the number z and write $w = \sqrt[n]{z}$.

Suppose $z = r(\cos\phi + i\sin\phi) \neq 0$, $w = \rho(\cos\theta + i\sin\theta)$; then, by (26),

$$\rho^n(\cos n\theta + i\sin n\theta) = r(\cos\phi + i\sin\phi),$$

whence, comparing moduli and arguments, we have

$$\rho^n = r, \qquad n\theta = \phi + 2k\pi,$$

where k is *any* integer. These last equations define a unique (positive) value of ρ and an infinite number of values of θ:

$$\rho = \sqrt[n]{r}, \qquad \theta = \theta_k = \frac{\phi + 2k\pi}{n}. \tag{27}$$

Putting $k = 0, 1, \ldots, n-1$ in turn in (27) we find n successive values of θ_k: $\theta_0, \theta_1, \ldots, \theta_{n-1}$. Each of the remaining θ_k differs from one of these by an integral multiple of 2π. Formula (27) thus shows that there are *exactly n* different values of $\sqrt[n]{z}$ when $z \neq 0$:

$$w_0 = (\sqrt[n]{z})_0 = (\sqrt[n]{r})\left(\cos\frac{\phi}{n} + i\sin\frac{\phi}{n}\right),$$

$$w_1 = (\sqrt[n]{z})_1 = (\sqrt[n]{r})\left(\cos\frac{\phi+2\pi}{n} + i\sin\frac{\phi+2\pi}{n}\right), \ldots,$$

$$w_{n-1} = (\sqrt[n]{z})_{n-1} = (\sqrt[n]{r})\left(\cos\frac{\phi+2(n-1)\pi}{n} + i\sin\frac{\phi+2(n-1)\pi}{n}\right);$$

for, any complex number is unchanged by increasing its argument by an integral multiple of 2π. The points $w_0, w_1, \ldots, w_{n-1}$ are the vertices of a regular n-gon inscribed in the circle of radius $\rho = \sqrt[n]{r}$ with centre at the origin of coordinates: the moduli of all the w_k are equal and the passage from w_k to w_{k+1} is accompanied by the increment $2\pi/n$ in the argument. After n such steps we return to the initial value of the root; if continued, the process merely repeats the values already constructed.

From what has been said it follows that for n *odd*, the nth root of a positive number has n complex values, of which exactly one is real and positive; for n *even*, the nth root of such a number also has n complex values, of which *two* are real (one positive and one negative). The reader should verify these results himself and also show that the nth root of zero has the single value zero.

Example. Let us find all values of $\sqrt[4]{(1+i)}$. We have

$$1+i = (\sqrt{2})\left(\cos\frac{\pi}{4} + i\sin\frac{\pi}{4}\right),$$

so that

$$w_0 = \left[\sqrt[4]{(1+i)}\right]_0 = (\sqrt[8]{2})\left(\cos\frac{\pi}{16} + i\sin\frac{\pi}{16}\right).$$

The remaining values of the root are obtained from w_0 by rotations through the angle $2\pi/4 = \pi/2$:

$$w_1 = [\sqrt[4]{(1+i)}]_1 = iw_0,$$
$$w_2 = [\sqrt[4]{(1+i)}]_2 = -w_0,$$
$$w_3 = [\sqrt[4]{(1+i)}]_3 = -iw_0.$$

The points w_k lie at the vertices of a square inscribed in the circle $|w| = \sqrt[8]{2}$ (Fig. 6).

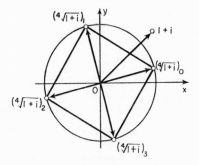

FIG. 6

4. Complex powers. Logarithms

Definition. The operation of raising the number e to the power $z = x+iy$ is *defined* by the equation

$$e^{x+iy} = e^x(\cos y + i\sin y). \tag{28}$$

This definition may appear to be artificial. Even in real analysis the definition of the power e^x for arbitrary real x is a source of difficulty. One method of approach is to define e^x as the limit of a sequence:

$$e^x = \lim_{n\to+\infty}\left(1+\frac{x}{n}\right)^n.$$

In the next chapter we introduce the concept of the *limit* of a sequence of complex numbers and show that our definition (28) is equivalent to the definition

$$e^z = \lim_{n \to +\infty} \left(1 + \frac{z}{n}\right)^n$$

(see Example, Art. 7). In justification of (28) we note that, for $y = 0$, when z is a real number, the power e^z reduces to the ordinary power e^x (this follows directly from the definition), and that the ordinary properties of powers are preserved:

$$e^{z_1} e^{z_2} = e^{z_1 + z_2}, \qquad e^{z_1}/e^{z_2} = e^{z_1 - z_2}. \tag{29}$$

To prove these relations we note that by (28) the complex power $e^{x_k + iy_k}$ has modulus e^{x_k} and argument y_k; hence, by the rules for multiplication and division of complex numbers we have

$$e^{z_1} e^{z_2} = e^{x_1 + x_2}[\cos(y_1 + y_2) + i\sin(y_1 + y_2)] = e^{z_1 + z_2},$$

and

$$\frac{e^{z_1}}{e^{z_2}} = \frac{e^{x_1}}{e^{x_2}}[\cos(y_1 - y_2) + i\sin(y_1 - y_2)] = e^{z_1 - z_2}.$$

Complex powers have properties with no analogue in real analysis. For example, if k is any integer (positive, negative, or zero) it follows from (28) that

$$e^{2k\pi i} = \cos 2k\pi + i\sin 2k\pi = 1, \tag{30}$$

whereas a real power of the number e is equal to unity only when the index of the power is zero. Furthermore, it follows from (30) and the first of the properties (29) that, for any integer k,

$$e^{z + 2k\pi i} = e^z e^{2k\pi i} = e^z; \tag{31}$$

that is, the power e^z is not changed by adding any integral multiple of $2\pi i$ to the index z.

Putting $x = 0$ and $y = \phi$ in (28) we obtain *Euler's formula*:

$$e^{i\phi} = \cos\phi + i\sin\phi. \tag{32}$$

Thus, if $r(\cos\phi + i\sin\phi)$ is the trigonometrical form of a complex number z, then

$$z = re^{i\phi}. \tag{33}$$

The last expression is called the *exponential form* of the complex number; its compactness makes it more convenient than the equivalent trigonometrical form. As $r = |z|$ and

$$\phi = \operatorname{Arg} z = \arg z + 2k\pi,$$

where k is an arbitrary integer, the exponential form of a complex number can be written as

$$z = |z|e^{i\operatorname{Arg} z} = |z|e^{i\arg z}. \tag{33'}$$

Examples:

$$i = e^{i\pi/2}, \quad -1 = e^{i\pi}, \quad -i = e^{-i\pi/2}, \quad 1+i = (\sqrt{2})e^{i\pi/4}.$$

Definition. The number w is called the (natural) logarithm of the complex number $z \neq 0$ (the notation is $w = \operatorname{Ln} z$) if $e^w = z$.

Putting $w = u + iv$ it follows from this definition that

$$z = e^u e^{iv};$$

comparing this with (33'), we get

$$e^u = |z|, \qquad v = \operatorname{Arg} z = \arg z + 2k\pi.$$

From the first equation, $u = \ln|z|$, where ln denotes the ordinary natural logarithm of the positive number $|z|$, so that

$$w = \operatorname{Ln} z = \ln|z| + i\operatorname{Arg} z = \ln|z| + i(\arg z + 2k\pi). \tag{34}$$

Formula (34) defines an infinity of complex numbers which are logarithms of the non-zero number z. Of these, the particular value corresponding to $k = 0$ is called the *principal value of the logarithm* and is denoted by $\ln z$:

$$\ln z = \ln|z| + i\arg z. \tag{35}$$

When z is real and positive, $\arg z = 0$, and the principal value of the logarithm is identical with the ordinary natural logarithm: $\ln z = \ln|z|$.

Examples:

$$\operatorname{Ln} i = \left(\frac{\pi}{2} + 2k\pi\right)i, \qquad \ln i = \frac{\pi}{2}i, \qquad \operatorname{Ln}(-1) = (2k+1)\pi i,$$

$$\ln(-1) = \pi i.$$

For $a > 0$ we have $\operatorname{Ln} a = \ln a + 2k\pi i$; thus, of the infinite number of logarithms of a positive number, one and only one is real (namely, the principal value).

In conclusion, we indicate the fundamental properties of the logarithmic function. From the rule for multiplication of complex numbers ($z_1 \neq 0 \neq z_2$),

$$\operatorname{Ln}(z_1 z_2) = \ln|z_1 z_2| + i \operatorname{Arg}(z_1 z_2)$$

$$= \ln|z_1| + \ln|z_2| + i(\operatorname{Arg} z_1 + \operatorname{Arg} z_2) = \operatorname{Ln} z_1 + \operatorname{Ln} z_2; \qquad (36)$$

similarly,

$$\operatorname{Ln} \frac{z_1}{z_2} = \operatorname{Ln} z_1 - \operatorname{Ln} z_2. \qquad (37)$$

Thus, the ordinary rules for taking logarithms of a product and a quotient are preserved. However, unlike the corresponding results in elementary real algebra, equations (36) and (37) are relations between infinite classes of numbers. For example, the difference $\operatorname{Ln} z_1 - \operatorname{Ln} z_2$ must be interpreted as

$$\ln z_1 + 2k_1\pi i - (\ln z_2 + 2k_2\pi i) = \ln z_1 - \ln z_2 + 2k\pi i$$

where $k = k_1 - k_2$ is an arbitrary integer. In particular, if $z \neq 0$, $\operatorname{Ln} z - \operatorname{Ln} z = 2k\pi i$, where k is an arbitrary integer, and it is wrong, without proper qualification, to assert that $\operatorname{Ln} z - \operatorname{Ln} z = 0$. In the same way, $\operatorname{Ln} z + \operatorname{Ln} z = 2\ln z + 2k\pi i$; as $2\operatorname{Ln} z = 2\ln z + 4k\pi i$, it is wrong to say that $\operatorname{Ln} z + \operatorname{Ln} z = 2\operatorname{Ln} z$.

Alternative treatments of the topics discussed in this Introduction are given by Knopp, *Elements of the Theory of Functions* (Dover, 1952); and by Estermann, *Complex Numbers and Functions* (Athlone Press, 1962).

Exercises

1. Find the trigonometrical and exponential forms of $1 + i\sqrt{3}$, $1 - \cos\alpha + i\sin\alpha$.

2. Given that $|z_1| = |z_2| = |z_3|$ and $z_1 + z_2 + z_3 = 0$, prove that the points z_k lie at the vertices of an equilateral triangle.

3. Given three vertices z_1, z_2, z_3 of a non-degenerate parallelogram, find the three possible positions of the fourth vertex.

4. Find the centre of mass of point masses $m_1, m_2, \ldots, m_n$ located at the respective points $z_1, z_2, \ldots, z_n$.

5. Given two consecutive vertices z_0 and z_1 of a regular n-gon, find the remaining vertices.

6. Prove the identity $|z_1+z_2|^2+|z_1-z_2|^2 = 2\{|z_1|^2+|z_2|^2\}$ and illustrate it geometrically.

7. Express $\cos 4\phi$ in terms of $\sin \phi$ and $\cos \phi$.

8. Find $\sqrt{(3+4i)}$, $\sqrt[6]{(-64)}$, $\sqrt[3]{(i-1)}$.

9. Solve the equations $z^2-(2+3i)z-1+3i = 0$, $z^2-2iz-5 = 0$.

10. Solve the systems of equations

$$\left.\begin{array}{l} z_1+2z_2 = 1+i, \\ 3z_1+iz_2 = 2-3i, \end{array}\right\} \text{and} \left\{\begin{array}{l} (1+i)z_1-(1-i)z_2 = 0, \\ (2+i)z_1-(1-2i)z_2 = 0. \end{array}\right.$$

(In the following problems, $a, b, \ldots$ denote complex constants and $\alpha, \beta, \ldots$ real constants.)

11. What geometrical point-loci are represented by the following relations?

    (a) $|z-a| = |z-b|$.

    (b) $\mathrm{Re}(az+b) = \alpha$.

    (c) $\alpha < \arg z < \beta, \qquad \gamma \leqslant \mathrm{Re}\, z \leqslant \delta,$

$$\left(-\frac{\pi}{2} < \alpha < \beta < \frac{\pi}{2}, \ \gamma > 0\right).$$

    (d) $|z-a|+|z-b| = \alpha$.

    (e) $|z| < 1-\mathrm{Re}\, z$.

*(f) $0 < \arg\dfrac{z-i}{z+i} < \dfrac{\pi}{4}.$

12. Investigate the following families of curves.

    (a) $\mathrm{Re}\dfrac{1}{z} = \alpha.$

    (b) $\arg\dfrac{z-1}{z+1} = \alpha.$

    (c) $\left|\dfrac{z-1}{z+1}\right| = \alpha.$

*(d) $|z-1| \cdot |z+1| = \alpha$. (Discuss the cases $0 < \alpha < 1$, $\alpha = 1$, $\alpha > 1$ separately.)

*(e) $|z^2+2az+b| = \alpha$.

13. Express each of the equations $x^2+2x+y^2-y = 1$, $x^2-y^2 = 1$ in complex form.

14. Express the formulae of geometrical inversion in Cartesian coordinates.

15. What is the inverse, with respect to the circle $|z| = 1$, of the following curves?

    (a)   The straight line $\alpha x+\beta y+\gamma = 0$. (Make a special examination of the case $\gamma = 0$.)

    (b)   The circle $\alpha(x^2+y^2)+\beta x+\gamma y+\delta = 0$.

    (c)   The hyperbola $x^2-y^2 = 1$.

    (d)   The parabola $y^2 = 2px$.

CHAPTER I

THE FUNDAMENTAL IDEAS OF COMPLEX ANALYSIS

5. The sphere of complex numbers

WE have seen that complex numbers can be represented as vectors or as points of a plane. Another geometrical representation which is often useful will now be described. We construct the sphere S (of, say, unit radius) touching the z-plane so that its "south pole" coincides with the origin O, and suppose that each point of the plane is joined to the "north pole" P by a straight line. Each point z of the plane will then correspond with the uniquely defined point Z at which the sphere intersects the straight line Pz internally. Conversely, each point Z of the sphere (other than the north pole P) will correspond with the uniquely defined point z at which the straight line PZ intersects the plane (Fig. 7). This one–one correspondence between the points of the sphere S (excluding the north pole) and the points of the plane is called *stereographic projection*.

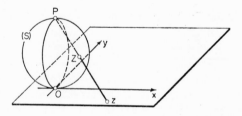

We shall consider the point Z which is the image of z under stereographic projection as a new representation of the complex number z. In order to carry out operations on complex numbers given by points of the sphere we shall pass to their stereographic projections on the plane, operate with their projections according to the rules in Arts. 2–4, and then return to the sphere.

The point P, the north pole of the sphere, will not correspond with any of the complex numbers so far defined. We introduce a new "complex number" ∞ (read *infinity*) to denote the point P. From this geometrical point of view the "number" $z = \infty$ plays the same role as, say, the numbers $z = 2+5i$, $z = 3$, $z = i$: it indicates the position of the corresponding point on the sphere. However, the new "number" cannot participate in ordinary arithmetical operations, because these are defined only for complex numbers (points of the sphere) which correspond with points of the plane (see, however, Art. 18).

The point P is said to be *infinitely distant* and is called the *point at infinity*; all the remaining points of the sphere (the remaining complex numbers) are called *finite*. If, later in the book, we do not wish to make special distinction of the point P (the number $z = \infty$), we shall refer the discussion to the sphere S (called the *sphere of complex numbers*). If, however, the point P (the number $z = \infty$) is excluded from the discussion we shall use the plane.

The plane sketches in the text are to be regarded as "geographical maps" of the corresponding diagrams on the sphere. We shall refer to the set of all finite complex numbers (points) as the *finite* or *open* plane; the set of *all* the numbers (including $z = \infty$) will be termed the *extended* or *closed* plane. The term "open plane" is equivalent to "plane of complex numbers" (see Art. 1), and the term "closed plane" to "sphere of complex numbers".

Stereographic projection maps any point-locus in the plane on to a corresponding locus on the sphere, and *vice versa*. For example, the image on the sphere of an arbitrary circle c of the plane is a circle C which does not pass through the pole P; similarly, any straight line l corresponds with some circle L passing through P (Fig. 8). (The proof of the first of these statements is a simple exercise in geometrical inversion in three dimensions; the second statement is obviously true.) We thus see that the images on the sphere of straight lines and circles in the plane are not distinguished from one another geometrically. Hence it is natural to consider that, *in the extended plane of the complex variable, straight lines are particular cases of circles* (more explicitly, circles passing through the point at infinity). With this convention, any two non-parallel straight lines intersect at *two* points, of which one is the point at infinity. Similarly, parallel straight lines are circles touching one another at the point at infinity.

The term "circle" will thus refer equally to a (non-degenerate) circle on the sphere and the image of this circle on the plane. Without qualification, then, we may say that any circle divides the sphere into two spherical caps; each of these (and its image on the plane) is called a *circular region*. In particular, any half-plane is a

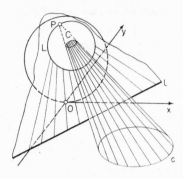

FIG. 8

circular region; for example, the upper half-plane Im $z > 0$ is the rear hemisphere of S. If a circle C does not pass through P (that is, it is a proper circle in the plane) then one of the two spherical caps bounded by it contains P; this particular cap (its boundary C is supposed not included) is called the *exterior* of the circle C; the other cap (likewise divorced from its boundary) is called the *interior* of C.

6. Domains and their boundaries

A domain D (on the sphere or complex plane) is defined as a non-empty set of points having the following properties:

(*a*) If z is a finite point of D then z belongs to the *interior* I of some circle, where I is itself contained in D; if $z = \infty$ is a point of D then there is some circle whose *exterior* E is contained in D. (In each case, by definition, the circle is not a degenerate point-circle and does not pass through the point at infinity.) Alternatively, we may say that z is a point of D if, and only if, it is the vertex of a spherical cap contained in D.

(*b*) Any two points z_1, z_2 of D can be joined by a continuous curve consisting wholly of points of D. (If either z_1 or z_2 is the point at infinity we think of the curve as drawn on the sphere.)

The interior and exterior of a circle are domains; each is called a *circular* domain. Thus, the circular regions $|z| < 1$, $|z-1| > 2$ are domains (the latter contains the point at infinity if it is considered as a domain in the extended plane); the region $|z| \leqslant 1$ is not a domain because condition (*a*) is not satisfied for points on the bounding circle $|z| = 1$.

The term *disc* is used to describe bounded circular regions and domains. Thus, the domain $|z-i| < 1$ is the *open* disc of unit radius with centre i, and $|z-a| \leqslant 2$ is the *closed* disc with radius 2 and centre a. In the absence of further qualification the term *unit disc* will usually refer to the open disc of unit radius with centre at the origin.

The *boundary* or *frontier* B of a domain D is defined as the set of points satisfying the following conditions: (a) the points of B do not belong to D; (b) any circular domain containing a point of B will also contain a point of D. For example, the circle $|z| = 1$ is the boundary of the (circular) domain $|z| < 1$; the boundary of the domain $\operatorname{Re} z > 0$ consists of the imaginary axis and (if we are considering sets in the extended plane) the point $z = \infty$.

A *region R* is a domain D together with none, some, or all, of the boundary points of D; if R contains *all* the boundary points of D it is called a *closed region* and is denoted by $\bar{D}$.

Fig. 9

In Fig. 9 the boundary of the domain D consists of two closed curves C_0 and C_1 separating D from "exterior" points, two "cuts" γ_1 and γ_2 and the point a. (We say z is an *exterior* point of a domain D if z belongs to some circular domain which is not contained in D.) In what follows we shall assume that the boundaries of all the domains considered have such a structure; that is, consist of a finite number of cuts, points, and closed curves separating the domain from exterior points.

The number of connected components into which the boundary is separated is called the *order of connectivity* of the domain. For example, the domain represented in Fig. 9 is quadruply connected, its boundary consisting of four distinct continua:

(1) C_0 and γ_2, (2) C_1, (3) γ_1, and (4) the point a.

In particular, if the boundary of D consists of one continuous part, D is called a *simply connected domain*.† (A different convention is sometimes adopted in connection with domains of the *open* plane. See Art. 37.)

We shall frequently consider domains whose boundaries are associated with a prescribed sense of description. For example, Fig. 9 indicates a sense of description such that the domain always remains on the left-hand side.

We now define what is meant by a "neighbourhood". A general *neighbourhood* of a point z_0 on the sphere (or plane) is any *domain* containing z_0. It is often convenient to consider a "standard" neighbourhood. For a finite point z_0 these are usually chosen to be the circular domains

$$|z - z_0| < \epsilon;$$

the corresponding *deleted* neighbourhoods (*excluding* z_0) are the domains $0 < |z - z_0| < \epsilon$. For $z = \infty$ the standard neighbourhood is a domain

$$|z| > \epsilon,$$

and the corresponding deleted neighbourhood a domain

$$\epsilon < |z| < +\infty.$$

(We adopt the convention that $|\infty| = +\infty$.) Neighbourhoods such as these are called *epsilon–neighbourhoods*.

We conclude with some definitions relating to a general set of points in the plane. We say that $z = a$ is a *limit point*, or *point of accumulation*, of a set of points S if *every* neighbourhood of $z = a$

---

† We do not define the concepts of curve, cut and connected part since their strict definition would lead us outside the limits of this book. In spite of their apparent simplicity they involve several rather subtle topological difficulties. (See, e.g., Newman, *Topology of Plane Sets*, Cambridge, 1952; and Estermann, *Complex Numbers and Functions*, Athlone Press, 1962.)

contains an infinite number of points of S. A limit point of S may, or may not, belong to S. The set S is said to be *closed* if it contains *all* of its limit points. A point $z = b$ is called an *interior point* of a set S if there exists a neighbourhood of b which consists entirely of points of S; we say that S is *open* if each of its points is an interior point of S. A point $z = c$ is called a *frontier point* or *boundary point* of a set S if every neighbourhood of c contains at least one point of S and at least one point which does not belong to S; it will be clear in this case that, if c belongs to S, c will be a limit point of the *complement* of S (the *complement* of S is the set of all points in the plane which do not belong to S); and that, if c does not belong to S, c will be a limit point of S. The *closure*, $\bar{S}$, of a general set of points S is defined as the set formed by adding to S the set of all limit points of S; it follows that S is closed if, and only if, $S = \bar{S}$.

7. The limit of a sequence

Consider the sequence of complex numbers

$$z_n = x_n + i y_n \quad (n = 0, 1, 2 \ldots)$$

where x_n and y_n are real functions of the integer variable n.

Definition. We say that z is the *limit of the sequence* $\{z_n\}$ or that $\{z_n\}$ *tends to the limit* z, and write

$$z = \lim_{n \to +\infty} z_n, \quad \text{or } z_n \to z \text{ as } n \to +\infty, \tag{1}$$

if, given *any* $\epsilon > 0$, it is possible to find a number N such that z_n belongs to the ϵ-neighbourhood of z whenever $n > N$; in other words we require that, if z is finite,

$$|z - z_n| < \epsilon \text{ whenever } n > N, \tag{2}$$

and, if $z = \infty$,

$$|z_n| > \epsilon \text{ whenever } n > N. \tag{3}$$

If there exists a finite real number M such that, for all n,

$$|z_n| \leqslant M,$$

the sequence $\{z_n\}$ is said to be *bounded*. Using the plane representation, a sequence is bounded if, and only if, all its points are contained in the interior of a finite circle.

Any sequence $\{z_n\}$ of finite points converging to a finite limit z is bounded. For, by (2), z_n lies within a finite circular domain K' for

$n \geqslant N+1$. The only points of $\{z_n\}$ which could possibly lie outside K' are $z_1, \ldots, z_N$. However, as this finite number of finite points can be covered by a finite circular domain K'' (say), it remains only to construct a finite circle containing K' and K'' in its interior.

Let the limit be $z = x+iy \neq \infty$; then the inequality (2) can be written in the form

$$|z - z_n| = \sqrt{\{(x-x_n)^2+(y-y_n)^2\}} < \epsilon \quad \text{for } n > N. \tag{4}$$

From (4) it follows that the real sequences $\{x_n\}$ and $\{y_n\}$ converge to the limits x and y:

$$\lim_{n \to +\infty} x_n = x, \qquad \lim_{n \to +\infty} y_n = y. \tag{5}$$

We leave as an exercise for the reader the proof of the converse result that if the (real) sequences $\{x_n\}$, $\{y_n\}$ converge to finite limits x, y respectively, then the sequence $z_n = x_n+iy_n$ converges to the (finite) limit $z = x+iy$.

A similar result holds for polar coordinates. Suppose

$$\lim_{n \to +\infty} z_n = z \quad (z \neq 0, \infty)$$

where z does not lie on the negative real axis. Then, if $z_n = r_n\, e^{i\phi_n}$, $z = r\, e^{i\phi}$, where ϕ_n and ϕ denote the principal values of the arguments, we have

$$\lim_{n \to +\infty} r_n = r, \qquad \lim_{n \to +\infty} \phi_n = \phi. \tag{6}$$

For, $r_n = \sqrt{(x_n^2+y_n^2)}$, so that, by (5) and the continuity of the root,

$$\lim_{n \to +\infty} \sqrt{(x_n^2+y_n^2)} = \sqrt{(x^2+y^2)}.$$

As the argument function is continuous in any finite neighbourhood which does not contain points of the negative real axis (see Art. 12), the second of the relations (6) follows similarly. If z is a negative real we choose some other suitable single-valued branch of the argument; for example, we may restrict the values of ϕ and of the ϕ_n to the interval $[0, 2\pi)$, the corresponding branch having discontinuities along the positive real axis; on this understanding the second of the relations (6) holds in this case also. Accordingly, we have:

Theorem 1. *If the sequence* $\{z_n\}$ *where* $z_n = x_n + iy_n = r_n\, e^{i\phi_n}$ *converges to the finite limit* $z = x + iy$, *then*

$$\lim_{n \to +\infty} x_n = x, \quad \lim_{n \to +\infty} y_n = y; \tag{5}$$

if, further, $z = r\, e^{i\phi} \neq 0$, *then, with a suitable choice of the values of* ϕ_n *and* ϕ,

$$\lim_{n \to +\infty} r_n = r, \quad \lim_{n \to +\infty} \phi_n = \phi. \tag{6}$$

The converse results hold less restrictively. *If* $\{x_n\}$, $\{y_n\}$, $\{r_n\}$, $\{\phi_n\}$ *are real sequences with the respective finite limits* x, y, r, ϕ *then the sequences* $z_n = x_n + iy_n$ *and* $z_n = r_n e^{i\phi_n}$ *converge, respectively, to the (finite) limits* $x + iy$ *and* $re^{i\phi}$. It will be clear that $\lim\limits_{n \to +\infty} (x_n + iy_n) = \infty$ if, and only if, $\lim\limits_{n \to +\infty} \sqrt{(x_n^2 + y_n^2)} = +\infty$, and that $\lim\limits_{n \to +\infty} (r_n e^{i\phi_n}) = \infty$ if, and only if, $\lim\limits_{n \to +\infty} |r_n| = +\infty$.

Example. Let $z = x + iy$ be any finite complex number. We show that the sequence

$$a_n = \left(1 + \frac{z}{n}\right)^n$$

converges to the finite limit e^z. By the rules for operating with complex numbers we have

$$|a_n| = \left|1 + \frac{z}{n}\right|^n = \left[\sqrt{\left\{\left(1 + \frac{x}{n}\right)^2 + \left(\frac{y}{n}\right)^2\right\}}\,\right]^n = \left(1 + \frac{2x}{n} + \frac{x^2 + y^2}{n^2}\right)^{n/2}$$

and

$$\theta_n = n \arctan \frac{y}{n + x},$$

where θ_n is some value of Arg a_n and arc tan denotes the value of Arc tan between $-\pi/2$ and $\pi/2$. Using certain elementary inequalities from real analysis it can be shown that $(x^2 + y^2)/n^2$ can be neglected in comparison with $2x/n$, so that

$$\lim_{n \to +\infty} |a_n| = \lim_{n \to +\infty} \left(1 + \frac{2x}{n}\right)^{n/2} = e^x;$$

and that arc tan$\{y/(n+x)\}$ can be replaced by $y/(n+x)$, so that

$$\lim_{n\to+\infty} \theta_n = \lim_{n\to+\infty} \frac{ny}{n+x} = y.$$

Thus, by Theorem 1, $\lim_{n\to+\infty} a_n$ exists, its trigonometrical form being given by

$$\lim_{n\to+\infty} \left(1 + \frac{z}{n}\right)^n = e^x(\cos y + i \sin y).$$

As in real analysis, this result can be taken as the definition of the complex power e^z (see Art. 4 and the references given at the end of Art. 4).

Remark. It is meaningless to introduce symbols $x+i(\pm\infty)$ or $(\pm\infty)+iy$, where x and y are finite, to represent different complex numbers. There is only one point at infinity on the complex number sphere. All complex sequences $z_n = x_n + iy_n$ for which either (or each) of the sequences $\{x_n\}$, $\{y_n\}$ becomes infinitely great converge to this point. (We say $\{x_n\}$ becomes "infinitely great" if

$$\lim_{n\to+\infty} |x_n| = +\infty;$$

that is, given any $\epsilon > 0$ there is a positive integer N such that $|x_n| > \epsilon$ whenever $n > N$.) Symbols of the above form are used merely to indicate the direction of certain lines on the plane. Thus, we may say that the real axis goes from "$-\infty$ to $+\infty$" or that the line $x = 3$ goes from "$3+i\infty$ to $3-i\infty$"; the axes being chosen as usual, these statements mean that the real axis is traversed from left to right and the line $x = 3$ from above to below.

By repeating the arguments used in real analysis, the reader can show that all the usual rules for operating with limits are preserved in the complex domain.

8. Complex functions of a real variable

Definition. If, to each value t in some real interval I, there corresponds a complex number $z = z(t)$, we say that $z(t)$ is a *complex function of the real variable t on this interval.*

If each value of z is finite, the function $z(t)$ defines (on I) the two real functions $x = x(t)$, $y = y(t)$ such that

$$z = z(t) = x(t) + iy(t). \qquad (7)$$

Definition. We say that z_0 is the *limit of $z(t)$ as t tends to t_0* and write

$$z_0 = \lim_{t \to t_0} z(t), \qquad \text{or } z(t) \to z_0 \text{ as } t \to t_0, \qquad (8)$$

if, given any $\epsilon > 0$, there is a $\delta > 0$ such that the points $z(t)$ all belong to the ϵ-neighbourhood of z_0 for all values of t satisfying the inequalities $0 < |t - t_0| < \delta$.

Note that the value $t = t_0$ is excluded in this definition. As in real analysis, the function $z(t)$ may not be defined at the point t_0. (For example, $(\sin x)/x \to 1$ as $x \to 0$ although the function $(\sin x)/x$ is not defined at $x = 0$.)

If $\lim_{t \to t_0} z(t) = z_0 = x_0 + iy_0$ $(\neq \infty)$ it is easily shown (the reader should carry out the proof for himself) that

$$\left. \begin{aligned} \lim_{t \to t_0} x(t) &= x_0, \\ \lim_{t \to t_0} y(t) &= y_0. \end{aligned} \right\} \qquad (9)$$

Definition. If $\lim_{\Delta t \to 0} z(t + \Delta t)$ exists finitely and equals the value of the function $z = z(t)$ at the point t, that is,

$$\lim_{\Delta t \to 0} z(t + \Delta t) = z(t), \qquad (10)$$

we say that $z = z(t)$ is *continuous at the point t*.

We shall restrict our discussion to functions continuous at every point of their interval of definition. As t varies, the point $z = z(t)$ describes in the z-plane a certain curve; in the vector calculus this curve is called the *hodograph* of the vector $z(t)$.

Definition. Provided the limits on the right exist finitely, we define

$$\dot{z}(t) = \lim_{\Delta t \to 0} \frac{z(t+\Delta t) - z(t)}{\Delta t}$$

$$= \lim_{\Delta t \to 0} \left\{ \frac{x(t+\Delta t) - x(t)}{\Delta t} + i\, \frac{y(t+\Delta t) - y(t)}{\Delta t} \right\} = \dot{x}(t) + i\dot{y}(t) \qquad (11)$$

to be the *derivative* of the function $z = z(t)$ at the point t. The reader can see for himself from Fig. 10 that the vector derivative $\dot{z}(t)$ (assumed non-zero) is directed along the tangent to the curve

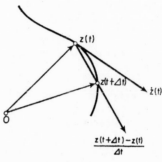

Fig. 10

$z = z(t)$ at the point t; hence the existence of a non-zero derivative $\dot{z}(t)$ implies the existence of the tangent. The points of the curve where $\dot{z}(t) = 0$ (that is, $\dot{x}(t) = \dot{y}(t) = 0$) may turn out to be special points (cusps, angular points, and so on) on the curve.

Example. The function

$$z = z_0 + re^{it}, \quad -\pi < t \leqslant \pi, \qquad (12)$$

where z_0 is a given (finite) complex number and r is a positive constant, represents the circle of radius r with centre at the point $z_0 = x_0 + iy_0$. For, by (12), the vector $z - z_0 = re^{it}$ joining the point z_0 to the point z has constant modulus r, and argument t ranging from $-\pi$ to π. (Here we have chosen the principal branch of the argument.) The complex function (12) defines the two real functions

$$x = x_0 + r \cos t, \\ y = y_0 + r \sin t. \quad \Bigg\} \tag{13}$$

The equations (13) are the ordinary parametric equations of a circle. The derivative of the function (12) is

$$\dot{z} = \dot{x} + i\dot{y} = -r \sin t + ir \cos t$$
$$= ir(\cos t + i \sin t) = ire^{it} = i(z - z_0)$$

and represents a vector parallel to the tangent to the circle at the point $z_0 + re^{it}$.

Certain additional concepts must now be introduced for use in later sections. A plane curve is said to be *smooth* if it can be represented by a function $z = z(t)$, $t_1 \leqslant t \leqslant t_2$, having a derivative $\dot{z}(t)$ which is *continuous and non-zero* on the closed interval $[t_1, t_2]$. Here, the values of the derivative at the end points t_1, t_2 are to be understood as the corresponding limits (11) taken on the right and on the left, respectively; also, if the curve is *closed* (that is, $z(t_1) = z(t_2)$) we require that $\dot{z}(t_1) = \dot{z}(t_2)$. It will be clear that, for a smooth curve, the gradient of the tangent varies continuously as the point of tangency moves continuously along the curve.

A curve is said to be *sectionally smooth* or *piecewise smooth* if it consists of a finite number of smooth curves joined in sequence at their ends. At the points of junction of these components, such a curve does not, in general, have a tangent. It is easily shown that any sectionally smooth curve (and, in particular, any smooth curve) has finite length. *In the later developments we shall consider only piecewise smooth curves.*

A *Jordan arc* is a (continuous) curve which does not cut itself (that is, has no multiple points). If such an arc is defined by $z = z(t)$ ($\alpha \leqslant t \leqslant \beta$) then $z(t)$ is continuous on the closed interval $[\alpha, \beta]$ and $z(t') \neq z(t'')$ for *all* pairs of *distinct* points t', t'' of this interval. If, in addition, this arc is piecewise smooth we shall call it a *Jordan path* (or, simply, a *path*) connecting the point $a = z(\alpha)$ to the point $b = z(\beta)$.

A *closed* Jordan curve C is obtained by a continuous deformation of a circle, the deformation being such that C does not cut itself at any point. If C is defined by $z = z(t)$ $(\alpha \leqslant t \leqslant \beta)$ then $z(t)$ is continuous on $[\alpha, \beta]$ and $z(\alpha) = z(\beta)$ while $z(t') \neq z(t'')$ whenever $\alpha \leqslant t' < t'' < \beta$. If, in addition, C is piecewise smooth we shall call it a *Jordan contour* (or, simply, a *contour*). The *Jordan curve theorem* states that a closed Jordan curve C separates the plane into two domains, each having C as frontier; of these domains, one is bounded and is called the *interior* domain defined by C; the other is unbounded and is called the *exterior* domain defined by C. This theorem seems obvious; however, its strict proof is lengthy and difficult (see, e.g. Newman, *Topology of Plane Sets*, Cambridge, 1952).

9. The complex form of an oscillation

Complex functions of a real variable play a useful role in the study of oscillations and waves. We shall consider simple harmonic oscillations, described by the trigonometrical functions

$$A_0 \cos(\omega t + \phi) \quad \text{and} \quad A_0 \sin(\omega t + \phi). \tag{14}$$

In place of the two functions (14) we introduce the single complex function of time

$$
\begin{aligned}
A(t) &= A_0\{\cos(\omega t + \phi) + i \sin(\omega t + \phi)\} \\
&= A_0 e^{i(\omega t + \phi)} = A e^{i\omega t}, \tag{15}
\end{aligned}
$$

where $A = A_0 e^{i\phi}$. Here, $A_0 = |A|$ defines the amplitude, $\phi = \operatorname{Arg} A$ is the initial phase angle, and ω is the angular frequency of the harmonic oscillation. The functions in (14) are the real and imaginary parts of (15). We call (15) *the complex representation of the harmonic oscillations* or, briefly, a *complex oscillation*.

The complex oscillation $A(t) = A e^{i\omega t} = A_0 e^{i(\omega t + \phi)}$ can be represented geometrically by a vector of constant modulus A_0 rotating with angular velocity ω. In the theory of alternating currents with fixed angular frequency ω, the oscillation is sometimes represented conventionally by a constant vector with modulus A_0 and argument ϕ; that is, in our notation, by the complex number $A = A_0 e^{i\phi}$.

The complex representation of the oscillation simplifies certain calculations. To illustrate, we discuss a simple physical problem. Consider a circuit, consisting of an ohmic resistance R and a self-inductance L connected in series (Fig. 11), to which is applied an external electromotive force (e.m.f.) $\mathscr{E}$. It is known that the steady current $\mathscr{I}$ satisfies the following differential equation:

$$\mathscr{E} - L\frac{d\mathscr{I}}{dt} = R\mathscr{I}. \tag{16}$$

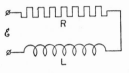

Fig. 11

Let the external e.m.f. be cosinusoidal or sinusoidal, that is, equal to $E_0 \cos(\omega t + \phi)$ or $E_0 \sin(\omega t + \phi)$); as indicated above, we consider the complex e.m.f. $\mathscr{E} = E e^{i\omega t}$ where $E = E_0 e^{i\phi}$. The steady current $\mathscr{I}$ satisfying (16) is then to be sought in the form $\mathscr{I} = J e^{i\omega t}$ where $J = J_0 e^{i\psi}$. (This is a simple consequence of certain basic results in the theory of linear differential equations with constant coefficients.) As $d\mathscr{I}/dt = Ji\omega e^{i\omega t} = i\omega\mathscr{I}$ (see Example, Art. 8), (16) gives

$$\mathscr{E} - i\omega L\mathscr{I} = R\mathscr{I},$$

or

$$\mathscr{I} = \mathscr{E}/(R + i\omega L) = \mathscr{E}/Z, \tag{17}$$

where

$$Z = R + i\omega L. \tag{18}$$

We call Z the *complex resistance* or *impedance* of the circuit. The relation (17) can be considered as a generalization of Ohm's law. Put $Z = Z_0 e^{i\delta}$, where

$$Z_0 = |Z| = \sqrt{(R^2 + \omega^2 L^2)}, \qquad \delta = \arg Z = \arctan\frac{\omega L}{R};$$

then (17) gives

$$\mathscr{I} = \frac{E_0}{Z_0} e^{i(\omega t + \phi - \delta)}. \tag{19}$$

Equation (19) shows that the amplitude of the current is obtained by dividing the amplitude of the e.m.f. by Z_0 and that there is a

4

time-lag of amount δ/ω. The quantity $Z_0 = \sqrt{(R^2 + \omega^2 L^2)}$, the modulus of the complex impedance, is called the *total* or *apparent resistance* of the circuit. Separating real and imaginary parts in (19) we obtain the currents corresponding to cosinusoidal and sinusoidal e.m.f's.

Let us consider the alternating vectors $\mathscr{E}$ and $\mathscr{I}$ representing the complex e.m.f. and current respectively. From the above results it follows that these vectors rotate with the same angular velocity ω, the phase of $\mathscr{I}$ differing from that of $\mathscr{E}$ by a constant amount δ. Consequently the vectors $\mathscr{I}$ and $\mathscr{E}$ rotate like a rigid body. In the usual accounts of alternating current theory, $\mathscr{E}$ and $\mathscr{I}$ are represented by two fixed vectors, as shown in Fig. 12.

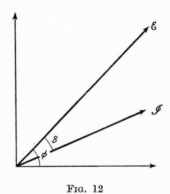

FIG. 12

In other, more difficult, problems, it may happen that a complex e.m.f. $\mathscr{E} = E_0 e^{i(\omega t + \phi)}$ is associated with a current $\mathscr{I}$ whose amplitude and phase (relative to $\mathscr{E}$) vary with time. In this case the vectors $\mathscr{E}$ and $\mathscr{I}$ no longer rotate like a rigid body, and it is often convenient to adopt a conventional diagram in which $\mathscr{E}$ appears as a constant vector $E = E_0 e^{i\phi}$, and which shows the curve traced out by the end point of the vector $\mathscr{I}$ (the current diagram).

We introduce the quantities

$$Z_R = R, \qquad Z_L = i\omega L$$

and call them the impedance of the ohmic resistance and self-inductance, respectively. Equation (18) shows that, with R and L connected in series, their impedances are added. It can be shown that equation (17) also holds when R and L are connected in parallel, provided the impedance Z is calculated according to the law for parallel connexion:

$$\frac{1}{Z} = \left\{ \frac{1}{R} + \frac{1}{i\omega L} \right\}.$$

In the same way, we represent the impedance of a capacitor as $Z_C = 1/(i\omega C)$. It is shown in alternating current theory that the generalized form (17) of Ohm's law also holds for arbitrary R, L, C combinations, provided the net complex impedance Z is calculated according to the usual laws of connexion. This method of calculating steady-state currents, etc., in A.C. circuits is formally simpler than that involving solution of differential equations.

10. Functions of a complex variable

We consider an arbitrary non-empty set M of points of the complex sphere. The set M may, or may not, contain the point $z = \infty$.

Definition. We say that

$$w = f(z) \tag{20}$$

is defined as a *function of the complex variable z on the set M* if, to each z of M, there corresponds one or more values of w (which may include the value $w = \infty$).

We call z the *independent variable* and w the *dependent variable* or *function*. If, to each value of z, there corresponds only one value of w, the function (20) is said to be *single-valued* or *uniform*; otherwise, (20) is said to be *many-valued* or *multiform*.

In discussing many-valued functions, the study of their single-valued branches is of great importance. A single-valued function $f(z)$ is called a *single-valued branch* (or, simply, a *branch*) of a many-valued function $F(z)$ on M if the value of $f(z)$ at each point z of M coincides with one of the values of $F(z)$ at this point.

If the set of points w corresponding by (20) to all possible points z of M is denoted by N we say that (20) establishes a *mapping* of the set M onto N. If M and N do not contain the point ∞, we shall represent them as sets of points of the z- and w-planes.

In particular, if M is the set of all positive integers, the function of a complex variable (20) (supposed single-valued) reduces to the sequence considered in Art. 7. If M is a set of real numbers, (20) reduces to a complex function of a real variable (see Art. 8).

By virtue of the correspondence (20), each point w of N corresponds to one or more points z of M (the latter case holds when the function $f(z)$ assumes the value w at two or more points of M). This means that on N there is defined a function

$$z = \phi(w) \tag{21}$$

mapping N onto M; the function (21) is called the *inverse* of the function (20).

A case of special importance is that in which the function $w = f(z)$ is single-valued in M and its inverse function $z = \phi(w)$ is single-valued in N; we then say the transformation $w = f(z)$ is *one–one*, or *biuniform*, in M and that $f(z)$ is *univalent* (or *schlicht*) in M. Under a one–one transformation $w = f(z)$ any two distinct points of M map onto two distinct points of N; that is, in such a transformation two points cannot be "merged" into one another.

It often happens that we have to deal with transformations involving composite functions. Let the function $\omega = f_1(z)$ map the set M onto the set N, and let $w = f_2(\omega)$ map N onto Q (M, N and Q are sets on the spheres of z, ω and w). The mapping of the set M onto Q is effected by the composite function

$$w = f(z) = f_2[f_1(z)] \tag{22}$$

called the *superposition* or *resultant* of the transformations f_1 and f_2. Later we shall consider the superposition of three or more transformations.

We note that the definition of a function of a complex variable $w = f(z)$ on the set M is equivalent to the definition on M of two real functions

$$u = u(x,y), \qquad v = v(x,y)$$

of the real variables x and y (we put $z = x+iy$, $w = u+iv$).

In what follows we shall usually be concerned with cases in which the sets M and N are *domains* on the complex z- and w-spheres†; we shall denote them by the letters D and Δ.

11. Examples

We illustrate the ideas introduced in Art. 10 by the following examples.

---

† See Art. 23, on the principle of preservation of domains.

Example 1. Suppose

$$w = kz \tag{24}$$

where k is a positive constant. In polar coordinates $z = re^{i\phi}$, $w = \rho e^{i\theta}$, the transformation (24) is expressed by the equations†

$$\rho = kr, \qquad \theta = \phi; \tag{25}$$

these throw immediate light on the geometrical content of (24). Thus, the second of the equations (25) shows that, under this mapping, the image of any point z ($z \neq 0$) is on the radius vector Oz, while the first shows that the modulus of z is increased (or, if $k < 1$, decreased) by a factor k. Accordingly, (24) expresses a *magnification* (or *compression*, if $k < 1$) of the z-plane with coefficient k. In Fig. 13, $k = \frac{1}{2}$. For example, if D is the circular domain (disc) $|z| < 1$, its image Δ is the similar domain $|w| < k$; if D is the upper half-plane Im $z > 0$, then Δ is also the upper half-plane Im $w > 0$.

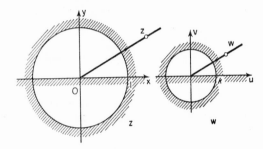

FIG. 13

Example 2. Suppose

$$w = e^{i\alpha}z, \tag{26}$$

where α is a real constant. Writing $z = re^{i\phi}$, $w = \rho e^{i\theta}$, we obtain

$$\rho = r, \qquad \theta = \phi + \alpha.$$

Thus, under the mapping (26), any point z on the circle $|z| = r$ has as image a point w on the same circle, the radius vector Oz being rotated through the angle α to give Ow. Accordingly, the transformation (26) is equivalent to a rotation of the z-plane

---

† Strictly speaking, the second of these relations should be written $\theta = \phi + 2k\pi$. It is clear, however, that the addition of $2k\pi$ is of no geometrical significance. We proceed as above in dealing with similar examples in Art. 11.

through an angle α about the origin (Fig. 14). If, in particular, $\alpha = \pi/2$, (26) becomes $w = iz$ and represents a rotation through a right angle; for $\alpha = \pi$, (26) becomes $w = -z$ and represents a rotation through an angle π.

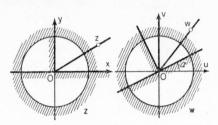

FIG. 14

Example 3. Suppose

$$w = z + b \tag{27}$$

where $b = \beta_1 + i\beta_2$ is a complex constant. If we put $z = x + iy$ and $w = u + iv$, (27) becomes

$$u = x + \beta_1, \qquad v = y + \beta_2,$$

whence it is clear that (27) is equivalent to a *parallel translation* of the *z-plane* represented by the vector b. For example, if D is the disc $|z| < r$, then Δ is the disc $|w - b| < r$ (Fig. 15).

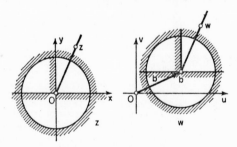

FIG. 15

Example 4. More generally, suppose

$$w = az + b, \tag{28}$$

where $a = ke^{i\alpha}$ and $b = \beta_1 + i\beta_2$ are complex constants; w is then an arbitrary *linear function* of the complex variable z. We can consider the transformation (28) to be the result of superposing the three transformations

$$\omega = kz, \qquad \omega_1 = e^{i\alpha}\omega, \qquad w = \omega_1 + b.$$

It will be clear that the transformation (28) is equivalent to *a rotation with magnification (or compression, if $k < 1$) followed by a parallel translation.* We call it the general *linear transformation.*

Example 5. Suppose

$$w = z^2; \tag{29}$$

putting $z = re^{i\phi}$, $w = \rho e^{i\theta}$, we can write (29) in the form

$$\rho = r^2, \qquad \theta = 2\phi.$$

It follows that, under the mapping (29), points lying on the ray $\arg z = \phi_0$ are transformed into points of the ray $\operatorname{Arg} w = 2\phi_0$, and points on the circle $|z| = r_0$ become points on the circle $|w| = r_0^2$. Let D be the upper half-plane $0 < \phi < \pi$ $(r > 0)$; as we then have $0 < \theta < 2\pi$, it is clear that (29) gives a one–one mapping of D on the domain Δ obtained from the w-plane by deleting the origin and the ray $\theta = 0$. If we adjoin to Δ the point $w = 0$ and suppose that the cut in the w-plane has *two* edges (*upper* and *lower*), the mapping from the closed region $\bar{D}$ will also be one–one: here the ray $\phi = 0$ maps on the upper edge $(\theta = 0)$ and the ray $\phi = \pi$ on the lower edge $(\theta = 2\pi)$ (Fig. 16).

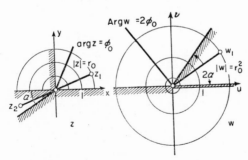

Fɪɢ. 16

If, now, D is the sector $0 < \phi < \pi + \alpha$ $(r > 0)$, where α is positive, the image of D under the mapping $w = z^2$ fills the w-plane (with the exception of the point $w = 0$); that the mapping will not be one–one in D is clear from Fig. 16, from which it can be seen that the points z_1 and $z_2 = -z_1$ (the one being situated in the first quadrant, the other in the third) both map on the same point $w_1 = z_1^2 = z_2^2$.

Example 6. Suppose $w = f(z)$ is defined on the closed disc $|z| \leqslant 1$ by

$$f(z) = \frac{1}{1-|z|} \quad \text{for} \quad |z| < 1; \qquad f(z) = \infty \quad \text{for} \quad |z| = 1. \qquad (30)$$

(The second equation in (30) is necessary because division by zero is not defined.) This function maps the closed disc $|z| \leqslant 1$ on the closed line-segment $1 \leqslant u \leqslant +\infty$, $v = 0$ in the complete w-plane; that is, on the lesser of the two closed great-circle arcs on the w-sphere joining the points $w = 1$ and $w = \infty$. It is clear that the mapping is *not* one–one.

Example 7. Consider the function

$$w = |z|z. \qquad (31)$$

Writing $z = re^{i\phi}$, $w = \rho e^{i\theta}$, we have

$$\rho = r^2, \qquad \theta = \phi.$$

The transformation (31) resembles (29), but is not identical with it. In particular, the mapping (31) is one–one throughout the whole of the disc $|z| < 1$.

Later (Art. 14) we show that Examples 1–5 differ essentially in character from the last two examples.

Example 8. Let the function $w = F(z)$ be defined in the upper half-plane $0 < \arg z < \pi$ by the equation $w = \sqrt[3]{z}$.

As we saw in Art. 3, this function is many-valued. It establishes a correspondence between any given point z of the upper half-plane and three corresponding points of the w-plane: $w_0 = (\sqrt[3]{z})_0$, $w_1 = (\sqrt[3]{z})_1$, $w_2 = (\sqrt[3]{z})_2$; of these, the first lies in the sector $0 < \arg w < \pi/3$, the second in the sector $2\pi/3 < \arg w < \pi$, and the third in the sector $-2\pi/3 < \arg w < -\pi/3$. These relations define in the upper half of the z-plane three single-valued functions $w_0(z)$, $w_1(z)$, $w_2(z)$, respectively, each being a single-valued branch of the function $w = F(z)$.

By setting up a correspondence between each point in the upper half-plane and *one* of the corresponding values w_0, w_1, w_2 we can construct each of the infinitely-many single-valued branches of $F(z)$; in general, such branches will not be continuous at all points in $\operatorname{Im} z > 0$. For example, we can define a branch $\tilde{w}(z)$ to be equal to $(\sqrt[3]{z})_0$ in the (first) quadrantal *region* $0 < \arg z \leqslant \pi/2$ and to $(\sqrt[3]{z})_1$ in the quadrant $\pi/2 < \arg z < \pi$; it will be clear that $\tilde{w}(z)$ will then be discontinuous along the ray $\arg z = \pi/2$.

12. The limit of a function

Let a single-valued function of a complex variable be defined in some neighbourhood of a point z_0, except, perhaps, at the point z_0 itself (see remark on the second definition of Art. 8).

Definition. If, given any $\epsilon > 0$, we can find $\delta > 0$ such that $w = f(z)$ maps all the points of the δ-neighbourhood of z_0 (except, perhaps, z_0 itself) into the interior of the ϵ-neighbourhood of some fixed point w_0, then we say that the number w_0 is the *limit of the function $f(z)$* as $z \to z_0$, and we write

$$w_0 = \lim_{z \to z_0} f(z). \tag{32}$$

It is important to note that this definition holds equally for infinite as well as for finite z_0 and w_0. For cases where both the points z_0 and w_0 are finite, (32) is true if the inequality

$$0 < |z - z_0| < \delta \tag{33}$$

implies the inequality

$$|f(z) - w_0| < \epsilon. \tag{34}$$

When, for example, $z_0 \neq \infty$ but $w_0 = \infty$, then (32) is true if the inequality

$$0 < |z - z_0| < \delta$$

implies that

$$|f(z)| > \epsilon. \tag{35}$$

It is left to the reader to formulate the inequalities expressing the meaning of the relations

$$\lim_{z \to \infty} f(z) = w_0 \neq \infty \quad \text{and} \quad \lim_{z \to \infty} f(z) = \infty.$$

It follows from the definition that, if (32) holds and z_n is an arbitrary sequence converging to z_0, then the sequence $w_n = f(z_n)$

converges to w_0 in the sense of Art. 7; and that, if $z = z(t)$ is an arbitrary continuous curve passing through $z_0 = z(t_0)$, then the real-variable function $f[z(t)]$ tends to w_0 as $t \to t_0$ in the sense of Art. 8. We express these two results in words as follows: *the limit in the complex domain does not depend on the way in which z approaches z_0*.

We note that *any function $w = f(z)$ which tends to a finite limit as $z \to z_0$ is bounded in some deleted neighbourhood of z_0* (that is, a neighbourhood of z_0 from which the point z_0 is itself excluded). The proof is similar to the corresponding proof for sequences in Art. 7, and is left to the reader.

In exactly the same way as for Theorem 1, Art. 7, we can prove

THEOREM 2. *If the function*

$$w = f(z) = u(x,y) + iv(x,y) = \rho(r,\phi)e^{i\theta(r,\phi)}$$

tends to the finite limit w_0 as $z \to z_0$, where $w_0 = u_0 + iv_0$ and $z = x + iy = re^{i\phi}$, then

$$\lim_{z \to z_0} u(x,y) = u_0, \qquad \lim_{z \to z_0} v(x,y) = v_0; \tag{36}$$

if, further, $w_0 = \rho_0 e^{i\theta_0} \neq 0$, then, with a suitable choice of the values of the arguments,

$$\lim_{z \to z_0} \rho(r,\phi) = \rho_0, \qquad \lim_{z \to z_0} \theta(r,\phi) = \theta_0.$$

The converse results hold generally when w_0 ($= u_0 + iv_0 = \rho_0 e^{i\theta_0}$) is finite. It will be clear that $\lim\limits_{z \to z_0} (u+iv) = \infty$ if, and only if, $\lim\limits_{z \to z_0} \sqrt{(u^2 + v^2)} = +\infty$, and that $\lim\limits_{z \to z_0} (\rho e^{i\theta}) = \infty$ if, and only if, $\lim\limits_{z \to z_0} |\rho| = +\infty$.

The standard rules for operating with limits, known to the reader from real analysis, carry over unchanged when applied to limits of functions of a complex variable. We shall not stop to formulate and prove them.

13. Continuity

Definition. We say that the (single-valued) function $w = f(z)$ is *continuous at the point* $z = z_0$ *if*

$$\lim_{z \to z_0} f(z)$$

exists finitely and equals $f(z_0)$:

$$\lim_{z \to z_0} f(z) = f(z_0) \neq \infty. \tag{38}$$

This definition can be expressed by inequalities: for example, if z_0 is finite, we say $f(z)$ is continuous at the point $z = z_0$ if, given any $\epsilon > 0$, we can find $\delta > 0$ such that, for *all* points z satisfying the inequality

$$|z - z_0| < \delta, \tag{39}$$

the inequality

$$|f(z) - f(z_0)| < \epsilon \tag{40}$$

will hold. Note that (40) implies that $f(z)$ is defined finitely at z_0, and that (39) permits z to assume the value z_0, the reason being that (40) holds automatically when $z = z_0$. The limit concept differs essentially from that of continuity in that the definition of the former (see Art. 12) depends in no way on the functional value *at* z_0 *itself.* Thus, for example, if (34) were to hold for $z = z_0$ we would have $|f(z_0) - w_0| < \epsilon$; as $f(z_0)$ and w_0 are constants and ϵ is an *arbitrary* positive number it would follow that $f(z_0) = w_0$.

As in real analysis, we write $z - z_0 = \Delta z$ (the *increment in the independent variable*) and $f(z) - f(z_0) = \Delta w$ (the *increment in the function*). In terms of increments, the condition (38) for continuity of $w = f(z)$ at the (finite) point z_0 becomes

$$\lim_{\Delta z \to 0} \Delta w = 0; \tag{41}$$

that is, Δw (which *vanishes* for $\Delta z = 0$) becomes *vanishingly small* as $\Delta z \to 0$.

Definition. A function $w = f(z)$ continuous at every point of a domain D is said to be *continuous in this domain.*

We illustrate our definitions with examples. The functions in Examples 1–5 and 7 of Art. 11 are continuous in the whole of the open z-plane. The function of Example 6 is continuous in the (open) unit disc $|z| < 1$. The functions $w_0(z)$, $w_1(z)$, $w_2(z)$ of Example

8 are continuous in the upper half of the z-plane, and it can be shown that these three functions exhaust the whole class of one-valued, *continuous* branches of the function $w = F(z)$ in the upper half-plane: each of the remaining single-valued branches of this function in the upper half-plane (for example, the branch $\tilde{w}(z)$) is discontinuous at points of some subset of $\operatorname{Im} z > 0$.

We discuss two further examples:

Example 1. *The principal branch of* $\operatorname{Arg} z$ *is continuous whenever* $z \neq 0, \infty$ *and z does not lie on the negative real axis.*

Thus, let z_0 be any such point and let ϵ be any positive number less than π. Let δ be the radius of the greatest circle, with centre at the point z_0, which does not contain points of the negative real-axis and lies in the interior of a sectoral region whose vertex is at O and whose angle is 2ϵ. Then, $|\arg z - \arg z_0| < \epsilon$ whenever $|z - z_0| < \delta$.

As $\operatorname{Arg} z$ is not defined for $z = 0$ and $z = \infty$, it is meaningless to speak of its continuity at these points. At any point z_0 on the negative real axis, $\arg z$ is discontinuous: for, $\arg z_0 = \pi$ while $\arg z \to -\pi$ as z tends to z_0 through points of the *lower* half-plane.

Example 2. Suppose

$$w = f(z) = \frac{1}{2i}\left(\frac{z}{\bar{z}} - \frac{\bar{z}}{z}\right), \quad (z \neq 0, \infty). \tag{42}$$

Writing $z = re^{i\phi}$ and using Euler's formula (32), Art. 4, we have

$$w = \frac{1}{2i}(e^{2i\phi} - e^{-2i\phi}) = \sin 2\phi.$$

From this it is seen that in *any* deleted neighbourhood of the origin the function assumes all values in the interval $[-1, 1]$. Consequently, if we stipulate merely that $\epsilon < 2$, there is no w_0 such that the inequality (34) holds for all z of an arbitrarily small deleted neighbourhood of $z_0 = 0$; that is, the function does not tend to a limit as $z \to 0$. We note that, as $z \to 0$ along any path $z = z(t)$ which has a *tangent* at $z = 0$, the function $f[z(t)]$ *does* tend to a finite limit. In general (as in the present case) different limiting values can be obtained when we choose different paths of approach.

The basic theorems on continuity in real analysis carry over unchanged to complex analysis; we shall not stop to formulate and prove them. Among the theorems concerning functions continuous in a region, we note the following two (proofs can be found elsewhere):

1. *A function $f(z)$ continuous on a closed region $\bar{D}$ is bounded in this region; that is, a finite real constant M exists such that, for all of z of $\bar{D}$, we have $|f(z)| \leqslant M$.*

2. *If $f(z)$ is continuous on a closed region $\bar{D}$ then so is $|f(z)|$; and $|f(z)|$ attains at points of $\bar{D}$ its upper and lower bounds on $\bar{D}$.*

These theorems also hold when $\bar{D}$ is a closed curve on the sphere or is a curvilinear arc (likewise on the sphere) which *includes* its *end-points*.

14. The Cauchy–Riemann conditions

Let the single-valued function $w = f(z)$ be defined in some neighbourhood of a finite point z. We choose a general point $Z = z + \Delta z$ in this neighbourhood and write

$$\Delta w = f(z + \Delta z) - f(z).$$

Definition. If $\lim\limits_{\Delta z \to 0} \dfrac{\Delta w}{\Delta z}$ exists finitely we say that the function $f(z)$ is *differentiable* at the point z. This limiting value is called the *derivative* of $f(z)$ at the point z and we write

$$f'(z) = \lim_{\Delta z \to 0} \frac{\Delta w}{\Delta z}. \tag{43}$$

As in real analysis, it is easily shown that differentiability of a function at a point implies its continuity at that point. The converse statement is not true in general.

Suppose $w = f(z) = u(x, y) + iv(x, y)$. We shall find conditions which must be imposed on the functions $u(x, y)$ and $v(x, y)$ in order that $f(z)$ should be differentiable at the point z. We assume that $f'(z)$ exists. From (43) and the definition in Art. 12 it follows that, given any $\epsilon > 0$, there corresponds $\delta > 0$ such that

$$\left| \frac{\Delta w}{\Delta z} - f'(z) \right| < \epsilon \tag{44}$$

whenever $0 < |\Delta z| < \delta$. In particular, taking $\Delta z = te^{i\alpha}$, where

$t = |\Delta z|$ and α is an arbitrary real constant, we see that (44) holds, independently of the choice of α, when $0 < t < \delta$ (see Art. 12); this implies that

$$\lim_{t \to +0} \Delta w / \Delta z$$

exists and equals $f'(z)$, independently of the choice of α. If $\alpha = 0$ then $\Delta z = t = \Delta x$ (say) is real and it follows from (43) that

$$f'(z) = \lim_{\Delta x \to +0} [\{u(x + \Delta x, y) - u(x, y)\} + i\{v(x + \Delta x, y) - v(x, y)\}]/(\Delta x)$$
$$= \partial u / \partial x + i \partial v / \partial x. \tag{45}$$

(We obtain the same result by taking $\alpha = \pi$.) If $\alpha = \pi/2$, then $\Delta z = it = i\Delta y$ (say) and we have

$$f'(z) = \lim_{\Delta y \to +0} [\{u(x, y + \Delta y) - u(x, y)\} + i\{v(x, y + \Delta y) - v(x, y)\}]/(i\Delta y)$$
$$= -i \partial u / \partial y + \partial v / \partial y. \tag{46}$$

(We obtain the same result by taking $\alpha = -\pi/2$.) Comparing the right-hand sides of (45) and (46) we find that

$$\frac{\partial u}{\partial x} = \frac{\partial v}{\partial y}, \qquad \frac{\partial u}{\partial y} = -\frac{\partial v}{\partial x}. \tag{47}$$

These equations are called the *Cauchy–Riemann* or *d'Alembert–Euler* conditions. We have shown that the partial derivatives $\partial u/\partial x$, $\partial u/\partial y$, $\partial v/\partial x$, $\partial v/\partial y$ must exist and satisfy the Cauchy–Riemann equations (47) at any point z at which $f(z)$ is differentiable; these conditions are *necessary* for the existence of $f'(z)$. We now find *sufficient* conditions for differentiability by showing that $f'(z)$ exists whenever the functions $u(x, y)$, $v(x, y)$ are *totally differentiable* at the point z and satisfy the Cauchy–Riemann relations at this point.† For, from the definition of total differentiability of

---

† It is well known that the mere existence of $\partial u/\partial x$, $\partial u/\partial y$, $\partial v/\partial x$, $\partial v/\partial y$ at the point z does not imply that u and v are totally differentiable at this point; however, both u and v will be totally differentiable at z when all four partial derivatives are *continuous* at this point.

functions of two real variables it follows that the increments in u and v can be expressed in the form

$$\left.\begin{aligned} \Delta u &= \frac{\partial u}{\partial x}\Delta x + \frac{\partial u}{\partial y}\Delta y + \eta_1|\Delta z|, \\[2mm] \Delta v &= \frac{\partial v}{\partial x}\Delta x + \frac{\partial v}{\partial y}\Delta y + \eta_2|\Delta z|, \end{aligned}\right\} \tag{48}$$

where $|\Delta z| = \sqrt{[(\Delta x)^2 + (\Delta y)^2]}$ and η_1 and η_2 tend to zero as $\Delta z \to 0$. From (48) we have:

$$\frac{\Delta w}{\Delta z} = \frac{\Delta u + i\Delta v}{\Delta x + i\Delta y}$$

$$= \frac{\left(\dfrac{\partial u}{\partial x}\Delta x + \dfrac{\partial u}{\partial y}\Delta y\right) + i\left(\dfrac{\partial v}{\partial x}\Delta x + \dfrac{\partial v}{\partial y}\Delta y\right) + (\eta_1 + i\eta_2)|\Delta z|}{\Delta x + i\Delta y}.$$

We now use the Cauchy–Riemann conditions, replacing $\partial u/\partial y$ by $-\partial v/\partial x$ and $\partial v/\partial y$ by $\partial u/\partial x$: simple rearrangement gives

$$\frac{\Delta w}{\Delta z} = \frac{\left(\dfrac{\partial u}{\partial x} + i\dfrac{\partial v}{\partial x}\right)\Delta x + i\left(i\dfrac{\partial v}{\partial x} + \dfrac{\partial u}{\partial x}\right)\Delta y}{\Delta x + i\Delta y} + (\eta_1 + i\eta_2)\frac{|\Delta z|}{\Delta z}$$

$$= \left(\frac{\partial u}{\partial x} + i\frac{\partial v}{\partial x}\right) + (\eta_1 + i\eta_2)\frac{|\Delta z|}{\Delta z}.$$

Accordingly,

$$\left|\frac{\Delta w}{\Delta z} - \left(\frac{\partial u}{\partial x} + i\frac{\partial v}{\partial x}\right)\right| = |\eta_1 + i\eta_2|$$

$$\to 0 \text{ as } \Delta z \to 0,$$

so that $f'(z)$ exists and is given by

$$f'(z) = \lim_{\Delta z \to 0}\frac{\Delta w}{\Delta z} = \frac{\partial u}{\partial x} + i\frac{\partial v}{\partial x}.$$

The above argument establishes the following

THEOREM. *In order that the function $f(z) = u(x, y) + iv(x, y)$ be differentiable at the point $z = x + iy$ it is necessary that the partial derivatives $\partial u/\partial x$, $\partial u/\partial y$, $\partial v/\partial x$, $\partial v/\partial y$ exist at this point and satisfy the Cauchy–Riemann conditions*

$$\frac{\partial u}{\partial x} = \frac{\partial v}{\partial y}, \qquad \frac{\partial u}{\partial y} = -\frac{\partial v}{\partial x}. \tag{47}$$

The Cauchy–Riemann conditions are also sufficient for the differentiability of $f(z)$ provided the functions $u(x, y)$ and $v(x, y)$ are totally differentiable at the point considered.

We note that the rules and formulae for differentiation in real analysis carry over unchanged to complex analysis. For, these rules and formulae are based on laws of algebraic operation, theorems on limits, and definitions of derivatives, all of which are formally the same in the complex as in the real domain. Thus, for example, the functions of Examples 1–5 in Art. 11 are differentiable at all points of the finite z-plane. We can verify this directly by showing that each of the functions concerned satisfies the Cauchy–Riemann conditions at every finite point z. (It is immediately clear in each case that the requirement that u and v be totally differentiable at every such point z is satisfied.) Consider, say, the function $w = z^2$ (Example 5); we have

$$u = x^2 - y^2, \qquad v = 2xy,$$

and

$$\frac{\partial u}{\partial x} = \frac{\partial v}{\partial y} = 2x, \qquad \frac{\partial u}{\partial y} = -\frac{\partial v}{\partial x} = -2y.$$

The function

$$w = |z|z \tag{31}$$

of Example 7 is differentiable at $z = 0$; for, at this point, $\Delta z = z$ and $\Delta w = w = z|\Delta z|$, so that $f'(0)$ exists and is given by

$$\lim_{\Delta z \to 0} \frac{\Delta w}{\Delta z} = \lim_{z \to 0} |z| = 0.$$

The same function is not differentiable at any point $z \neq 0$, for it is easily verified that the functions $u = x\sqrt{(x^2 + y^2)}$ and

$v = y\sqrt{(x^2+y^2)}$ do not satisfy the Cauchy–Riemann conditions whenever $z \neq 0$. It is also easy to show that the function of Example 6 is not differentiable at any point of the disc $|z| < 1$.

We conclude this chapter with two definitions which are of fundamental importance in the whole theory:

Definition 1.   A function $f(z)$ which is single-valued and differentiable at each point of a domain D of the plane is said to be *regular in this domain*.

Definition 2.   The function $f(z)$ is said to be *regular at the point* z if $f(z)$ is regular in some neighbourhood of this point.

We emphasize that our definitions refer to single-valued functions and to *finite* points z: so far we have *not* defined differentiability and regularity at the point at infinity (see Art. 6).

The requirement that a single-valued function $f(z)$ be differentiable at each point of a domain D of the plane is identical with the requirement that $f(z)$ be regular in this domain. On the other hand, the regularity of $f(z)$ at a point z of the plane demands more than that $f(z)$ be differentiable at this point. For example, the function (31) is differentiable at $z = 0$ but is not regular at $z = 0$ because it is not differentiable *throughout* some neighbourhood of this point.

An alternative account of many of the topics discussed in this chapter is given in the references quoted at the end of Art. 4.

Exercises

1. Write down the formulae of stereographic projection in Cartesian coordinates. What are the images under stereographic projection of (*a*) the pair of points z and $-z$, (*b*) the pair of points z and $\bar{z}$?

2. D_1 is the set of all finite points z such that $|z^2-1| \leqslant 1$. D_2 is the set of all finite points $z = re^{i\phi}$, where $r \geqslant 0$ and ϕ is real, such that $\cos \phi < r < 2 \cos \phi$. Are both these sets domains? (Give proofs.)

3. Find the limit of the sequence $\{z_n\}$ where

$$z_n = \sum_{k=0}^{n} \frac{i^k}{2^k} \quad (n = 0, 1, \ldots).$$

Illustrate your solution with a diagram.

5

4. Discuss the curves represented by the following complex functions of the real variable t:

(a) $z = \alpha e^{it} + \beta e^{-it}$,   ($\alpha, \beta$ real),   (b) $z = e^{at}$, (a complex).

5. Let $z = z(t)$ define the position at time t of a point moving on the plane. Find the components of velocity and acceleration in the direction Oz and in the direction perpendicular to Oz.

6. Let the point z trace the circle $|z| = R$ in the positive sense so that Oz has constant angular velocity unity. Find the vector velocity of the point w whose motion is related to that of z according to the law $w = f(z)$.

7. Find the *steady* current in a circuit consisting of a resistance R and capacitance C, in series, when connected across a sinusoidal e.m.f. $E_0 \sin(\omega t + \alpha)$.

8. Find the image under the mapping (42) of the set D of all points z such that $0 < |z| < +\infty$. (D is obtained from the closed plane by deleting the points $z = 0, \infty$.)

9. The transformation represented by the pair of real functions of two variables

$$u = \alpha_1 x + \beta_1 y + \gamma_1, \ v = \alpha_2 x + \beta_2 y + \gamma_2,$$

($\alpha_1 \beta_2 - \alpha_2 \beta_1 \neq 0$), is called an *affine* transformation. Show that: (a) an affine mapping transforms any square of the plane $z = x + iy$ into a parallelogram of the plane $w = u + iv$; (b) if the image of any one square is also a square, then $u + iv$ is a linear function of the complex variable $z = x + iy$.

10. What are the images under the mapping $w = z^2$ of (a) the family of straight lines $y = \alpha$ ($\alpha > 0$), and (b) the family of half-lines $x = \beta, y > 0$?

11. Find the transforms of:
(a) the lines $x = \alpha$ and $y = \beta$ under the mapping $w = 1/z$;
(b) the family of rays $\arg z = \alpha$ under the mapping

$$w = (1+z)/(1-z);$$

(c) the circle $|z| = r$ ($0 < r < 1$) and the line-segment $\arg z = \alpha$, $0 < |z| \leqslant 1$ under the mapping $w = \frac{1}{2}\{z + (1/z)\}$;

(d) the circle $|z| = 1$ under the mapping $w = \sqrt{(z+1)}$.

12. Find the image of the sector S defined by $0 < \arg z < 2\pi/3$ under the mapping $w = z^3$. Find the loci in S giving rise to the families $\operatorname{Re} w = \alpha$ and $\operatorname{Im} w = \beta$.

*13. Give an example of a function $f(z)$ which tends to a limit as $z \to 0$ along any straight line through the origin, the limiting value being independent of the particular line chosen, but is such that

$$\lim_{z \to 0} f(z)$$

does *not* exist.

14. Discuss the continuity of the function $w = \tan(\arg z)$.

15. Show that if a function $w = f(z)$ is regular in a domain D and is real then it is constant in D.

16. Show that if $w = f(z)$ is regular in a domain D and $f'(z)$ vanishes at every point of D then $f(z)$ is a constant in D.

17. Discuss the regularity of the following functions:

    (*a*) $w = z^3$,   (*b*) $w = (1/z)^2$,   (*c*) $w = \sqrt[3]{z}$,

    (*d*) $w = z \operatorname{Re} z$.

CHAPTER II

CONFORMAL MAPPINGS

15. Conformal mappings

Let the function $w = f(z)$ be single-valued and continuous in some neighbourhood of a (finite) point z_0 at which $f(z)$ is differentiable, with $f'(z_0) \neq 0$. Suppose $f'(z_0) = Ae^{i\alpha}$ where $\alpha = \arg f'(z_0)$, and let $z = z_0 + \Delta z$ be a neighbouring point, where $\Delta z = \Delta r \cdot e^{i\phi} \neq 0$. Write $f(z) - f(z_0) = \Delta\rho \cdot e^{i\theta}$. We suppose ϕ, θ chosen so that, for sufficiently small positive Δr, $\theta - \phi$ lies in the interval $(-\pi, \pi)$ if $-\pi < \alpha < \pi$ and in $[0, 2\pi)$ if $\alpha = \pi$. Then, by Theorem 2 of Art. 12 and the definition of a derivative,

$$|f'(z_0)| = A = \lim_{\Delta r \to +0} \frac{\Delta\rho}{\Delta r}, \qquad \arg f'(z_0) = \alpha = \lim_{\Delta z \to 0} (\theta - \phi). \qquad (1)$$

If z tends to z_0 along some curve C through z_0, the corresponding point $w = f(z)$ will tend to $w_0 = f(z_0)$ along a curve γ which is the image of C under the mapping $w = f(z)$ (Fig. 17). Thus, if C

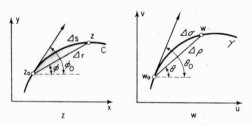

Fig. 17

is defined by the complex function $z = z(t)$, where t is a real variable and $z_0 = z(t_0)$, then γ will be given by $w = w(t) = f[z(t)]$, the image of z_0 being $w_0 = w(t_0)$. Suppose C has a tangent at z_0 (that is, $\dot{z}(t_0) \neq 0$); we have $f'(z_0) \neq 0$ so that, by the rule for differentiation of a composite function, $\dot{w}(t_0) = f'(z_0) \cdot \dot{z}(t_0) \neq 0$; accordingly, γ has a tangent at w_0. In what follows we shall suppose the tangents to C and γ at the respective points z_0, w_0 to be *directed* lines drawn in the sense of t *increasing*, as indicated by arrows in Fig. 17. Let these (directed) tangents make angles ϕ_0, θ_0 with the positive x- and u-axes, respectively. For definiteness, suppose $-\pi < \phi_0 \leqslant \pi$, and choose values for ϕ from a continuous branch of Arg Δz which contains ϕ_0 in the interior of its range. Then, as $t \to t_0 + 0$ (that is, as z approaches z_0 along C from "the positive side") the ϕ and θ of (1) tend to the respective limits ϕ_0 and θ_0, where

$$\arg f'(z_0) = \theta_0 - \phi_0. \tag{2}$$

Equation (2) shows that:

(a) *the angle through which a smooth curve C is rotated at the point z_0 in the mapping $w = f(z)$ is independent of the form and orientation of C* (we suppose throughout that the directions of the axes of x and u, and of y and v, coincide; the angle of rotation is then interpreted as the angle between the original and transformed directions) and expresses this rotation in terms of the argument of the derivative: *the angle of rotation at z_0 under the mapping $w = f(z)$ is* $\alpha = \arg f'(z_0)$.

Suppose the element of C joining z_0 and z to be rectifiable and of length Δs. (This requirement is satisfied if C is *smooth*.) Then, if $f(z)$ is sufficiently well-behaved in some domain D containing this element (it is sufficient, for example, that $f(z)$ be *regular* in D) the corresponding element of γ will be rectifiable and have length $\Delta\sigma$ (say). To the first order, Δs and $\Delta\sigma$ will be equal to Δr, $\Delta\rho$, respectively, and it follows readily that the first relation in (1) can be written

$$|f'(z_0)| = A = \lim_{\Delta z \to 0} \frac{\Delta\sigma}{\Delta s}. \tag{3}$$

This limiting value is the coefficient of (linear) magnification for the curve C at z_0.

Equation (3) shows that:

(b) *under the mapping $w = f(z)$* (now supposed regular at z_0) *the coefficient of linear magnification A at z_0 for any* (smooth) *curve C through z_0 is independent of the form and orientation of C*; accordingly, for such a mapping $w = f(z)$ we may say that *the coefficient of linear magnification at a point of regularity z_0 is* $A = |f'(z_0)|$.

The above properties (a) and (b) can be expressed otherwise. Before proceeding we note certain conventions concerning measurement of angles: the angle between two directions (that is, directed

lines) in the plane, given in order, is taken numerically equal to
the *non-reflex* angle included between them and is associated with
the sign $+$ or $-$ according as the rotation of the *first* direction
towards the *second* (we think of them as vectors drawn outward
from a common base-point) through this non-reflex angle is counter-
clockwise or clockwise; for example, with the usual reference
frame, the angle between the positive axes of x and y is $+\pi/2$; if
the two directions are *antiparallel* they are said to include an
angle π. With this understanding, the property (a) can be expressed
as that of *conservation of angles*:

(a') *under the above mapping* $w = f(z)$, *the angle between two
smooth curves* C_1, C_2, *intersecting at* z_0 (*that is, the angle between
the corresponding positively-directed tangents at* z_0) *is equal* (*in magnitude and sign*) *to the corresponding angle between the respective image-
curves* γ_1, γ_2 *at* $w_0 = f(z_0)$. (See Fig. 18.)

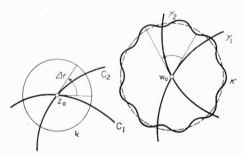

FIG. 18

Also, we have seen above that, under the transformation $w = f(z)$,
a point z whose distance from z_0 is some given small quantity Δr is
mapped on a point w separated from $w_0 = f(z_0)$ by a distance
which is, to the first order of small quantities, $A \cdot \Delta r$. Thus,
property (b), in conjunction with (a), can be expressed as the
property of *preservation of small neighbourhoods*:

(b') *under the mapping* $w = f(z)$ (*supposed regular at* z_0) *the
image of any circle* k *with centre* z_0 *and sufficiently small radius* Δr
is a closed curve κ *whose maximum radial deviation from the circle*
κ_0 *with centre* w_0 *and radius* $A \cdot \Delta r$ *is a small quantity of order higher
than* Δr.

Definition. A mapping which, at a certain point z_0, has the
properties (a) and (b), or—equivalently—the properties (a') and
(b'), is said to be *conformal* at z_0.

The above results can be formulated as:

THEOREM 1. *If $f(z)$ is regular at the point z, with $f'(z) \neq 0$, the mapping $w = f(z)$ is conformal at z; at any such point the angle of rotation of the mapping is $\arg f'(z)$ and the corresponding coefficient of linear magnification is $|f'(z)|$.*

We have shown above that a conformal mapping preserves the angles between curves, not only in magnitude but also in sense. This last characteristic is not exhibited by, say, the mapping $w = \bar{z}$ which reduces to the reflexion of all figures in the axis of abscissae. The mapping $w = \bar{z}$ preserves the magnitude of any angle but reverses it in sign.

Let us now consider the superposition of the mappings $w = f(\zeta)$ and $\zeta = \bar{z}$, where $f(\zeta)$ is a regular function of ζ; that is, the mapping $w = f(\bar{z})$. Both $w = f(\zeta)$ and $\zeta = \bar{z}$ preserve the magnitudes of angles, so that $w = f(\bar{z})$ also leaves angles unchanged in magnitude. The mapping $w = f(\zeta)$ preserves the sense of angles, but $\zeta = \bar{z}$ reverses them in sign; it follows that $w = f(\bar{z})$ changes the sign of angles. A mapping such as $w = f(\bar{z})$ is sometimes termed a conformal mapping of the *second kind*, or an *indirect* conformal mapping, in distinction from the conformal mapping described above (termed a conformal mapping of the first kind, or a direct conformal mapping).

We conclude this article with certain remarks on the nature of conformal mappings.

Remark 1. The condition $f'(z) \neq 0$ imposed in Theorem 1 is essential. For, consider the function $w = z^2$ of Example 5, Art. 11. It is regular at the point $z = 0$ but its derivative vanishes at this point:

$$\left[\frac{dw}{dz}\right]_{z=0} = [2z]_{z=0} = 0.$$

In Art. 11 we saw that the mapping $w = z^2$ doubles, and does not preserve, angles at the origin of coordinates, so that it cannot be conformal at this point.

Remark 2. From (b) it follows that, if we neglect small quantities of higher order, the area enclosed by the curve κ is equal to $A^2\pi \cdot (\Delta r)^2$. Thus, to the order of approximation stated, the coefficient A^2 is the ratio of the areas enclosed by the curves k and κ and it follows that A^2 is the coefficient of superficial magnification at the point z_0. Accordingly, at a point z where $f(z)$ is regular and $f'(z) \neq 0$, *the coefficient of superficial magnification* in the mapping $w = f(z)$ is equal to $|f'(z)|^2$. We obtain the same result if we use the Cauchy–Riemann equations. The Jacobian of the equivalent transformation $u = u(x, y)$, $v = v(x, y)$ is

$$\frac{\partial(u, v)}{\partial(x, y)} = \begin{vmatrix} \dfrac{\partial u}{\partial x} & \dfrac{\partial u}{\partial y} \\ \dfrac{\partial v}{\partial x} & \dfrac{\partial v}{\partial y} \end{vmatrix} = \left(\frac{\partial u}{\partial x}\right)^2 + \left(\frac{\partial v}{\partial x}\right)^2 = |f'(z)|^2. \qquad (4)$$

It is a familiar result in real analysis that the modulus of the Jacobian gives the coefficient of superficial magnification under this transformation.

Remark 3. If the mapping function $f(z)$ is regular at the point z_0, with $f'(z_0) \neq 0$, it can be shown that $f'(z)$ exists and is *non-zero* at all points z in some neighbourhood of z_0; it follows, as in the proof of (4), that the Jacobian $\partial(u, v)/\partial(x, y)$ is non-vanishing throughout this neighbourhood. It is shown in real analysis that this implies that the mapping $w = f(z)$ is *one–one* in the neighbourhood concerned. A converse result can be stated: if the function $w = f(z)$ is regular at the point z_0 and $f'(z_0) = 0$ then the mapping $w = f(z)$ is *not* one–one in any neighbourhood of z_0.

16. Conformal mapping of domains

Definition. A mapping $w = f(z)$ which is single-valued and continuous in a domain D of the plane is said to be *conformal* in D if it is conformal at every point of D.

From Theorem 1 it follows that, for the mapping $w = f(z)$ to be conformal in the domain D, it is sufficient that the function $f(z)$ be regular in D and have a non-vanishing derivative at all points of D. The mappings of Examples 1–4, Art. 11, are obviously conformal throughout the whole of the open plane. Further examples of conformal mappings are given below.

Let us assume that the mapping $w = f(z)$ is conformal and, for simplicity, one–one in the domain D. Let Δ be the image of D under this mapping. In the domain Δ we consider two families of straight lines $u = c_1$, $v = c_2$ parallel to the coordinate axes of the

w-plane. The inverse mapping transforms these into two families
of curves in D whose representative equations have the respective
forms

$$u(x,y) = c_1, \qquad v(x,y) = c_2. \tag{5}$$

Thus, when z moves in D along a curve which is a member of, say,
the first family, then, as the first of the equations (5) shows, the
function $u(x,y)$ remains constant in value. This implies that the
image point w moves in Δ along some line $u = $ const., parallel to
the v-axis.

Suppose now that the parametric values c_1 and c_2 in (5) have
been chosen at equal intervals Δc. This implies the construction of
a *Cartesian coordinate net* in Δ, the basic element of the net being a
square of side Δc. To this net there corresponds in D a net formed
by curves belonging to the families (5). The latter net is called the
conformal equivalent of the Cartesian net. If Δc is *small*, it follows
from the properties (a') and (b) that the general element of the
equivalent net approximates closely to a square. (Consider the
typical curvilinear element shown shaded in Fig. 19: (a') ensures
that its sides meet at right-angles and (b) that its sides differ in
length only by quantities of a higher order of smallness than Δc.)

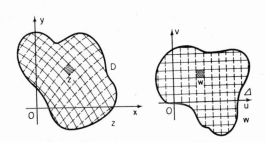

Fig. 19

Example. The function

$$w = z^2 \tag{6}$$

gives a one–one mapping of the upper half-plane $\operatorname{Im} z > 0$ onto
the w-plane slit along the positive real axis (see Art. 11). This

mapping is conformal at every point z of the upper half-plane, because we then have

$$\frac{dw}{dz} = 2z \neq 0;$$

at the boundary point $z = 0$ the mapping doubles angles (see Art. 11). We have

$$u = x^2 - y^2, \qquad v = 2xy, \tag{7}$$

so that the conformal equivalent of the Cartesian net consists essentially of parts of hyperbolas

$$x^2 - y^2 = c_1, \qquad 2xy = c_2 \tag{8}$$

lying in the upper half-plane (Fig. 20). An alternative is to consider the conformal equivalent of the *polar-coordinate net*. The polar net consists of circles $|w| = c_1$ (omitting the point $w = c_1$) and rays $\text{Arg } w = c_2$ ($c_1 > 0$, $0 < c_2 < 2\pi$); its conformal equivalent consists of the semi-circles $|z| = \sqrt{c_1}$ ($\text{Im } z > 0$) and rays $\arg z = \frac{1}{2}c_2$ (see Fig. 16).

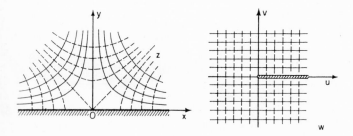

Fig. 20

17. Geometric significance of the differential dw

Suppose $f(z)$ differentiable at z. Then, with the usual notation ($\Delta z \neq 0$),

$$\frac{\Delta w}{\Delta z} - f'(z) = \eta, \quad \text{where} \quad \lim_{\Delta z \to 0} \eta = 0,$$

whence

$$\Delta w = f'(z) \cdot \Delta z + \eta \cdot \Delta z. \tag{9}$$

If $f'(z) \neq 0$, $\Delta z \neq 0$, the quantity $f'(z) \cdot \Delta z$ differs from the increment Δw by a quantity $\eta \cdot \Delta z$ of a "higher order of smallness" than $f'(z) \cdot \Delta z$. (As in real analysis, this means that, as $\Delta z \to 0$, $\{\Delta w - f'(z) \cdot \Delta z\}/\{f'(z)\Delta z\} \to 0$). Adopting the usual terminology, we call $f'(z) \cdot \Delta z$ the *principal part* of Δw or the *differential* in $f(z)$ corresponding to the increment Δz in the variable, and write $dw = f'(z)\Delta z$; it is clear that, for fixed z, dw depends *linearly* on Δz. Taking $f(z) = z$, we have $f'(z) = 1$ and $dz = \Delta z$; accordingly, we write the differential of $w = f(z)$ as

$$dw = f'(z) \cdot dz. \tag{10}$$

We now bring out the geometric meaning of the differential by considering the images $w = f(z)$ and $W = w + \Delta w = f(z + \Delta z)$ of neighbouring points z and $Z = z + \Delta z$. Supposing z given, the correspondence between Z and W can be expressed by the relation between $\Delta z = Z - z$ and $\Delta w = W - w$. We limit our discussion to some sufficiently small neighbourhood of the point z and assume that $f'(z) \neq 0$. If, in (9), we neglect $\eta \cdot \Delta z$ as a term which is of a higher order of smallness than the others appearing there, we obtain the approximate formula

$$\Delta w \approx f'(z) \cdot \Delta z = dw. \tag{11}$$

Equation (11) expresses a very simple linear relationship between Δz and dw. Using geometrical language we can say that, if the function $f(z)$ is differentiable at the point z, with $f'(z) \neq 0$, the mapping of a sufficiently small ϵ-neighbourhood of this point can be effected (if we neglect errors of an order of smallness higher than ϵ) by the *linear* mapping

$$W - w = f'(z) \cdot (Z - z). \tag{10'}$$

The right-hand side of this relation is called the *principal linear part* of the mapping at z. Thus, at a point z where $f'(z) \neq 0$, the principal linear part of the mapping $w = f(z)$ is the *differential* $dw = f'(z) \cdot \Delta z$.

An analogous procedure in real analysis is the representation of the function $f(x)$ in the neighbourhood of a given point x by its differential; geometrically this is equivalent to our representing a small curvilinear segment of the graph $y = f(x)$ by a corresponding segment of the tangent, the latter having equation

$$Y - y = f'(x) \cdot (X - x).$$

By (11),

$$W - w \approx f'(z)(Z - z),$$

or

$$W \approx f'(z) \cdot Z + w - f'(z) \cdot z = aZ + b,$$

where $a = f'(z)$ and $b = w - f'(z) \cdot z$ are constants for a fixed point z. This is the linear mapping considered in Example 4, Art. 11. Recalling the result obtained there, we arrive at the following theorem:

THEOREM 2. *If the function $f(z)$ is differentiable at the point z_0, with $f'(z_0) \neq 0$, the mapping $w = f(z)$ of a sufficiently small ϵ-neighbourhood of this point reduces (if we neglect errors of an order of smallness higher than ϵ) to a linear mapping consisting of*
  (1) *a parallel translation from the point z_0 to $w_0 = f(z_0)$,*
  (2) *a magnification with coefficient $|f'(z_0)|$,*
and
  (3) *a rotation through an angle $\arg f'(z_0)$.*
Thus, *locally* (that is, within some neighbourhood of the given point z_0), the conformal mapping is, to the degree of approximation indicated, a *similarity transformation*; it is this property that gives rise to the term conformal ("form-preserving") mapping.

In the following article we study an important class of elementary conformal mappings.

18. Bilinear mappings

To avoid tedious discussion of special cases we shall extend our arithmetic to include the "number" ∞. The set of all finite complex numbers and the number ∞ will form the set of *extended complex numbers* (the number sphere). We adopt the following conventions:
  (1) if a is any *finite* number, then

$$a + \infty = \infty + a = \infty, \quad a/\infty = 0;$$

(2) if A is any *non-zero extended complex number*, then

$$A\infty = \infty A = \infty, \qquad A/0 = \infty;$$

(3) $|\infty| = +\infty$.

Note that we do *not* define the combinations (∞/∞), $(0 \cdot \infty)$, $(0/0)$ $(\infty \pm \infty)$; and that the above rules do not in any way clash with the "finite" arithmetic developed earlier.

The general *bilinear mapping* is defined on the z-sphere by

$$w = \frac{az+b}{cz+d} \quad (z \neq \infty), \qquad w = \frac{a}{c} \text{ for } z = \infty, \qquad (12)$$

where a, b, c, d are finite and

$$ad - bc \neq 0. \qquad (13)$$

(If we permitted $ad - bc$ to vanish, so that $a/c = b/d$, then the ratio

$$(az+b)/(cz+d)$$

would reduce to a constant or be indeterminate.) This gives a *one–one* mapping of the *z-sphere* onto the *w*-sphere, the image of $z = -d/c$ being $w = \infty$; the inverse mapping,

$$z = \frac{b - dw}{cw - a} \quad (w \neq \infty), \qquad z = -\frac{d}{c} \text{ for } w = \infty,$$

is also bilinear and is defined and single-valued on the *w-sphere*. Note that $z = -d/c$ maps on $w = \infty$ and $z = \infty$ on $w = a/c$.

For $c = 0$, the transformation (12) reduces to the linear mapping $w = (a/d)z + (b/d)$ already considered in Art. 11 (Example 4). For $c \neq 0$, it can be expressed as

$$w = \frac{a}{c} + \frac{bc - ad}{c(cz+d)}$$

and can be obtained by superposition of the simpler mappings

$$\left.\begin{array}{l} \zeta = cz + d, \\[2mm] \omega = \dfrac{1}{\zeta}, \\[2mm] w = \dfrac{a}{c} + \dfrac{bc - ad}{c}\omega. \end{array}\right\} \qquad (14)$$

With the conventions adopted above it will be clear that $\omega = 0$ for $\zeta = \infty$, $\omega = \infty$ for $\zeta = 0$, and that the first and third mappings transform the point at infinity into the point at infinity.

The first and third of the mappings (14) are linear: each reduces to a magnification (or compression) followed by a rotation and a translation. It remains to determine the geometrical meaning of the second mapping; changing the notation, we write it as

$$w = \frac{1}{z}. \tag{15}$$

We suppose the z- and w-planes superposed so that corresponding coordinate axes coincide. The mapping (15) is then equivalent, in general, to the passage from the complex number z to the number $1/z$. The corresponding construction was considered in Art. 3 (Fig. 5); it reduces to carrying out two mappings in succession: (1) inversion with respect to the unit circle (that is, passage from the point z to the point $\zeta = 1/\bar{z}$, a process leaving the argument unchanged, but replacing the modulus r (say) by $1/r$); and (2) reflexion

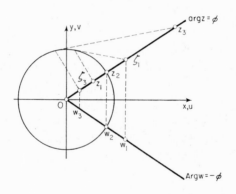

Fig. 21

in the real axis (that is, passage from the point ζ to the point $w = \bar{\zeta} = 1/z$, a process leaving the modulus unchanged but reversing the sign of the argument). It is obvious that, under this mapping (15), the disc $|z| < 1$ transforms into the circular domain $|w| > 1$ with centre at the point at infinity, the domain $|z| > 1$ into the disc $|w| < 1$, the circle $|z| = 1$ into the circle $|w| = 1$, and the ray $\arg z = \phi$ into the ray $\operatorname{Arg} w = -\phi$ (Fig. 21).

The derivative of the function $w = 1/z$ exists everywhere, except at the points $z = 0$ and $z = \infty$, and is given by $dw/dz = -1/z^2 (\neq 0)$. By Theorem 1, it follows that the mapping (15) is conformal throughout the entire closed plane, except at the points indicated.

In order to examine the character of the mapping at these exceptional points it is necessary to introduce the concept of the angle between two curves intersecting at infinity. As the angle between two curves is measured by the angle between their tangents, we may limit our definition to that of the angle between two straight lines intersecting at infinity. We use the fact that, in stereographic projection, the angle between two lines intersecting at a finite point is preserved (we omit the proof of this proposition). This gives the basis for our definition of the angle between *any* two straight lines (even when they intersect only at the point at infinity) as the angle between their representations on the sphere as circles intersecting at the north pole. With this convention we may say that the mapping (15) preserves angles even at the exceptional points. To illustrate this, consider two lines I and II, in the z-plane, intersecting at angle α at $z = 0$; under (15), these are transformed into lines I′ and II′, in the w-plane, intersecting at the same angle α, for it is clear that any ray arg $z = \phi$ maps on the ray Arg $w = -\phi$ (Fig. 21). The stereographic images of I′ and II′ on the w-sphere are

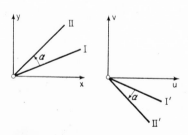

Fig. 22

great circles intersecting at $w = 0$ at angle α; these circles also intersect at the same angle α at the north pole $w = \infty$, and it was this angle which was taken in our definition as the angle between I′ and II′ at their intersection at infinity. The above argument shows that the mapping (15) preserves angles at $z = 0$; a similar argument shows that it has the same property at $z = \infty$.

It will also be clear that the mapping (15) transforms any closed disc with centre at the origin into a circular region $\bar{\Delta}$ whose representation on the sphere has for boundary a circle whose points are all at the same distance δ from the north pole (a situation justifying our description of $\bar{\Delta}$ as having "centre at infinity"), and *vice versa*. Interpreting a circle with centre at infinity (or a circular domain with centre at infinity) as having a "radius" determined in the same way as the distance δ, above, we can say that (15) has the properties (a'), (b') characterizing conformal mappings, not only for finite non-zero z, but also for the points $z = 0$, ∞ (see Art. 15).

It is clear that the other components in (14) of the bilinear mapping (12) are also conformal in the closed plane. As the result of superposing conformal mappings is, obviously, itself a conformal mapping, we conclude that the general bilinear mapping (12) is conformal in the closed plane.

The basic results obtained in this article can be formulated as

THEOREM 3. *The general bilinear function*

$$w = \frac{az+b}{cz+d} \quad (ad-bc \neq 0) \tag{12}$$

(*we suppose* $w = a/c$ *for* $z = \infty$) *gives a one–one conformal mapping of the closed z-plane onto the closed w-plane.*

19. The circle property

The equation of an arbitrary circle in the z-plane is

$$A(x^2+y^2)+Bx+Cy+D = 0, \tag{16}$$

where A, B, C, D are real, with A, B, C not all zero. Substituting

$$x = \frac{z+\bar{z}}{2}, \qquad y = \frac{z-\bar{z}}{2i}$$

it can be written

$$A z\bar{z}+\alpha z+\bar{\alpha}\bar{z}+D = 0, \tag{17}$$

where $\alpha = \frac{1}{2}(B-iC)$. For $A = 0$, equation (16) represents a straight line; we recall from Art. 5 that the locus in this case is considered to be a circle through the point at infinity.

Under the transformation (15), equation (17) becomes

$$A + \alpha \bar{w} + \bar{\alpha} w + D w \bar{w} = 0, \tag{18}$$

representing a circle on the w-sphere. Accordingly, (15) transforms any circle on the z-sphere into a circle on the w-sphere. A circle through $z = 0$ is transformed by (15) into a straight line, and any straight line of the z-plane is mapped onto a circle through $w = 0$; for, in the first case, the locus and its image are obtained from (17) and (18), respectively, by putting $D = 0$; in the second, they are obtained by taking $A = 0$ in the same equations. It will be clear that any line through $z = 0$ (obtained by taking $A = D = 0$ in (17)) is transformed into a line through $w = 0$.

The other components in (14) of the mapping (12) also transform any circle into another circle; it follows that (12) has the same property. This result expresses what is called the *circle property* of bilinear mappings:

THEOREM 4. *The general bilinear mapping*

$$w = \frac{az + b}{cz + d} \quad (ad - bc \neq 0)$$

(*we suppose* $w = a/c$ *for* $z = \infty$) *transforms any circle on the z-sphere into a circle on the w-sphere.*

Remark. Neglecting errors of order higher than ϵ, we can say that a general conformal mapping preserves the form of *small* circles of radius ϵ. The bilinear mapping preserves the form of *all* circles exactly.

20. Invariance of the conjugate points

Definition. We say the points z and ζ are *conjugate* or *inverse* with respect to a (proper) circle C in the plane if they lie on the same radius (and its continuation) as shown in Fig. 23 and satisfy

$$Oz \cdot O\zeta = R^2, \tag{19}$$

where O is the centre, and R is the radius, of C. We also say that the centre O is conjugate to the point at infinity.

In Arts. 3 and 18 we have met the particular case in which $R = 1$ and the centre of C coincides with the origin of coordinates. The method of constructing pairs of symmetrical points indicated in Fig. 5 holds good in the general case.

6

Let us construct a pencil of circles (Γ) each member Γ passing through points z and ζ which are conjugate with respect to the circle C (Fig. 23). Every circle Γ intersects C at right angles. For, by a well-known theorem of elementary geometry, the square of the length $O\omega$ of the tangent from O to the circle Γ is equal to the product of the secants from the external point O. By (19), this product equals R^2, so that $O\omega$ equals the radius R of C; it follows that the circles C, Γ are orthogonal.

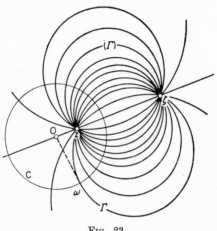

Fig. 23

Conversely, if the points z and ζ are the vertices of a pencil of circles, each member Γ being orthogonal to C, then these points are conjugate with respect to C. For the line $z\zeta$ belongs to the pencil and is orthogonal to C; accordingly, it passes through O. Also, Γ is orthogonal to C so that $O\omega = R$; by the theorem quoted above, $Oz \cdot O\zeta = O\omega^2 = R^2$. This gives the required result. We have thus established the following theorem:

THEOREM 5. *The necessary and sufficient condition that the points z and ζ be conjugate with respect to the circle C is that C be orthogonal to each member Γ of the pencil of circles (Γ) having vertices at z and ζ.*

It will be clear that this holds for the special case in which one of the points z, ζ is the point at infinity. (If $\zeta = \infty$, the pencil consists of lines through z, and C is any circle with centre z.) It extends to the case in which C is a line (that is, a circle through the point at infinity) by virtue of the following:

Definition. The (finite) points z and ζ are said to be *conjugate with respect to the line* C if every member of the pencil of circles with vertices z, ζ is orthogonal to C. This means simply that z and ζ are *symmetrical* with respect to the line C.

Interpreting "circle" as a proper circle or a straight line, we have:

THEOREM 6. *The general bilinear mapping transforms any pair of distinct points z and ζ which are conjugate with respect to the circle C into points w and ω which are conjugate with respect to the image C' of this circle.*

To prove this, we construct a pencil (Γ) of circles Γ passing through z and ζ; by Theorem 5 each Γ is orthogonal to C. By Theorem 4, C is transformed into the circle (or straight line) C', the pencil (Γ) into the pencil (Γ') of circles with vertices at the points w and ω. By Theorem 3, the pencil (Γ') is orthogonal to C' so that, by Theorem 5, the points w and ω are conjugate with respect to C'. (The case in which C' is a straight line clearly does not form an exception.)

Example. Let us find the net conformally equivalent to the polar-coordinate net in the mapping

$$w = \frac{z - z_1}{z - z_2}, \tag{20}$$

where z_1 and z_2 are arbitrary distinct points of the finite z-plane. Under the transformation (20), the points $z = z_1$ and $z = z_2$ map on the points $w = 0$ and $w = \infty$. It follows from Theorem 4 that the rays $\arg w = c_1$ (that is, the "semi-circles" joining the points $w = 0$ and $w = \infty$) correspond with arcs of circles joining the points z_1 and z_2 (these arcs are shown dotted in Fig. 24). Further, the points $w = 0$ and $w = \infty$ are conjugate with respect to any circle $|w| = c_2$. Hence, by Theorems 4 and 6, these circles correspond with the circles for which z_1 and z_2 are conjugate points (these circles are shown by full lines in Fig. 24). The two families of circles in the z-plane are mutually orthogonal.

Remark. We have shown in passing that the locus of a point z moving so that the ratio of its distances from two given points remains constant, a locus represented by the equation

$$|w| = \left| \frac{z - z_1}{z - z_2} \right| = \text{const.},$$

is a circle. This result is the well-known theorem of Apollonius; the circles

$$\left|\frac{z - z_1}{z - z_2}\right| = \text{const.}$$

are for this reason called the Circles of Apollonius.

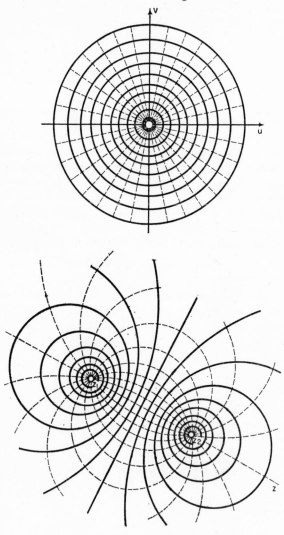

Fig. 24

21. Conditions determining bilinear mappings

The general bilinear mapping (12) depends on *three* complex parameters. At least *two* of the coefficients a, b, c, d must be non-zero; supposing, for example, that $c \neq 0$, we can write $(az+b)/(cz+d)$ as the function $(a'z+b')/(z+d')$ containing the *three* parameters $a' = a/c$, $b' = b/c$, $d' = d/c$.

The simplest problem involving the construction of a bilinear mapping is the following: given three distinct points z_1, z_2 and z_3 of the z-sphere and three distinct points w_1, w_2 and w_3 of the w-sphere, it is required to find the mapping (12) transforming z_k into w_k ($k = 1, 2, 3$). For finite z_k and w_k the required transformation is

$$\frac{w-w_1}{w-w_2} \cdot \frac{w_3-w_2}{w_3-w_1} = \frac{z-z_1}{z-z_2} \cdot \frac{z_3-z_2}{z_3-z_1}. \tag{21}$$

It is clear that, in this case, (21) is bilinear and maps z_k on w_k ($k = 1, 2, 3$). If one of the points z_k, or one of the points w_k, is the point at infinity, then the required mapping is obtained from (21) by substituting 1 for each difference involving the number (or numbers) concerned. For example, if $z_3 = \infty$ and $w_1 = \infty$, the required transformation is given by

$$\frac{1}{w-w_2} \cdot \frac{w_3-w_2}{1} = \frac{z-z_1}{z-z_2} \cdot \frac{1}{1},$$

or

$$w = w_2 + (w_3-w_2)\frac{z-z_2}{z-z_1}; \tag{22}$$

we easily verify that $w = \infty$ for $z = z_1$ and $w = w_2$ for $z = z_2$; the fact that $w = w_3$ for $z = \infty$ follows from the usual convention that $(az+b)/(cz+d)$ equals a/c when $z = \infty$ (see (12)).

We shall prove that the solution of the above problem represented by (21), or (for the case in which not all of the z_k and w_k are finite) by a formula such as (22), is unique. Suppose there exist *two* bilinear transformations $w = l_1(z)$ and $w = l_2(z)$, each mapping z_k onto w_k ($k = 1, 2, 3$). We construct the bilinear mapping $\omega = l(w)$ which transforms the w_k into $0, 1, \infty$ and consider the composite mappings

$$\omega' = l[l_1(z)] = L_1(z), \qquad \omega'' = l[l_2(z)] = L_2(z).$$

It is clear that each of these is a bilinear mapping which transforms the points z_k into the points 0, 1 and ∞. We now consider the transformation

$$\omega'' = L_2[L_1^{-1}(\omega')]$$

where L_1^{-1} is the mapping inverse to L_1. It is bilinear (that is, $\omega'' = [(a\omega'+b)/(c\omega'+d)]$) and maps each of the points 0, 1, ∞ onto itself. As $\omega'' = a/c = \infty$ for $\omega' = \infty$, we have $c = 0$, $a \neq 0$; as $\omega'' = b/d = 0$ for $\omega' = 0$, we have $b = 0$, $d \neq 0$, and it follows that $\omega'' = a\omega'/d$; finally, $\omega'' = 1$ for $\omega' = 1$, so that $a = d$, and we have $\omega'' = \omega$. Accordingly, L_1^{-1} is the inverse of L_2, so that $L_1 = L_2$. It follows that $l_1 = l_2$. We formulate this result as a theorem:

THEOREM 7. *There exists one and only one bilinear mapping transforming three given (distinct) points z_k on the z-sphere into three given (distinct) points w_k on the w-sphere, in order.*

This result ensures that we can find a mapping of the form (12) which transforms a given circle C on the z-sphere into a given circle C' on the w-sphere: by Theorem 4, it suffices to construct a bilinear mapping l which transforms any three points of C into three points of C'. For definiteness, suppose C and C' are *proper* circles, the former defining an interior domain D_i and exterior domain D_e; let the corresponding domains for C' be Δ_i and Δ_e. Suppose, if possible, that points z', z'' of D_i map on the respective points w', w'' where w' is in Δ_i and w'' in Δ_e, the rectilinear segment $z'z''$ having as image the arc $\overset{\frown}{w'w''}$; then the segment $z'z''$ does not intersect C, whereas its image $\overset{\frown}{w'w''}$ must intersect C'; clearly, this is impossible. It follows that the image of D_i must be either Δ_i or Δ_e. The general result will be clear.

In order to establish whether D_i maps on Δ_i or Δ_e, it suffices to find the image w of only a single point z of D_i: the image of D_i will be Δ_i or Δ_e according as whether w belongs to Δ_i or Δ_e. Alternatively, we may fix any three points z_1, z_2, z_3 taken in order on C so as to define a sense of description of C (indicated by the arrow in Fig. 25). If the corresponding images w_1, w_2, w_3 define a like sense of description of C', then the interior of C is mapped onto the interior of C' (Fig. 25, a); if they define the opposite sense of description of C', then D_i maps on the exterior of C' (Fig. 25, b). For, let us consider a point z on the radius of C passing through z_2.

The line segment z_2z maps onto a circular arc $\overparen{w_2w}$ orthogonal to C'. As the mapping is conformal, the angle $+\pi/2$ between the radius z_2z and the arc $\overparen{z_2z_1}$, must equal the angle between the arcs $\overparen{w_2w}$ and $\overparen{w_2w_1}$. It will be clear from Fig. 25 that w lies inside C' in case (a) and outside C' in case (b).

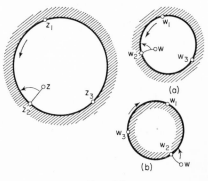

F<small>IG</small>. 25

We note that, in the chosen sense of description of C, the domain D_i (the interior of C) remains on the left. Under the bilinear mapping concerned, the corresponding sense of description of C' is such as to keep the image of D_i on the left, in both cases (a) and (b). Accordingly, we may say that the general bilinear mapping (12) preserves the sense of description of the boundary of any circular domain or region.

22. Particular examples

We find a bilinear mapping which transforms the upper half-plane onto the interior of the unit disc ($|w| < 1$) so that some given point z_0 of Im $z > 0$ maps on $w = 0$. By Theorem 6, $\bar{z}_0$ (the conjugate of z_0 with respect to the real axis) must map on $w = \infty$ (the conjugate of $w = 0$ with respect to the circle $|w| = 1$). Accordingly, the required mapping is of the form

$$w = k\frac{z - z_0}{z - \bar{z}_0}.$$

The coefficient k is determined by the requirement that points of the real axis $z = x$ map onto points of the circle $|w| = 1$: if z is real, then $\bar{z} = z$ and $\overline{z - z_0} = z - \bar{z}_0$ so that $|(z - z_0)/(z - \bar{z}_0)| = 1$; accordingly, $|k| = 1$ so that $k = e^{i\theta}$, and the required mapping is

$$w = e^{i\theta} \frac{z - z_0}{z - \bar{z}_0} \quad (\theta \text{ real}). \tag{23}$$

A solution is obtained by taking any given (real) value for θ in (23): for, any such transformation maps the "boundary circle" $y = 0$ onto the circle $|w| = 1$ and the point z_0 of the upper half-plane onto a point of the disc $|w| < 1$. Changing θ in the formula (23) is geometrically equivalent to rotating the disc $|w| < 1$ about the origin $w = 0$; a rotation such as this does not vary the conditions of the problem. Figure 26 shows the conformal equivalent of the polar-coordinate net in the disc $|w| < 1$. It is obviously part of the net shown in the upper part of Fig. 24.

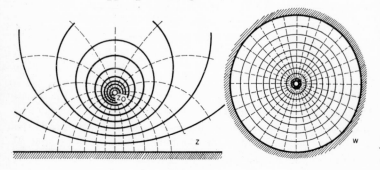

FIG. 26

We now find a bilinear mapping of the unit disc $|z| < 1$ onto the unit disc $|w| < 1$ such that some given point $z = z_0$ of the first domain maps onto the centre of the second domain. The point $1/\bar{z}_0$, the conjugate of z_0 with respect to $|z| = 1$, must map onto the point $w = \infty$; the desired mapping thus has the form

$$w = k_1 \frac{z - z_0}{z - (1/\bar{z}_0)} = k \frac{z - z_0}{1 - \bar{z}_0 z},$$

where $k = -k_1 \bar{z}_0$ is some constant. In order to determine k we use the fact that points $z = e^{i\phi}$ of the circle $|z| = 1$ must transform into points of $|w| = 1$:

$$1 = \left| k \frac{e^{i\phi} - z_0}{1 - \bar{z}_0 e^{i\phi}} \right| = |k| \cdot |e^{i\phi}| \cdot \left| \frac{1 - z_0 e^{-i\phi}}{1 - \bar{z}_0 e^{i\phi}} \right|.$$

As $|e^{i\phi}| = 1$ and the conjugate of $1 - \bar{z}_0 e^{i\phi}$ is $1 - z_0 e^{-i\phi}$, it follows that $|k| = 1$ so that $k = e^{i\theta}$ (θ real); accordingly, the required mapping is of the form

$$w = e^{i\theta}\frac{z - z_0}{1 - \bar{z}_0 z} \quad (\theta \text{ real}). \tag{24}$$

For each (real) value of θ, (24) provides a solution of the proposed problem; changing θ is equivalent to rotating the disc $|w| < 1$ about the origin $w = 0$. Clearly, we may suppose $-\pi < \theta \leqslant \pi$.

The derivative of the function (24) at the point $z = z_0$ is

$$w_0' = \left[e^{i\theta}\frac{1 - z_0\bar{z}_0}{(1 - \bar{z}_0 z)^2} \right]_{z=z_0} = e^{i\theta}\frac{1}{1 - r_0^2} ,$$

where $r_0 = |z_0| < 1$. It follows that $\theta = \arg w_0'$, so that θ gives the angle of rotation of the mapping (24) at the point z_0. Thus, by a suitable choice of z_0 and θ, we can always ensure that any given point of $|z| < 1$ is mapped on $w = 0$ and that any given direction at this point is made to correspond with the direction of the positive u-axis: for, under the transformation (24), any curve touching the ray $\mathrm{Arg}\,(z - z_0) = -\theta$ at its end-point z_0 is mapped onto a curve touching the axis $v = 0$ at $w = 0$.

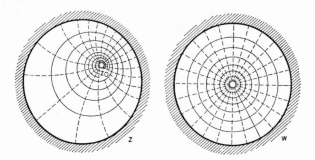

Fig. 27

Figure 27 shows the conformal equivalent of the polar-coordinate net in the disc $|w| < 1$. This is also part of the net in Fig. 24. Our mapping deforms the interior and boundary of the region $|z| \leqslant 1$, leaving each unchanged as a whole.

We note that the bilinear transformation of the *disc* $|z| < R$ onto the disc $|w| < 1$ such that the point z_0 ($|z_0| < 1$) maps onto the origin $w = 0$ is

$$w = e^{i\theta}\frac{R(z-z_0)}{R^2-\bar{z}_0 z}\,.\tag{25}$$

This formula is obtained from (24) by replacing z by z/R and z_0 by z_0/R.

23. General principles of the theory of conformal mapping

The bilinear function gives a one–one conformal mapping of the closed z-plane onto the closed w-plane. It can be shown that no other type of function has this property: if $w = f(z)$ is not bilinear and gives a one–one conformal mapping of a domain D on a domain Δ then D and Δ are both *proper* subsets of their corresponding spheres.

In the preceding sections we saw that it is always possible to carry out a one–one conformal mapping of an arbitrary circular domain of the z-sphere onto an arbitrary circular domain of the w-sphere by finding a suitable bilinear function; one, or both, of these domains may degenerate into a half-plane.

The question arises as to whether we can always find a one–one conformal mapping of an arbitrary domain D onto an arbitrary domain Δ. In general, no such mapping exists. For example, it is not possible to find a one–one conformal mapping of a multiply-connected domain D onto a simply-connected domain Δ. Not stopping for a complete proof, we shall indicate briefly why such a mapping is not possible. Let us suppose there exists a one–one conformal mapping of D onto the domain Δ. We may suppose D does not contain the point at infinity. (As D is multiply-connected its frontier consists of *at least two* separate components and hence contains at least one finite point z_0. Under the bilinear mapping $\zeta = 1/(z-z_0)$, the point z_0—which does not belong to the open set D—maps on $\zeta = \infty$, and D maps on a domain D' in the open ζ-plane. If necessary we can, in this way, replace D by a domain consisting of finite points only.) We think of D as represented on the plane and Δ as represented on the sphere. Let C be a closed curve in D which encloses points not belonging to D; as D is multiply-connected, such a curve always exists. In the mapping of D onto Δ, the image of C is a closed curve γ consisting of points of Δ. As Δ is simply-connected, it is possible to shrink γ into a point (of Δ) by a continuous deformation in which γ remains within Δ. By the continuity of the inverse mapping, the corresponding curve C in D must also shrink to a point in D without leaving D; clearly, this is impossible.

For simply-connected domains, however, the following is true:

THEOREM *on existence and uniqueness of mappings of simply-connected domains: Let D and Δ be any simply-connected domains, each having a frontier (on the sphere) consisting of more than one point. Let z_0 and w_0 be any finite points of D and Δ, respectively, and let θ_0 be any number of the interval $(-\pi, \pi)$. Then, there exists a unique one–one conformal mapping of D onto Δ satisfying the conditions*

$$f(z_0) = w_0, \qquad \arg f'(z_0) = \theta_0. \qquad (26)$$

The proof of this theorem is beyond the scope of the present book and is therefore omitted. Reasons for demanding that each frontier contain more than one point (so that neither domain coincides with the *complete* sphere or is obtained therefrom by abstracting a *single* point) are given later, in Art. 53.

Remark 1. The possibility of the above mapping will be established if it can be shown that each of the domains D and Δ can be mapped, one–one and conformally, onto the upper half-plane or onto the unit disc. For example, let the functions $\zeta = f(z)$ and $\zeta = g(w)$ give one–one conformal mappings of the respective domains D and Δ onto the disc $|\zeta| < 1$; and let $w = \phi(\zeta)$ be the mapping inverse to $\zeta = g(w)$. Then, the composite function

$$w = \phi[f(z)] = F(z)$$

gives a one–one conformal mapping of the domain D onto Δ.

If, however, we know one such mapping $\zeta = f(z)$ of the domain D onto the unit disc we can construct infinitely many of them by means of a supplementary general mapping of the unit disc $|\zeta| < 1$ onto the disc $|w| < 1$. The latter is obtained from (24) by replacing z by ζ and z_0 by ζ_0; the point ζ_0 chosen to be mapped on $w = 0$ is an arbitrary point of the disc, and the angle of rotation at ζ_0 can be made to have any given value by a suitable choice of θ.

Remark 2. The relations (26) show that the mapping in the above theorem depends on three real parameters (the first relation expresses an equality between complex numbers and is equivalent to two equations between real numbers). The conditions (26), which determine the mapping uniquely, can be replaced by others also depending on three real parameters. For example, suppose the boundary C of D is a piecewise-smooth closed curve, so that any point of the boundary can be defined by its distance along C (in the positive sense) from some fixed point of C; if, then, the position of a boundary point of either domain can be defined in some such way by a single real parameter, the conditions (26) can be replaced by prescribing the image w_0 of some interior point z_0 of D and the image w_1, of some point z_1 on the boundary of D:

$$f(z_0) = w_0, \qquad f(z_1) = w_1$$

(here, w_0 is an interior point of Δ and w_1 is a point on the boundary Γ of Δ); alternatively, we could prescribe the images w_k ($k = 1, 2, 3$) on Γ of three selected points z_k on C:

$$f(z_k) = w_k \quad (k = 1, 2, 3).$$

Conditions such as the above are said to *normalize* the conformal mapping considered in our theorem.

We emphasize that in the basic theory we are only concerned with mapping the *interior* of the domain D onto the *interior* of the unit circle. What is the correspondence between the boundaries in the mapping? Before answering this question we must remind the reader of the restrictions imposed in Art. 6: a domain D will be *admissible* if its frontier C is bounded and consists of a finite number of simple closed curves, cuts, and isolated points (all curves and cuts being piecewise smooth), as indicated by Figs. 9 and 28; or if D is the image of such a domain under a bilinear mapping. We shall also suppose that the two *edges* of any cut represent distinct parts of the boundary and that other singular points on the boundary are accorded a similar multiplicity corresponding to the number of times any such point is encountered in one complete circuit of the boundary; for example, in the case shown in Fig. 28, only one boundary point lies at z_1, whereas *four* coincide at z_3, *two* at z_2, and *two* at z_4. With this understanding we can show, in the context of the above theorem, that, if the domain Δ has a boundary Γ consisting of finite points only, the mapping function $f(z)$ can be defined uniquely and finitely at each point z of C (the boundary of D) as the limit of $f(z_n)$ where $\{z_n\}$ is any sequence of points in

D which tends to z as $n \to +\infty$; the function thus defined on $\overline{D}$ is called the *extension* of f to $\overline{D}$. Under these conventions we have the following:

THEOREM *on the correspondence of boundaries. If, in the above theorem, the domains D and Δ are admissible, Δ having a boundary lying in the open plane, and $f(z)$ denotes the extension of the mapping function to $\overline{D}$, then*

(a) $w = f(z)$ *establishes a one–one correspondence between the boundaries C and Γ (multiplicity of boundary points being considered, as indicated above); and*

(b) *if C also lies in the open plane and if we define the derivative of $f(z)$ at a point z of C as the limit of $\{f(z') - f(z)\}/(z' - z)$ as $z' \to z$ through points of C, then this derivative is continuous (on the set C) at all boundary points where C has a continuously-turning tangent; at angular points of C this derivative either does not exist or is equal to 0 or ∞.*

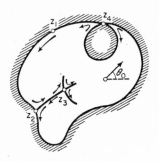

FIG. 28

We also note that the property established in Art. 21 for the mapping (12) holds more generally:

If D and Δ satisfy the requirements of (a) *above, the sense of description of the boundary is preserved under the mapping $w = f(z)$.* Thus, if C is traversed so that D remains on the left, the corresponding circuit of Γ will be such as to leave Δ on the left. (In advanced courses on real analysis it is shown that this property is characteristic of one–one continuous mappings having a non-negative Jacobian; it is clear from (4) in Art. 15 that this requirement is satisfied for conformal mappings.)

A result of great importance in practical applications is the following:

Principle of correspondence of boundaries: Let D and Δ be simply-connected domains whose boundaries (C and Γ) are closed curves, with $\overline{D}$ and $\overline{\Delta}$ contained in the finite plane; and let $w = f(z)$, regular in D and continuous on $\overline{D}$, establish a one–one mapping of C on Γ. Then, $w = f(z)$ gives a one–one conformal mapping of D onto Δ.

In conclusion, we state the important *principle of preservation of domains: If $w = f(z)$ is regular, and not constant, in the domain D then it maps D on a set Δ which is also a domain.*

It should be observed that this principle is of a very general nature. As noted in Remark 3 to Theorem 1 of the present chapter, if $f'(z_0) \neq 0$ the function $w = f(z)$ gives a one–one mapping of some neighbourhood γ of the point z_0 onto a neighbourhood of the point $w_0 = f(z_0)$ of the w-plane. In general, the mapping of the whole domain D onto Δ will not be one–one: Δ will be a domain on the "Riemann surface of the function $f(z)$". These surfaces will be studied in the next chapter. It will be shown that points where $f'(z) = 0$ correspond to "branch points" of the Riemann surface; in the neighbourhood of such points the mapping ceases to be one–one in the simple sense. However, the principle of preservation of domains holds even when D contains such points; it will be found that their images are interior points of Δ.

Accounts of the main results in this article are given by Carathéodory (*Theory of Functions*, Chelsea, 1954), Littlewood (*Theory of Functions*, Oxford, 1944), and Nehari (*Conformal Mapping*, McGraw-Hill, 1952).

Exercises

1. Let $w = f(z) = u(x, y) + iv(x, y)$ be defined in a neighbourhood of the point z. Show that for the differentiability of $f(z)$ at the point z it is necessary and sufficient that $du + i\,dv$, where du and dv are differentials of the real functions u and v, should be proportional to $dx + i\,dy$ (the coefficient of proportionality depending on z only).

2. Explain how to find the length of the image of the curve C and the area of the image of the domain D under the one–one conformal mapping $w = f(z)$.

3. Find the coefficient of magnification and the angle of rotation in the mapping $w = (z-i)/(z+i)$ at the points $z_1 = -1$ and $z_2 = i$.

4. Find the area of the image Δ of the square $0 < x < 1$, $0 < y < 1$ under the mapping $w = z^2$ and find the length of the boundary of Δ.

5. Find the length of the image of the circle $|z| = 1$ under the mapping $w = \sqrt{(z+1)}$. (See Exercise 11(d) of Chapter 1.)

6. Show that the conditions that the net $u(x, y) = c_1$, $v(x, y) = c_2$ be equivalent, under a simple conformal mapping $w = u+iv = f(z)$, to a Cartesian coordinate net are expressed by the relations $(\text{grad } u) \cdot (\text{grad } v) = 0$ (the dot denoting the usual scalar product) and $|\text{grad } u| = |\text{grad } v|$.

7. Find the principal linear part of the mapping $w = z^2$ at the point $z = i$. Estimate the extent to which the mapping diverges from this principal linear part in the circle $|z - i| < 0 \cdot 1$.

8. D is a bounded domain of the z-plane exterior to each of three circles which touch externally, in pairs, one point of contact being the origin. Find the image of D under the mapping $w = 1/z$.

9. Find the image of the half-strip $0 < x < 1$, $y > 0$ under the mapping $w = 1/z$.

10. Find a one–one conformal mapping of the annulus between the circles $|z| = 1$ and $|z-1| = 5/2$ onto an annulus $1 < |w| < R$. Determine the value of R.

11. Find all bilinear transformations mapping each of the points $z = \pm 1$ onto itself.

12. Find the conformal mapping of the disc $|z| < 1$ onto the half-plane Im $w > 0$, in which the points -1, 1, i map onto the respective points ∞, 0, 1.

13. Find the conformal mapping of the upper half-plane onto itself which maps the points ∞, 0, 1 onto 0, 1, ∞, respectively.

14. Find the conformal mapping $w = f(z)$ of the upper half-plane Im $z > 0$ onto a disc $|w| < R$ such that $f(i) = 0$, $f'(i) = 1$. Determine the value of R.

15. What is the geometrical meaning of θ in formula (23)? Find the image of the Cartesian coordinate net in the z-plane under the mapping (23).

16. Find the bilinear mapping of the upper half-plane which transforms three given points a_1, a_2, and a_3 of the real axis $(a_1 < a_2 < a_3)$ into 0, 1 and ∞, respectively.

17. Find conditions under which $w = (az+b)/(cz+d)$ maps the upper half-plane onto itself. (The z- and w-planes are supposed to coincide.)

CHAPTER III

ELEMENTARY FUNCTIONS

24. The functions $w = z^n$ and their Riemann surfaces

The function

$$w = z^2 \tag{1}$$

was considered in Arts. 11 and 16. Taking polar coordinates $z = re^{i\phi}$, $w = \rho e^{i\theta}$, we can express (1) by two real equations

$$\rho = r^2, \qquad \theta = 2\phi \tag{2}$$

from which the geometrical meaning of this mapping is quite clear. If $z_1^2 = z_2^2$ then

$$z_1 = \pm z_2; \tag{3}$$

it follows that the images of distinct points z_1, z_2 will coincide if, and only if, they are situated symmetrically with respect to the origin. In order that (1) be one–one in the domain D it is necessary and sufficient that D should not contain any two (distinct) points connected by the relation (3).

This condition is satisfied, in particular, by the upper half-plane $0 < r < +\infty$, $0 < \phi < \pi$; as seen from (2), the function $w = z^2$ maps this half-plane onto the w-plane slit along the positive real axis. Figures 16 and 20 show the correspondence of the lines in this mapping; it is conformal everywhere, except at the points $z = 0$ and $z = \infty$ (see Art. 16). (Strictly speaking, the function (1) is not defined at the point $z = \infty$; we extend the definition by taking $\lim\limits_{z \to \infty} z^2 = \infty$ as the value of z^2 at $z = \infty$.)

Similarly, the lower half-plane $0 < r < +\infty$, $\pi < \phi < 2\pi$ is mapped onto the whole w-plane with a cut along the positive real axis. Clearly, (1) maps the whole of the z-plane onto the whole of the w-plane; the mapping is single-valued but not one–one: each point w, other than $w = 0$ and $w = \infty$, is the image of two distinct points z. This property entails certain consequences which cannot ensue for one–one mappings: for example, the arc $|z| = 1$, $0 \leqslant \phi < \pi$, a set which is not closed, is transformed by (1) into the *closed* circle $|w| = 1$.

It will be shown that there is a geometrical method of representing the complex numbers w which enables us to consider the mapping (1) as one–one in the whole z-plane. We take two planes ("sheets"), each representing the w-plane and each having a cut along the positive real axis; we consider the first sheet (I) to carry the images of points in $\text{Im } z > 0$ and the second (II) to carry the images of points in $\text{Im } z < 0$. Sheet II is placed above sheet I so that points with identical coordinates are one above the other. To ensure continuity of the mapping $w = z^2$ along the negative x-axis we join together the lower edge of the cut in I (the image of the negative x-axis in the mapping of the upper half-plane) and the upper edge of the cut in II (the image of the negative x-axis in the mapping of the lower half-plane), the join being closed by a ray l_1 lying above the positive u-axis (Fig. 29).

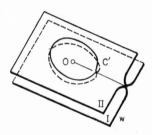

Fig. 29

It remains to ensure continuity of the mapping (1) along the positive x-axis. For this we join the remaining free edges of the cuts, the upper edge of the cut in I to the lower edge of the cut in II, with the help of a ray l_2 lying above the positive u-axis; to preserve biuniformity of the mapping (1), the ray l_2 must be considered to be distinct from the ray l_1 used to make the previous join, although these rays must coincide in any geometrical representation (see Fig. 29). Only the *ends* of these rays, lying above the points $w = 0$ and $w = \infty$ will be considered to be identical.

The two-sheeted surface R constructed above is called the

7

Riemann surface of the function $w = z^2$. It is distributed over the whole w-plane, so that above each point, other than $w = 0$ and $w = \infty$, there lie two distinct points of R belonging to its different sheets.[†] Above each of the points $w = 0$ and $w = \infty$ there is only one point of R. If the point z goes once round the point $z = 0$ along the circle $|z| = r$, then by virtue of equations (2) the image point w will go twice round the point $w = 0$ along the circle $|w| = \rho$. These circuits can be interpreted equally well (as is clear from the spherical representation) as circuits about the corresponding points at infinity. This is the reason for describing the points of R lying above $w = 0$, ∞ as *branch points of the second order*. At these points we consider the sheets of the surface R to be joined together.

By our construction, the function $w = z^2$ gives a *uniform and continuous map of the closed z-plane onto its Riemann surface*. To clarify this point, we consider the correspondence set up between points of the unit circle C and points of its image C' on the surface R. The upper semi-circle of C (defined by $0 < \phi < \pi$) is transformed into the circle $|w| = 1$, with the omission of the point $w = 1$, lying on sheet I. The lower semi-circle of C (defined by $\pi < \phi < 2\pi$) transforms into the same "broken" circle on sheet II. We now make a criss-cross join of the four free ends of our circles, adding two junction points which we shall consider *distinct* although they coincide geometrically. The resulting curve C', which is closed and free from self-intersections (double points) and lies on both sheets of the Riemann surface above the circle $|w| = 1$, will represent a one–one and continuous image of C (see Fig. 29).

Further light on the nature of the Riemann surface is supplied by the following analogues. The real analogue of (1), the function $y = x^2$, maps the x-axis onto the non-negative y-axis. This mapping is one-valued, but not one–one; each of the pair of points A and B, corresponding to abscissae differing only in sign, is transformed onto the same point $A'' = B''$ (Fig. 30). However, by taking two separate representations of the positive y-axis, joined together at the points $y = 0$ and $y = +\infty$ we may consider that A'' lies on the one and B'' on the other; the function $y = x^2$ can then be considered as giving a biuniform mapping of the x-axis onto the

---

[†] Points of the finite positive u-axis do not constitute exceptions, for we agreed to consider points of self-intersection of the surface R, arising from the crossing of its sheets, as non-existent.

"doubled" y-axis ($y \geqslant 0$). The geometrical meaning of the mapping $y = x^2$ becomes clearer if we draw the parabola $y = x^2$ in the (x, y) plane and consider that every point A'' is obtained from A by a double projection, first of A into A' and then of A' into A'' (Fig. 30). The doubled y-axis ($y \geqslant 0$) can be considered as the projection of the parabola $y = x^2$ or as its one-dimensional model.

A similar procedure can be carried out with the function $w = z^2$.

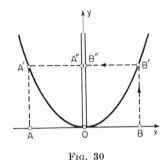

FIG. 30

The equation $w = z^2$ is equivalent to two real equations

$$u = x^2 - y^2, \qquad v = 2xy \qquad (4)$$

which define a two-dimensional surface in four-dimensional space (x, y, u, v)†. This surface cannot be exhibited in a three-dimensional space, just as the above parabola could not be exhibited on the y-axis, and we must consider its projection on the (u, v) plane of the four-dimensional space, a plane coinciding with the plane of $w = u + iv$. Our Riemann surface then appears from the "doubling" of a w-plane, just as a "doubled" y-axis rose in the representation of $y = x^2$.

Our analogy explains the presence of the disregarded self-intersections of the Riemann surface. Such self-intersections can emerge when a geometrical form is studied by some projection of this form. For example, if a plane curve in the form of a figure eight appears as the projection of a three-dimensional loop having no double points, then its point of self-intersection is not to be regarded as having any significance (Fig. 31).

---

† In this space there are four axes, x, y, u, v; each pair of axes defines a coordinate plane [there are six such pairs: (x,y), (x,u), (x,v), (y,u), (y,v), (u,v)].

The function

$$w = z^n \qquad (5)$$

has similar properties for any positive integral n (we put $w = \infty$ for $z = \infty$). Expressed in polar coordinates, (5) is equivalent to the two real equations

$$\rho = r^n, \qquad \theta = n\phi; \qquad (6)$$

the geometrical significance of these will be obvious.

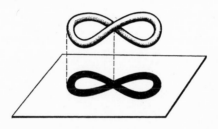

FIG. 31

In order that (5) be one–one in the domain D it is necessary and sufficient that D should not contain two distinct points with the same modulus and with arguments differing by a multiple of $2\pi/n$; two distinct points of the z-plane are merged under the mapping (5) if, and only if, they are related in this way. In particular, (5) is one–one in each of the sectors defined by

$$\frac{2\pi}{n}k < \phi < \frac{2\pi}{n}(k+1) \quad (k = 0, 1, \dots, n-1);$$

each such sector is mapped onto the w-plane cut along the positive real axis. We take n superposed planes, each cut in this way, and join them together by means of n rays arranged along the positive u-axis, in accordance with the scheme indicated in Fig. 32 for the case $n = 5$. We consider these n rays to be distinct from one another and attached only at their ends, situated at the points $w = 0$ and $w = \infty$. The n-sheeted surface so constructed is called the *Riemann surface* of the function $w = z^n$.

It will be seen from (6) that, when the point z goes once round the point $z = 0$ along the circle $|z| = r$, the image point w goes n times round the point $w = 0$ along the circle $|w| = \rho$. As before, these circuits may be considered as taken about the corresponding points at infinity. This is the reason for speaking of the points of R situated above $w = 0$ and $w = \infty$ as *branch points of order* n.

The function $w = z^n$ gives a one–one and continuous mapping of the closed z-plane onto the Riemann surface R. Like (1), the mapping (5) is conformal everywhere, except at the points $z = 0$ and $z = \infty$; at these branch points it increases angles by a factor n.

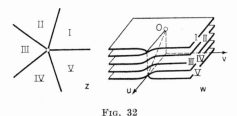

F<small>IG</small>. 32

25. The concept of a regular branch. The functions $w = \sqrt[n]{z}$.

Definition. A function $f(z)$ regular in the domain D is called a *regular branch* of the many-valued function $F(z)$ in this domain, if $f(z)$ coincides in value at each point z of D with one of the values of $F(z)$ at this point.

A regular branch of a many-valued function $F(z)$ is obviously a one-valued and continuous branch of $F(z)$.

Consider, for example, the function

$$w = \sqrt{z}, \tag{7}$$

the inverse of the function $z = w^2$. This function gives a single-valued (uniform) mapping of the two-sheeted Riemann surface R onto the w-plane when we adopt the following convention. Suppose $z = re^{i\alpha}$ $(0 < r < +\infty,\ 0 < \alpha < 2\pi)$. The corresponding values of $\sqrt{z}$ are $w_1 = (\sqrt{r})e^{i\alpha/2}$ and $w_2 = -(\sqrt{r})e^{i\alpha/2}$; the first (lying in the upper half-plane) is the image of the point on sheet I coinciding with z, the second (lying in the lower half-plane) is the image of the corresponding point on sheet II. The ray joining the lower edge of sheet I to the upper edge of II is associated with points on the positive u-axis; the ray joining the lower edge of sheet II to the upper edge of I is associated with points on the negative u-axis. The points $z = 0,\ \infty$ at which these rays are joined are associated with the respective values $w = 0,\ \infty$; these points are called *branch points* of the function $\sqrt{z}$.

If we examine the conditions which must be satisfied by a domain

D of the z-plane in order that a branch of $\sqrt{z}$ be regular in D, we see that these require that it be possible to exhibit D *without cuts* on the Riemann surface R, so that D does not meet branch points: it must be possible to arrange D on a single sheet of R or else descending from one sheet to the other (like a carpet on a spiral staircase). For example, the annulus $1 < |z| < 2$ can be displayed on R only by making a suitable cut (say, along a radius).

Assuming that D can be displayed on R in this way we can define a single-valued and continuous branch of $\sqrt{z}$ on D. Conversely, given any such branch, the arrangement of D on R is determined, since the value of $\sqrt{z}$ at any point z of D determines the sheet (or joining-ray) containing this point; at any such point we have (by the theorem on the derivative of an inverse function)

$$\frac{\mathrm{d}w}{\mathrm{d}z} = \frac{1}{2w} = \frac{1}{2\sqrt{z}}$$

where $\sqrt{z}$ denotes the value of w associated with the point z on R. It follows that the function concerned is a *regular* branch of $\sqrt{z}$.

For example, within the annulus $1 < |z| < 2$, cut along a radius, it is possible to construct a regular branch of $\sqrt{z}$; at matching points on the two edges of the cut this branch will assume distinct values, differing in sign. Within the complete annulus $1 < |z| < 2$ the function $\sqrt{z}$ does not have a regular branch. Similarly, $\sqrt{z}$ does not have a regular branch in the domain shown in Fig. 33 (a) since this domain contains the branch point $z = 0$. Regular branches of this function do exist in the domains shown in Fig. 33 (b) and (c), the branch points of $\sqrt{z}$ lying on their boundaries and not in their interiors.

If a domain D can be displayed continuously on the Riemann surface R, this arrangement can take either of two forms. For example, the open disc in Fig. 33 (b) can be arranged on R with the upper semi-disc on sheet I and the lower on sheet II; or with the upper semi-disc on II and the lower on I. These arrangements correspond with the two branches of $\sqrt{z}$ which are regular in the disc and differ only in sign at any point of the disc.

We note that the value taken for $\sqrt{z}$ determines the particular sheet on which z is displayed; it will be clear that the problem of constructing a regular branch of $\sqrt{z}$ in D is equivalent to that of constructing a continuous and uniform branch of $\operatorname{Arg} z$ in this domain.

Consider, for example, the domain D in Fig. 33 (c). We associate some fixed point, say $z_0 = 1$, with a particular value of its argument, say $\phi_0 = 0$, and take $\sqrt{z_0}$ to be

$$(\sqrt{z_0})_0 = +1.$$

At any other point z of D we take the argument of z to be ϕ where ϕ is the angle (measured positive in the anticlockwise sense) through which the radius vector $O\zeta$ rotates when ζ moves from z_0 to z along

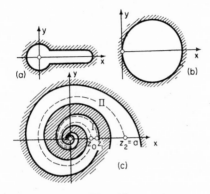

Fig. 33

any continuous path *lying in* D; the corresponding value of $\sqrt{z}$ is taken to be $(\sqrt{|z|})e^{i\phi/2}$. Thus, when z moves from z_0 to z_1 along path I, ϕ increases through positive values, then decreases to zero, and $\sqrt{z_1}$ is positive; if, however, z moves from z_0 to $z_2 = a$ $(a > 0)$ along path II, ϕ decreases, finally becoming equal to -2π, and we obtain a negative value for $\sqrt{z_2}$:

$$\sqrt{z_2} = (\sqrt{a})e^{-i\pi} = -\sqrt{a}.$$

Finally, let D denote the z-plane cut along the positive real axis; this domain can be arranged on the Riemann surface corresponding to $w = \sqrt{z}$ in two ways, each being associated with a regular branch of this function. We consider a branch of $\sqrt{z}$ which is regular in D and maps D on the upper half-plane $\text{Im } w > 0$. As $z = w^2$, we have

$$x = u^2 - v^2, \qquad y = 2uv.$$

First we put $u = \alpha$ and eliminate v; then we put $v = \beta$ $(\beta > 0)$

and eliminate u; the resulting equations,

$$x = \alpha^2 - \frac{y^2}{4\alpha^2}, \quad x = \frac{y^2}{4\beta^2} - \beta^2,$$

representing families of parabolas with axes along Ox (see Fig. 76), give the conformal equivalent of the Cartesian coordinate net in $\operatorname{Im} w > 0$.

For positive integral n the function $\sqrt[n]{z}$ has properties similar to those of $\sqrt{z}$. It is uniform on the appropriate n-sheeted Riemann surface placed over the z-plane and maps this surface onto the complete w-plane. It provides an example of a many-valued analytic function (see Art. 63), and can be separated into (one-valued) regular branches in any domain D in which it is possible to separate a single-valued *continuous* branch of Arg z.

As an example of a multiform function we now consider

$$w = \sqrt{\{(z-a)(z-b)\}}. \tag{8}$$

Putting $z-a = r_1 e^{i\phi_1}$, $z-b = r_2 e^{i\phi_2}$, we have

$$w = [\sqrt{(r_1 r_2)}]e^{i(\phi_1+\phi_2)/2}.$$

We superpose two z-planes, each being cut along the segment $[a, b]$. A regular branch of (8) exists in each of these domains. When z traces one complete circuit of the contour I (Fig. 34), a

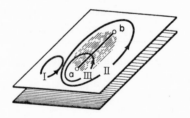

Fig. 34

contour which does not enclose the points a and b, the arguments ϕ_1 and ϕ_2 (supposed to vary continuously) return to their original values; and when z makes a positive circuit of the contour II enclosing both the points a and b, each of the arguments increases by 2π, so that $(\phi_1+\phi_2)/2$ also increases by 2π and w returns to its original value. The cut does not allow z to make a circuit of the contour III enclosing one only of the points a, b; were such a circuit possible it would be accompanied by a change in the value of w.

We now make the obvious criss-cross join of the edges of the cuts, with the help of two segments $[a, b]$; matching interior points of these segments are considered to be distinct, although geometrically they coincide. We shall call the resulting surface the *Riemann surface* for the function $w = \sqrt{\{(z-a)(z-b)\}}$; it is two-sheeted, with two branch points†, each of the second order, above the points $z = a$ and $z = b$. The function (8) is uniform and continuous on this surface and maps it onto the complete w-plane. This mapping is not one–one since the function

$$z = \frac{a+b}{2} + \sqrt{\left\{\left(\frac{a-b}{2}\right)^2 + w^2\right\}}$$

inverse to (8) is two-valued in the w-plane.

26. The function $w = \frac{1}{2}[z+(1/z)]$ and its Riemann surface

We first seek the conditions under which the mapping

$$w = \frac{1}{2}\left(z + \frac{1}{z}\right) \tag{9}$$

is one–one. The equation

$$z_1 + \frac{1}{z_1} = z_2 + \frac{1}{z_2}$$

can be written

$$(z_1 - z_2)\left(1 - \frac{1}{z_1 z_2}\right) = 0;$$

it follows that w has the same value at distinct points z_1, z_2 if, and only if,

$$z_1 z_2 = 1. \tag{10}$$

---

† Both branches of the function (8) have the common value ∞ at $z = \infty$; the two sheets are not, however, joined at the point $z = \infty$. The reason for this is clear when we study the function (8) in the neighbourhood of $z = \infty$: *one* complete circuit about $z = \infty$ along a contour such as II (Fig. 34) is accompanied by *one* complete circuit about the point $w = \infty$, and conversely. The reader should make a careful study of this feature of the function (8).

For this reason (9) is one–one in a domain D if, and only if, D does not contain two distinct points z_1, z_2 connected by equation (10). This condition is satisfied, for example, by the interior of the unit circle, $|z| < 1$, or by its exterior, $|z| > 1$.

To explain the geometrical meaning of the mapping (9) we write $z = re^{i\phi}$, $w = u+iv$; equation (9) is equivalent to the two real equations

$$u = \frac{1}{2}\left(r + \frac{1}{r}\right)\cos\phi, \qquad v = \frac{1}{2}\left(r - \frac{1}{r}\right)\sin\phi. \qquad (11)$$

It follows from (11) that (9) transforms the circle $|z| = r$ ($r < 1$) into an ellipse with semi-axes

$$a_r = \frac{1}{2}\left(r + \frac{1}{r}\right), \qquad b_r = -\frac{1}{2}\left(r - \frac{1}{r}\right),$$

the foci being the points $(\pm 1, 0)$. As $r - (1/r)$ is negative when $0 < r < 1$, it follows from (11) that when $|z| = r$ is described in the positive sense the corresponding ellipse is described in the negative sense. As $r \to +0$, the semi-axes a_r, b_r both tend to $+\infty$ while $a_r - b_r = r \to +0$; that is, the elliptical image expands, approximating more closely to a circle. As $r \to 1-0$, a_r and b_r tend, respectively, to 1 and 0; that is, the ellipse degenerates into the segment $[-1, 1]$ of the u-axis. It will thus be clear that (9) gives a one–one mapping of the disc $|z| < 1$ *onto the exterior of the segment* $[-1, 1]$ *of the real axis in the w-plane.*

The circle $|z| = 1$ maps onto the doubled segment $[-1, 1]$ each of the points -1 and 1 being transformed into itself. We think of the upper semi-circle as mapping on the lower of these segments (that is, on the lower edge of the *cut* $[-1, 1]$); for, when $0 < \phi < \pi$, it will be clear from (11) that $v \to -0$ as $r \to 1-0$. Similarly, we think of the lower semi-circle as transforming into the upper edge of this cut. The correspondence between the circle $|z| = 1$ and the edges of the cut $[-1, 1]$ is indicated in Fig. 35.

Eliminating r between the equations (11), we see that the family of radii $\arg z = \phi$ (the family orthogonal to the circles $|z| = r$) transforms into the family of hyperbolas

$$\frac{u^2}{\cos^2\phi} - \frac{v^2}{\sin^2\phi} = 1;$$

each of these curves (shown dotted in Fig. 35) has its foci at the points ($\pm 1, 0$).

It follows in the same way from (11) that (9) transforms the circles $|z| = r$ ($r > 1$) into ellipses with semi-axes

$$a_r = \frac{1}{2}\left(r + \frac{1}{r}\right), \qquad b_r = \frac{1}{2}\left(r - \frac{1}{r}\right).$$

These are the same ellipses as before, but each is described in the positive sense as the point z makes a positive circuit of the corresponding circle $|z| = r$. As $r \rightarrow 1+0$, the semi-axes a_r, b_r tend,

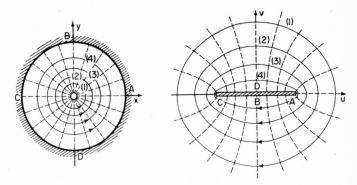

Fig. 35

respectively, to 1 and 0; that is, the elliptical image degenerates into the segment $[-1, 1]$. As $r \rightarrow +\infty$, the semi-axes a_r, b_r both tend to $+\infty$, while

$$a_r - b_r = \frac{1}{r} \rightarrow +0;$$

that is, the ellipse expands, approximating more closely to a circle. It will be clear that (9) gives a one–one mapping *of the exterior of the circle $|z| = 1$ onto the exterior of the segment $[-1, 1]$*. The circle $|z| = 1$ again corresponds to the doubled segment, or cut, along $[-1, 1]$; we consider that the upper semi-circle transforms into the upper edge of the cut and the lower semi-circle into the lower edge.

From the above it will be evident that, to obtain a biuniform and continuous image of the complete z-plane under (9) it will be necessary to take two superposed w-planes each cut along the segment $[-1, 1]$, the edges being joined criss-cross fashion as before. The two-sheeted surface so obtained, with branch points above $w = \pm 1$, serves as the Riemann surface of the function

$$w = \frac{1}{2}\left(z + \frac{1}{z}\right).$$

Geometrically it differs in no way from the Riemann surface of Fig. 34.

The function

$$z = w + \sqrt{(w^2 - 1)} \qquad (12)$$

inverse to (9) is single-valued on the Riemann surface constructed above; the different values which it assumes at the point w ($\neq 0, \infty$) are associated with the two different points on the Riemann surface situated above w. The method of construction of the regular branches of the function (12) is the same as in the preceding examples.

It should be noted that (12) has two distinct regular branches in the exterior of the segment $[-1, 1]$ of the u-axis. One of these branches maps the exterior of the segment onto $|z| > 1$ and the other maps it onto $|z| < 1$. It is not possible to characterize these branches by attaching different signs to the root: for example, the branch of (12) which maps the exterior of the segment onto $|z| > 1$ assumes the value $2 + \sqrt{3}$ at $w = 2$ and the value $-(2 + \sqrt{3})$ at $w = -2$.

Both mappings are one–one and conformal everywhere in the exterior of the segment $[-1, 1]$. The nets conformally equivalent to the polar-coordinate net are represented on Fig. 35; they form a family of confocal ellipses and hyperbolas.

27. Examples

The above results are often useful in the solution of problems on *conformal mappings*. These problems usually amount to that of finding a one–one (biuniform) conformal mapping of a given simply-connected domain onto a canonical domain (half-plane or unit disc); it will be seen in the next chapter that they are of considerable practical interest.

By the fundamental theorem of Art. 23, there are infinitely many solutions of this basic problem (depending on three real parameters) for each given simply-connected domain whose boundary contains more than one point. In general, none of these solutions can be expressed in terms of elementary functions; however, we shall now discuss certain examples in which the required mappings are given by such functions.

Example 1. We seek a one–one conformal mapping of the upper half-plane, with a cut of height h along the imaginary axis from the coordinate origin (Fig. 36,a), onto the upper half-plane. The problem amounts to our removing the cut and smoothing it into a segment of the real axis. In order to liquidate the angles on the boundary at B and D it is natural to use the mapping

$$\omega = z^2$$

which transforms ("smooths") the right angles ADC and ABC into angles of magnitude π. The mapping $w = z^2$ is one–one in the domain concerned, so that this operation is permissible. Under this transformation, the ray AD (the locus of points with zero

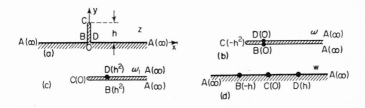

Fig. 36

argument) maps onto the upper edge of a cut along the positive real axis; the segment DC (a locus of points with argument $\pi/2$) maps onto the upper edge of the cut along the negative real axis from 0 to $-h^2$ (since $\omega = -h^2$ when $z = ih$); CB maps onto the lower edge of the same cut; and the ray BA (the locus of points with argument π) maps onto the lower edge of the cut along the positive real axis. Traversing the boundary $ABCDA$ (Fig. 36, a) in the sense indicated, the domain Δ in the z-plane remains on the left; the corresponding image-point ω traverses $ABCDA$ (Fig. 36, b) so that the image of Δ remains on the left; it follows that the image of Δ in the ω-plane is obtained from the complete ω-plane by taking a cut along the segment $\operatorname{Im} \omega = 0$, $\operatorname{Re} \omega \geqslant -h^2$. We now move the initial point of the cut to the origin in the ω_1-plane by writing

$$\omega_1 = \omega + h^2;$$

the points B and D transform into points B and D on the real axis of the ω_1-plane, each having abscissa $+h^2$ (Fig. 36, c). In the domain Δ_1 which is the image (in the ω_1-plane) of Δ we can separate a suitable regular branch of the function

$$w = \sqrt{\omega_1};$$

we take $\omega_1 = |\omega_1|e^{i\phi}$, where $|\omega_1| > 0$ and $0 < \phi < 2\pi$, and choose w to be $(\sqrt{|\omega_1|})e^{i\phi/2}$. It will be clear that the corresponding transformation maps Δ_1 onto the upper half-plane $\operatorname{Im} w > 0$; A falls on $w = \infty$, the points B and D map on $w = \pm h$, and C maps on $w = 0$.

Accordingly, with this interpretation of the branch of $\sqrt{\omega_1}$, the function giving the required conformal mapping of Δ onto $\operatorname{Im} w > 0$ is

$$w = \sqrt{\omega_1} = \sqrt{(\omega + h^2)} = \sqrt{(z^2 + h^2)}. \tag{13}$$

Example 2. We seek a conformal mapping onto $\operatorname{Im} w > 0$ of the domain Δ obtained from the z-plane by taking two cuts, defined

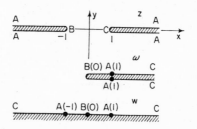

Fig. 37

by $-\infty \leqslant x \leqslant -1$ and $1 \leqslant x < +\infty$, along the real axis (on the z-sphere the cuts join at infinity, so that Δ is simply-connected; see Fig. 37). The bilinear mapping

$$\omega = \frac{z+1}{z-1} \tag{14}$$

transforms B into $\omega = 0$, C into $\omega = \infty$, $z = \infty$ into $\omega = 1$ (and $z = 0$ into $\omega = -1$); as the coefficients in (14) are real, ω is real whenever z is real. It follows readily that Δ maps onto a domain obtained from the ω-plane by taking a cut along the *positive* real axis from $\omega = 0$ to $\omega = \infty$. Taking a regular branch of $\sqrt{\omega}$ as in Example 1, we obtain the required mapping:

$$w = \sqrt{\omega} = \sqrt{\left(\frac{z+1}{z-1}\right)}. \tag{15}$$

Example 3. We seek a conformal mapping of the semi-circular domain $|z| < 1$, $\operatorname{Im} z > 0$ (Fig. 38) onto the upper half-plane $\operatorname{Im} w > 0$. Under a suitable bilinear mapping the semi-circle transforms into a half-line and the diameter into another such line; it suffices to choose the mapping so that one end of the diameter is transformed

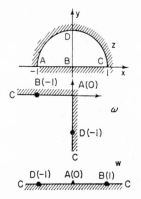

Fɪɢ. 38

into the point at infinity. (Were we to choose a mapping which transformed any other point of the semi-circle into the point at infinity, the image of the x-axis would not pass through the point at infinity and would therefore be a circle and not a straight line.) For example, we may take

$$\omega = \frac{z+1}{z-1};$$

this maps the diameter AC onto that part of the real axis which joins $\omega = 0$ and $\omega = \infty$ and contains the point $\omega = -1$ (the image of $z = 0$); consequently, the image of AC is the *negative* real axis (*cf.* Ex. 2, above). As the mapping is conformal at A, the semi-circle ADC is transformed into a ray, joining $\omega = 0$ and $\omega = \infty$, which is perpendicular to the real axis and contains the image, $\omega = (i+1)/(i-1) = -i$, of $z = i$; it follows immediately that this ray is the negative imaginary axis. The image domain must remain on the left when we traverse the contour $ABCDA$ in the sense indicated, so that it consists of the open third quadrant, $\pi < \mathrm{Arg}\ \omega < 3\pi/2$. On applying the mapping $w = \omega^2$ it will be clear that this domain maps onto $\mathrm{Im}\ w > 0$. Accordingly, the required mapping is

$$w = \omega^2 = \left(\frac{z+1}{z-1}\right)^2. \tag{16}$$

We note that

$$w = \frac{1}{2}\left(z + \frac{1}{z}\right)$$

gives a direct mapping of the semi-circular disc onto the lower half-plane, so that

$$W = -\frac{1}{2}\left(z + \frac{1}{z}\right) \tag{17}$$

is a mapping satisfying the requirements of the problem. However, the correspondence established by (17) ($A \leftrightarrow 1$, $B \leftrightarrow \infty$, $C \leftrightarrow -1$, $D \leftrightarrow 0$) differs from that established by the mapping (16) ($A \leftrightarrow 0$, $B \leftrightarrow 1$, $C \leftrightarrow \infty$, $D \leftrightarrow -1$). To show the relation between (16) and (17) we use formula (21) of Chapter II to find the bilinear mapping of $\mathrm{Im}\ w > 0$ onto $\mathrm{Im}\ W > 0$ under which the points $w = 0$, 1, ∞ have the respective images $W = 1$, ∞, -1; this auxiliary mapping is

$$W = \frac{1+w}{1-w}.$$

Substituting for w from (16), we have

$$W = \left\{1 + \left(\frac{z+1}{z-1}\right)^2\right\} \Big/ \left\{1 - \left(\frac{z+1}{z-1}\right)^2\right\} = -\frac{1}{2}\left(z + \frac{1}{z}\right).$$

Accordingly, the mappings (16) and (17) can be obtained from each other by a further bilinear mapping, in accordance with the theorem of Art. 23.

Example 4. A domain Δ is formed from the upper half-plane by excluding the semi-circular region $|z| \leqslant 1$, $\operatorname{Im} z > 0$ and the ray $y \geqslant 2$, $x = 0$ (Fig. 39, a). We seek a conformal mapping of Δ onto the half-plane $\operatorname{Im} w > 0$. The mapping

$$\omega = \frac{1}{2}\left(z + \frac{1}{z}\right)$$

is one–one in Δ and transforms the semi-circle into a line-segment without distorting the shape of the other parts of the boundary.

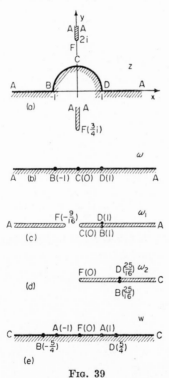

Fɪɢ. 39

The corresponding image-domain is shown in Fig. 39, b. The function $\omega_1 = \omega^2$ transforms this domain into a domain obtained

8

from the ω_1-plane by deleting two rays (Fig. 39, c). Under the further bilinear mapping

$$\omega_2 = \frac{1}{\omega_1}\left(\omega_1 + \frac{9}{16}\right) = 1 + \frac{9}{16\omega_1},$$

the image-domain is that obtained from the ω_2-plane by deleting the positive real axis. It remains to use the function

$$w = \sqrt{\omega_2},$$

where the root sign denotes the appropriate regular branch of the corresponding two-valued function. Combining these mappings we find the solution

$$w = \frac{\sqrt{(4z^4 + 17z^2 + 4)}}{2(z^2 + 1)}. \tag{18}$$

28. The Joukowski profile

The example now considered is of great importance in the theory of aerofoils. We find a conformal mapping of the set of points exterior to the arc AB of a certain circle (Fig. 40, a) onto the exterior domain whose frontier is the circle C (Fig. 40, b). The bilinear function

$$\zeta = \frac{z-2}{z+2} \tag{19}$$

maps the exterior of the arc AB in the z-plane onto the exterior (Δ) of the ray AB in the ζ-plane (A lies at $\zeta = \infty$, B at $\zeta = 0$).

As $d\zeta/dz > 0$ at $z = 2$ the angle of inclination of this ray to the negative real axis is equal to

$$\alpha = 2\arctan h.$$

For, from Fig. 40, a,

$$\sin\alpha = \frac{2}{r}, \qquad \cos\alpha = \frac{r-2h}{r} = 1 - h\sin\alpha,$$

where r is the radius of the arc AB, so that

$$h = (1 - \cos\alpha)/\sin\alpha = \tan\frac{\alpha}{2}.$$

Instead of finding a direct mapping of Δ onto the exterior of the circle C, we find an inverse mapping of this domain onto Δ. As a first step we again use a bilinear mapping

$$\omega = \frac{w-1}{w+1}$$

transforming C into a straight line through the origin B in the ω-plane (Fig. 40, c); as

$$\left[\frac{d\omega}{dw}\right]_{w=1} > 0,$$

this line makes an angle $\beta = (\pi/2) - \arctan h$ with the positive real axis (it is clear from Fig. 40, b that $\cot \beta = h$); it follows

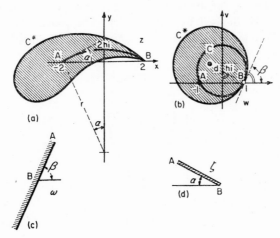

(a)

(b)

(c)

(d)

Fig. 40

readily that the exterior domain bounded by C maps on the half-plane $\beta - \pi < \arg \omega < \beta$. Finally, the mapping

$$\zeta = \omega^2 = \left(\frac{w-1}{w+1}\right)^2 \tag{20}$$

transforms this half-plane onto the exterior of a ray in the ζ-plane making an angle $2\beta = \pi - 2\arctan h = \pi - \alpha$ with the positive real axis. It will be clear that this ray is the ray AB of Fig. 40, d.

Eliminating ζ between the equations (19) and (20), we obtain the required mapping:

$$\left(\frac{w-1}{w+1}\right)^2 = \frac{z-2}{z+2},$$

whence we have

$$z = w + \frac{1}{w}, \qquad w = \tfrac{1}{2}[z + \sqrt{(z^2-4)}]. \qquad (21)$$

We now construct the circle C^* in the w-plane, touching C at the point B ($w = 1$). The mapping (21) transforms this circle into a certain closed curve C^* in the z-plane; the curve encloses the arc AB and touches AB at the point B ($z = 2$), so that it has a cusp at this point (see Fig. 40, a); it will be seen that it resembles the profile of an aerofoil.

This technique for obtaining a wing-section profile is the *method of encirclement* devised by Joukowski†. The profiles obtained by this method (called *Joukowski profiles*) greatly simplify certain aerodynamic calculations.

Fig. 41

The shape of these profiles depends on two parameters: h, characterizing the curvature of the wing; and d, the distance between the centres of C and C^*, characterizing the thickness of the section. (The dimensions of the wing are normalized by our taking A, B as the points $z = \pm 2$ in Fig. 40, a and as $w = \pm 1$ in Fig. 40, b.) Taking $h = 0$ we obtain a profile (*Joukowski's rudder*) which has axial symmetry (Fig. 41).

---

† Nikolai Egerovich Joukowski (1847–1921) was among the first to make extensive use of the methods of function theory in hydro- and aerodynamics; his contributions to aerodynamic theory are of fundamental importance.

29. The exponential function and its Riemann surface

The function $w = e^z$ (see Art. 4) is defined by

$$w = u+iv = e^z = e^x(\cos y+i\sin y). \tag{22}$$

We show that the function e^z is regular in the whole of the open plane. By (22),

$$u = e^x\cos y, \qquad v = e^x\sin y, \tag{23}$$

whence

$$\frac{\partial u}{\partial x} = \frac{\partial v}{\partial y} = e^x\cos y, \tag{24}$$

$$-\frac{\partial u}{\partial y} = \frac{\partial v}{\partial x} = e^x\sin y, \tag{25}$$

so that the Cauchy–Riemann conditions are satisfied at all finite points z; it is obvious that the functions u, v are totally differentiable everywhere (see Art. 14).

As in real analysis, the derivative of e^z is e^z:

$$\frac{\mathrm{d}}{\mathrm{d}z}e^z = \frac{\partial u}{\partial x}+i\frac{\partial v}{\partial x} = e^x\cos y+ie^x\sin y = e^z. \tag{26}$$

To study the mapping $w = e^z$ we put $z = x+iy$ and $w = \rho e^{i\theta}$, where, by (22),

$$\rho = e^x, \qquad \theta = y. \tag{27}$$

We find the conditions under which the mapping is one–one. From the equation $w_1 = w_2$ or $\rho_1 = \rho_2$, $\theta_1 = \theta_2+2k\pi$, it follows, with an obvious notation, that $x_1 = x_2$, $y_1 = y_2+2k\pi$; that is,

$$z_1 - z_2 = 2k\pi i, \tag{28}$$

where k is an arbitrary integer. Consequently, for $w = e^z$ to be one–one in the domain D it is necessary and sufficient that D should not contain any pair of points z_1, z_2 related by (28). In particular, this condition is satisfied by any horizontal strip of width 2π, for example the strips

$$\left.\begin{array}{l} -\infty < x < +\infty, \\ 2k\pi < y < 2(k+1)\pi \end{array}\right\} \ (k = 0, \pm 1, \pm 2, \ldots).$$

To every such strip S corresponds the set of values of $w = \rho e^{i\theta}$ for which

$$0 < \rho < +\infty, \qquad 2k\pi < \theta < 2(k+1)\pi;$$

that is, $w = e^z$ maps S onto the domain formed from the w-plane by taking a cut along the positive real axis. Under this mapping, the straight lines $y = $ const. are transformed into the rays $\theta = $ const., and the segments $x = $ const. become circles. In particular, *the function $w = e^z$ gives a one–one conformal mapping of the strip of width π defined by $-\infty < x < +\infty$, $0 < y < \pi$ onto the upper half-plane; and of the half-strip defined by $-\infty < x < 0$, $0 < y < \pi$ onto a unit semi-circular disc,* and so on (Fig. 42).

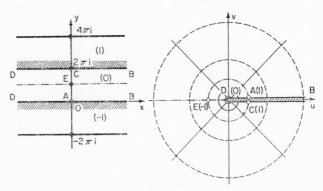

Fig. 42

The boundary lines of every strip S correspond with the edges of a cut, the lower line with the upper edge and the upper line with the lower edge. Consequently, in order to present a one–one and continuous mapping of the whole z-plane we must take an infinite number of superposed w-planes, each cut along the positive u-axis, the planes being labelled by the numbers $k = 0, \pm 1, \pm 2, \ldots$. The planes are connected in an order matching that in which the corresponding strips S abut on each other. We begin with the plane (0) and connect the lower edge of its cut to the upper edge of the cut in plane (1); the free (lower) edge of cut (1) is then joined to the upper edge of cut (2), and so on. On plane (0) the upper edge of the cut is free, so far; we join to it the lower edge of the cut (-1); the free (upper) edge of the cut (-1) is then attached to the lower edge of the cut (-2), and so on (Fig. 43).

The resulting surface R has an infinite number of sheets and is called the *Riemann surface of the function $w = e^z$*. This function gives a one–one and continuous mapping of the whole of the open z-plane onto R. (We cannot continuously extend our mapping to include the point $z = \infty$, as $\lim\limits_{z\to\infty} e^z$ does not exist: e.g. $e^z \to 0$ as $z \to \infty$ along the negative real axis, and $e^z \to \infty$ as $z \to \infty$ along the positive real axis.)

This mapping becomes clearer when we consider the mapping of the vertical strip $0 < x < a$: it is easily seen that this strip maps onto an infinite helical strip, arranged over the annulus $1 < |w| < e^a$ like a spiral staircase (Fig. 44).

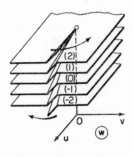

Fig. 43   Fig. 44

We note that the function $w = e^z$ does not assume the values $w = 0$ and $w = \infty$ at any point. Consequently, there are no points of R lying on $w = 0$ or $w = \infty$. Let us go round the points $w = 0$ and $w = \infty$, moving along R on the circle $|w| = r$ in one direction. As seen from Fig. 44, we move along a helix going round these points an infinite number of times. Accordingly, we say that the points $w = 0$ and $w = \infty$ are *branch points of R of infinite order*. (It is to be noted that these two points do not belong to R.)

30. The logarithmic function

In Art. 4 we defined the logarithmic function $w = \operatorname{Ln} z$ as the function inverse to the exponential function:

$$w = \operatorname{Ln} z \tag{29}$$

if, and only if,

$$e^w = z. \tag{30}$$

It was shown that

$$w = \operatorname{Ln} z = \ln|z| + i \operatorname{Arg} z = \ln|z| + i(\arg z + 2k\pi)$$
$$= \ln z + 2k\pi i. \tag{31}$$

The principal value of $\operatorname{Ln} z$ is

$$\ln z = \ln|z| + i \arg z. \tag{32}$$

The function $w = \operatorname{Ln} z$ is infinitely many-valued and maps the Riemann surface of the function $z = e^w$ onto the w-plane. It is defined for all finite non-zero z; as $\operatorname{Arg} z$ is not defined when $z = 0$, it will be clear from (31) that e^w cannot vanish for any value of w.

As seen in the preceding article, the points $z = 0$, ∞ are branch-points of infinite order for the Riemann surface concerned. These points are called *logarithmic branch points*.

We note that, from the definition of the logarithm and from (31),

$$e^{\operatorname{Ln} z} = z, \qquad \operatorname{Ln} e^z = z + 2k\pi i. \tag{33}$$

The function $w = \operatorname{Ln} z$ is a further example of a *many-valued analytic function* (see Art. 63). If follows from the definition of $w = \operatorname{Ln} z$ that a regular branch of this function exists in a domain D if, and only if, a continuous one-valued branch of $\operatorname{Arg} z$ exists in D. For example, let D be formed from the z-plane by taking a cut along the negative real axis. Clearly, we can arrange this domain on the Riemann surface of e^w in an infinite number of ways. Let us arrange it so that the upper half-plane falls on the sheet (0), and the lower on the sheet (-1): then $v = \operatorname{Arg} z$ ranges from $-\pi$ to π and coincides with the principal branch $\arg z$. The uniform branch of the logarithm so obtained is its principal value $\ln z$. This function is *regular* in the domain considered; for, by the theorem on the derivative of an inverse function, its derivative exists in this domain:

$$\frac{\mathrm{d}}{\mathrm{d}z} \ln z = 1 \bigg/ \left(\frac{\mathrm{d}}{\mathrm{d}w} e^w \right) = \frac{1}{e^w} = \frac{1}{z}. \tag{34}$$

The function (32) gives a one–one conformal mapping of Δ (*the domain obtained from the z-plane by taking a cut along the negative real axis*) onto the strip $-\infty < u < +\infty$, $-\pi < v < \pi$; for, (d/dz) ln $z \neq 0$ for all points of D (the mapping ceases to be conformal only at points $z = 0, \infty$ on the frontier of D). The mapping function assumes different values at matching points on the edges of the cut. Under this mapping the upper half-plane transforms into the strip $0 < v < \pi$, the semi-annulus $y > 0$, $a < |z| < b$ transforms into a rectangular domain, and so on (Fig. 45).

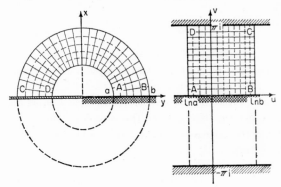

Fig. 45

31. Trigonometrical and hyperbolic functions

We define the *trigonometrical functions* of a complex variable z by the equations

$$\sin z = \frac{e^{iz} - e^{-iz}}{2i}, \qquad \cos z = \frac{e^{iz} + e^{-iz}}{2}, \qquad (35)$$

$$\tan z = \frac{\sin z}{\cos z}, \qquad \cot z = \frac{1}{\tan z}. \qquad (36)$$

Using Euler's formula it is easily shown that, for real z, these functions are the trigonometrical functions of real analysis. Many of the familiar properties of the latter carry over into the complex domain: for example, it follows readily from the periodicity of e^z that the functions (35) have period 2π and that the functions (36) have period π.

Similarly, $\sin z_1 \cos z_2 + \cos z_1 \sin z_2$ equals

$$\frac{1}{4i}\{(e^{iz_1} - e^{-iz_1})(e^{iz_2} + e^{-iz_2}) + (e^{iz_1} + e^{-iz_1})(e^{iz_2} - e^{-iz_2})\}$$

$$= \frac{1}{2i}\{e^{i(z_1+z_2)} - e^{-i(z_1+z_2)}\} = \sin(z_1 + z_2). \qquad (37)$$

The other standard trigonometrical formulae can be verified in exactly the same way.

From (36) and the fact that $de^z/dz = e^z$, we have

$$\left.\begin{array}{ll} \dfrac{d}{dz}\sin z = \cos z, & \dfrac{d}{dz}\cos z = -\sin z, \\[2ex] \dfrac{d}{dz}\tan z = \dfrac{1}{\cos^2 z}, & \dfrac{d}{dz}\cot z = -\dfrac{1}{\sin^2 z}. \end{array}\right\} \qquad (38)$$

It follows immediately that $\sin z$ and $\cos z$ are regular in the whole of the open plane, that $\tan z$ is regular for $z \neq (2k+1)(\pi/2)$, and that $\cot z$ is regular for $z \neq k\pi$.

Certain properties of the real trigonometrical functions are not preserved under the extension to the complex domain. In particular, it is incorrect to assert that $|\sin z|$ and $|\cos z|$ never exceed unity: for example,

$$\cos i = \frac{e + e^{-1}}{2} \approx 1 \cdot 54, \qquad \sin i = \frac{e^{-1} - e}{2i} \approx 1 \cdot 17i.$$

Let us consider the mapping

$$w = \cos z. \qquad (39)$$

It will be clear from (36) that this can be represented as the superposition of three mappings

$$\text{(I)}\ \zeta = iz, \qquad \text{(II)}\ \omega = e^\zeta, \qquad \text{(III)}\ w = \frac{1}{2}\left(\omega + \frac{1}{\omega}\right); \qquad (40)$$

each of these has been discussed earlier. First, we find the condition that (39) be one–one. Let (I) map a domain D_0 on D_1, let (II) map D_1 on Δ_1; and let (III) map Δ_1 on Δ. The mapping (I) is one–one everywhere; in order that (II) be one–one it is necessary and sufficient that D_1 should not contain distinct points ζ_1, ζ_2 such that $\zeta_1 - \zeta_2 = 2k\pi i$ (see (28)), or, what is the same thing, D_0 should not contain distinct points z_1, z_2 such that

$$z_1 - z_2 = 2k\pi. \qquad (41)$$

In order that (III) be one–one it is necessary and sufficient that Δ_1 should not contain distinct points ω_1, ω_2 such that $\omega_1\omega_2 = 1$ (see (10)); or, equivalently, D_0 should not contain distinct points z_1, z_2 such that

$$e^{iz_1} \cdot e^{iz_2} = e^{i(z_1+z_2)} = 1,$$

that is, such that

$$z_1 + z_2 = 2k\pi. \tag{42}$$

Accordingly, (39) will be one–one in D_0 if, and only if, D_0 does not contain distinct points z_1, z_2 satisfying either of the equations (41) and (42). This condition is satisfied by, for example, the half-strip D_0 defined by

$$0 < x < 2\pi, \qquad y > 0.$$

Figure 46 shows the three successive stages in which we have resolved the mapping $w = \cos z$. The half-strip D_0 finally maps on the domain Δ formed from the w-plane by removing the ray

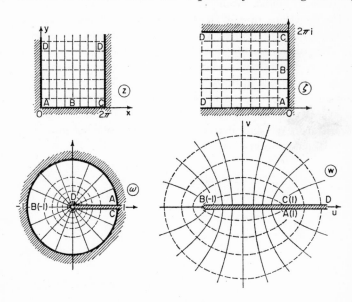

FIG. 46

$-1 \leqslant u \leqslant +\infty$, $v = 0$. (In connection with stage III we recall from Art. 26 that the unit disc $|\omega| < 1$ maps onto the exterior of the segment $[-1, 1]$ in the w-plane; the cut along the radius of this disc corresponds to the segment $[1, +\infty]$ of the u-axis.)

The Riemann surface of the function $w = \cos z$ is rather more complicated in structure than the examples encountered earlier. It will be clear that it has an infinite number of sheets; detailed investigation shows that it has an infinite number of branch points of the second order above the points $w = \pm 1$ and a logarithmic branch point above the point $w = \infty$. It is easily verified that, for example, the image of the real axis of the z-plane is an infinite zig-zag line on this surface composed of the segments $[-1, 1]$. We have

$$\sin z = \cos\left(z - \frac{\pi}{2}\right);$$

it will be clear that the mapping $w = \sin z$ can be obtained from the preceding mapping simply by making a preliminary translation of the z-plane. The mappings $w = \tan z$ and $w = \cot z$ can be analysed by similar methods.

The functions inverse to those in (35) and (36) are the *inverse trigonometrical functions*. As all the Riemann surfaces representing the trigonometrical functions have an infinity of sheets, the inverse functions are infinitely many-valued (they are also many-valued analytic functions in the sense of Art. 63). The functions (35) and (36) are expressed in terms of exponentials; it is therefore natural to expect that the inverse functions can be expressed in terms of logarithms. We shall derive such an expression for $w = \text{Arc}\cos z$. From the definition of this function we have:

$$z = \cos w = \frac{e^{iw} + e^{-iw}}{2},$$

whence

$$e^{2iw} - 2ze^{iw} + 1 = 0, \qquad e^{iw} = z + \sqrt{(z^2 - 1)},$$

and

$$w = \text{Arc}\cos z = -i\,\text{Ln}[z + \sqrt{(z^2 - 1)}].$$

We note that

$$\frac{1}{z - \sqrt{(z^2 - 1)}} = z + \sqrt{(z^2 - 1)},$$

so that changing the sign associated with the root is equivalent to changing the sign of the logarithm; as both root and logarithm in the above formula for w are many-valued functions the minus sign can be omitted and we write

$$w = \text{Arc}\cos z = i\,\text{Ln}[z + \sqrt{(z^2 - 1)}]. \tag{43}$$

The preceding discussion shows that $w = \mathrm{Arc}\cos z$ can be resolved in regular branches in any suitable domain D of the z-plane. For example, such a branch exists when D is the domain formed from the z-plane by deleting the ray $-1 \leqslant x \leqslant +\infty$, $y = 0$; the particular branch satisfying the conditions $0 < u < 2\pi$, $v > 0$ is usually chosen as the *principal branch* and is denoted by arc cos z.

Formulae similar to (43) can be given for the other inverse trigonometrical functions:

$$\left.\begin{aligned} \mathrm{Arc}\sin z &= \frac{\pi}{2} - \mathrm{Arc}\cos z = \frac{\pi}{2} - i\,\mathrm{Ln}[z + \sqrt{(z^2-1)}], \\ \mathrm{Arc}\tan z &= \frac{\pi}{2} - \mathrm{Arc}\cot z = \frac{1}{2i}\,\mathrm{Ln}\frac{i-z}{i+z}. \end{aligned}\right\} \quad (44)$$

The hyperbolic functions, defined in the complex domain by

$$\left.\begin{aligned} \sinh z &= \frac{e^z - e^{-z}}{2}, & \cosh z &= \frac{e^z + e^{-z}}{2}, \\ \tanh z &= \frac{\sinh z}{\cosh z}, & \coth z &= \frac{1}{\tanh z}, \end{aligned}\right\} \quad (45)$$

can easily be expressed in terms of trigonometrical functions:

$$\left.\begin{aligned} \sinh z &= -i\sin iz, & \cosh z &= \cos iz, \\ \tanh z &= -i\tan iz, & \coth z &= i\cot iz; \end{aligned}\right\} \quad (46)$$

accordingly, their properties are essentially similar. The *inverse hyperbolic functions* are defined as the inverses of the functions (45). They are easily expressed in terms of logarithms:

$$\left.\begin{aligned} \mathrm{Ar}\sinh z &= \mathrm{Ln}[z + \sqrt{(z^2+1)}], \\ \mathrm{Ar}\cosh z &= \mathrm{Ln}[z + \sqrt{(z^2-1)}], \\ \mathrm{Ar}\tanh z &= \tfrac{1}{2}\mathrm{Ln}\{(1+z)/(1-z)\}, \\ \mathrm{Ar}\coth z &= \tfrac{1}{2}\mathrm{Ln}\{(z+1)/(z-1)\}. \end{aligned}\right\} \quad (47)$$

32. The general power

The function $w = z^a$, where $a = \alpha + i\beta$ is an arbitrary complex number, is defined by the relation

$$z^a = e^{a \operatorname{Ln} z} \quad (z \neq 0, \infty). \tag{48}$$

Putting $z = re^{i\phi}$, we have $\operatorname{Ln} z = \ln r + i(\phi + 2k\pi)$, whence

$$z^a = e^{(\alpha + i\beta)\operatorname{Ln} z} = e^{\alpha \ln r - \beta(\phi + 2k\pi)} \cdot e^{i\{\alpha(\phi + 2k\pi) + \beta \ln r\}}. \tag{49}$$

Equation (49) shows that the function z^a is infinitely many-valued whenever $\beta \neq 0$; for fixed z and a its values are distributed on a system of circles

$$|w| = e^{\alpha \ln r - \beta(\phi + 2k\pi)} \quad (k = 0, \pm 1, \pm 2, \ldots).$$

The radii

$$\rho_k = e^{\alpha \ln r - \beta\phi} \cdot e^{-2k\pi\beta} = \rho_0 e^{-2k\pi\beta} \tag{50}$$

of these circles form two geometrical progressions; for positive k the common ratio is $e^{-2\pi\beta}$, and for negative k it is $e^{2\pi\beta}$. The arguments

$$\theta_k = \alpha(\phi + 2k\pi) + \beta \ln r = \theta_0 + 2k\pi\alpha \tag{51}$$

of the values of z^a form arithmetical progressions with common differences $\pm 2\pi\alpha$. For $\beta = 0$ (that is, for real a) it will be seen from (50) that all values of z^a lie on the circle

$$|w| = e^{a \ln r} = r^a; \tag{52}$$

the corresponding values for the argument given by (51) are

$$\theta_k = a\phi + 2k\pi a. \tag{53}$$

If a is a non-zero *rational* real number, equal to the irreducible fraction p/q, then any q successive values of the argument given by (53) yield all the values of z^a. Putting $k = 0, 1, 2, \ldots, q-1$ in turn in (53), the values obtained for θ_k are

$$\theta_0 = a\phi, \qquad \theta_1 = a\phi + \frac{p}{q}2\pi, \qquad \theta_2 = a\phi + \frac{p}{q}4\pi, \ldots,$$

$$\theta_{q-1} = a\phi + \frac{p}{q}(q-1)2\pi. \tag{54}$$

No two of these differ by a multiple of 2π. (If, for any integer $k < q$, we had $k(p/q)$ equal to a positive integer n, then $p/q = n/k$

this contradicts our initial hypothesis that p/q is irreducible.) It will be clear that further values of k yield values θ_k differing from those in (54) by a multiple of 2π.

We see that, *for rational real $a = p/q$, the function z^a is identical with the function $\sqrt[q]{z^p}$*:

$$z^{p/q} = \sqrt[q]{z^p}$$

(see Arts. 4 and 25), *and has a finite number of values for given $z \neq 0, \infty$.*

For *irrational* (real) a, no two of the values (53) can differ by a multiple of 2π. (Let us suppose that integers k_1, k_2 exist such that $k_1 \neq k_2$, $2\pi k_1 a - 2\pi k_2 a = 2\pi n$ where n is an integer; then, $a = n/(k_1 - k_2)$, contradicting the hypothesis that a is irrational.) It follows that, in this case, the function

$$z^a = e^{a\mathrm{Ln}z}$$

is *infinitely many-valued.*

Examples: 1. The function

$$w = z^i = e^{-(\phi+2k\pi)} \cdot e^{i\ln r}$$

is defined for $z \neq 0, \infty$ and is infinitely many-valued. For fixed z its values are distributed on the ray $\mathrm{Arg}\, w = \ln r$, their moduli forming two geometric progressions with ratios $e^{\pm 2\pi}$. The sequence of values corresponding to positive k converges to the point $w = 0$; that corresponding to negative k converges to the point $w = \infty$. In particular, all these values are real when $r = 1$.

2. The function

$$w = z^{3/4} = e^{(3/4)\ln r} \cdot e^{i[(3/4)\phi+(3k\pi/2)]} = \left(\sqrt[4]{r^3}\right) e^{i(3/4)(\phi+2k\pi)}$$

is four-valued; in order to obtain all values of w, it suffices to give k the values 0, 1, 2, 3, ($k = 4$ would yield the value obtained for $k = 0$).

3. The function

$$w = z^\pi = r^\pi e^{i\pi(\phi+2k\pi)}$$

is infinitely many-valued: for given z its values lie on the circle $|w| = r^\pi$, and it can be shown that their distribution on this circle is everywhere dense.

By definition of the general power a regular branch of $w = z^a$ exists in a domain D whenever D supports a regular branch of

Ln z; that is, whenever we can separate a single-valued and continuous branch of Arg z in D. For example, a regular branch of z^a can be separated in the domain D formed from the z-plane by taking a cut along the negative real axis; the particular branch defined on D by $w = e^{a \ln z}$ is called the *principal branch* of z^a on this domain. We verify that this branch is regular in D: by (34) and the rule for differentiation of a composite function we have

$$\frac{d}{dz}z^a = \frac{d}{dz}e^{a\ln z} = \frac{a}{z}\,e^{a\ln z} = az^{a-1}.$$

Let us now restrict discussion to positive values of a. For $a > 1$, the principal branch of z^a effects a one–one conformal mapping of the sector $-\pi/a < \arg z < \pi/a$ onto the domain Δ obtained from the w-plane by taking a cut along the negative real axis (see Fig. 47, where $a = 4/3$); under the same mapping, the sector $0 < \arg z < \pi/a$ is transformed into the upper half-plane.

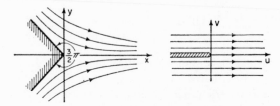

FIG. 47

For $a < 1$, a one–one mapping onto this domain Δ is not possible. However, for $\frac{1}{2} < a < 1$ it is possible to give a one–one mapping of the sector $0 < \arg z < \pi/a$ onto the half-plane Im $w > 0$ (see Fig. 48, where $a = 2/3$).

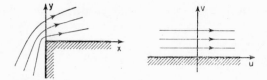

FIG. 48

33. Examples

We consider further problems in conformal mapping which can be solved by means of elementary functions.

Example 1. Let us find a mapping of the lune shown in Fig. 49, a on a strip $0 < \operatorname{Im} w < h$. First, we map the lune onto a sector (Fig. 49, b) by the bilinear transformation

$$\omega = \frac{z+a}{z-a}.$$

By means of a regular branch of the logarithm, defined by

$$\omega_1 = \operatorname{Ln} \omega = \ln|\omega| + i\operatorname{Arg}\omega \quad (0 \leqslant \operatorname{Arg}\omega < 2\pi),$$

we map this sector onto the strip $\pi + \alpha < \operatorname{Im} \omega_1 < \pi + \alpha + \beta$; the width of this strip is β. Under the transformations so far used, the

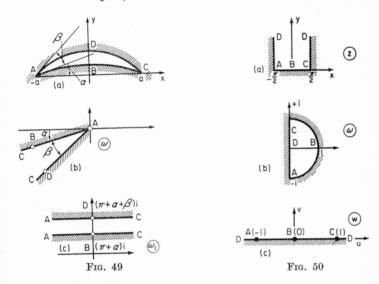

FIG. 49   FIG. 50

point $B[ia\tan(\alpha/2)]$ becomes $\omega = -(\cos\alpha + i\sin\alpha)$ and then $\omega_1 = (\pi+\alpha)i$; and the points A, C both become the point at infinity in the ω_1-plane. It follows immediately that the required mapping is given by

$$w = \frac{h}{\beta}\{\omega_1 - (\pi+\alpha)i\} = \frac{h}{\beta}\left\{\operatorname{Ln}\frac{z+a}{z-a} - (\pi+\alpha)i\right\}. \tag{56}$$

Example 2. We seek the mapping $w = f(z)$ of the half-strip $-\pi/2 < x < \pi/2$, $y > 0$ onto the half-plane $\operatorname{Im} w > 0$ such that $f(\pm\pi/2) = \pm 1$, $f(0) = 0$ (Fig. 50).

We rotate the half-strip through a right angle, anti-clockwise,

9

and apply the mapping (22): the combination, represented by

$$\omega = e^{iz},$$

maps the strip on the right-hand half of the unit disc (Fig. 50, b). Next, we rotate this semi-circular disc through a right angle, clockwise, and apply the transformation (9). The composite mapping so obtained is

$$w = \frac{1}{2}\left(-i\omega + \frac{1}{-i\omega}\right) = \frac{1}{2i}\left(\omega - \frac{1}{\omega}\right) = \frac{e^{iz} - e^{-iz}}{2i} = \sin z. \qquad (57)$$

It is easily verified that this maps the half-strip on the half-plane $\operatorname{Im} w > 0$ and that the points $z = \pi/2,\ -(\pi/2),\ 0$ map on the respective points $w = 1,\ -1,\ 0$. It is even simpler to use the results of Art. 31 directly.

Example 3. The cut strip shown in Fig. 51 is transformed, under the mapping $\omega = e^z$, into the domain Δ formed from the

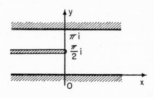

FIG. 51

half-plane $\operatorname{Im} \omega > 0$ by taking a cut along the imaginary axis from 0 to i. The mapping which transforms Δ into the half-plane $\operatorname{Im} w > 0$ is given by formula (13) of Art. 27. It follows that the function

$$w = \sqrt{(\omega^2 + 1)} = \sqrt{(e^{2z} + 1)} \qquad (58)$$

maps the cut strip on $\operatorname{Im} w > 0$. (Here, $\sqrt{\ }$ denotes the regular branch which equals $i\sqrt{3}$ when $\omega = 2i$.)

Example 4. The z-domain (D_0) is formed from the same strip by taking a vertical cut, as shown in Fig. 52, a. The function $\omega = e^z$ maps D_0 onto the domain Δ formed from the half-plane $\operatorname{Im} \omega > 0$ by taking a cut along an arc of the unit circle (Fig. 52, b). Under the further mapping $\omega_1 = (\omega - 1)/(\omega + 1)$, this arc becomes a vertical line segment, its end point C being at

$$\omega_1 = (e^{ih} - 1)/(e^{ih} + 1) = i \tan(h/2).$$

Again making use of formula (13) we see that D_0 is mapped on the half-plane $\operatorname{Im} w > 0$ by the function

$$w = \sqrt{\left(\omega_1{}^2 + \tan^2 \frac{h}{2}\right)} = \sqrt{\left\{\left(\frac{e^z-1}{e^z+1}\right)^2 + \tan^2 \frac{h}{2}\right\}}$$

$$= \sqrt{\left\{\tanh^2 \frac{z}{2} + \tan^2 \frac{h}{2}\right\}}. \tag{59}$$

Example 5. The z-domain (D_0) is formed from the z-plane by deleting the rays $-\infty \leqslant x \leqslant -a,\ a \leqslant x \leqslant +\infty$ $(y = 0)$. We wish to map D_0 on the strip $0 < \operatorname{Im} w < 2V_0$ (Fig. 53) so that the

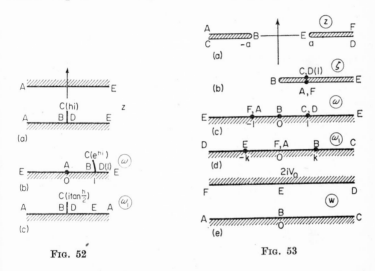

FIG. 52   FIG. 53

first ray is transformed into the lower edge of the strip and the second into the upper edge. (Note that these requirements determine only two of the parameters of the mapping; the third remains arbitrary.) The bilinear transformation

$$\zeta = \frac{z+a}{z-a}$$

maps the rays onto the positive real axis in the ζ-plane (Fig. 53, b). Accordingly,

$$\omega = \sqrt{\zeta} = \sqrt{\left(\frac{z+a}{z-a}\right)}$$

maps D_0 on the upper half-plane Im $\omega > 0$ (Fig. 53,c). This half-plane is mapped onto a strip by $w = \ln \omega$; however, in order to attain the required correspondence between boundaries, we must first transform the half-plane into itself so that the point A, F falls on the origin and the point C, D becomes the point at infinity. This is accomplished by the mapping

$$\omega_1 = k\frac{1+\omega}{1-\omega} = k\frac{\sqrt{(z-a)}+\sqrt{(z+a)}}{\sqrt{(z-a)}-\sqrt{(z+a)}} = -\frac{k}{a}[z+\sqrt{(z^2-a^2)}],$$

where k is an arbitrary positive constant. Finally we make the transformation

$$w = \frac{2V_0}{\pi}\ln \omega_1 = \frac{2V_0}{\pi}\ln[z+\sqrt{(z^2-a^2)}]+2iV_0+C, \quad (60)$$

where $C = \ln(k/a)$ is an arbitrary real constant; it will be seen that (60) satisfies the requirements of the problem. [Here, $\sqrt{(z^2-a^2)}$ denotes the regular branch which equals ia at $z = 0$.]

Exercises

1. Find the real and imaginary parts of the functions

$$w = \sin z, \quad w = \cos z, \quad w = \tan z.$$

2. Prove the formulae (46) and (47).

3. Prove the relations

$$\cosh^2 z - \sinh^2 z = 1, \qquad \cosh 2z = \cosh^2 z + \sinh^2 z,$$

$$\sinh 2z = 2 \sinh z \cosh z.$$

4. Show that we can separate a regular branch of the function $\sqrt[3]{[(1-z)z^2]}$ in the domain exterior to the segment $0 \leqslant x \leqslant 1$, $y = 0$. Find the value at the point $z = i$ of the regular branch which has a negative value at the point $z = 2$. Discuss the remaining values of the many-valued function at this point.

5. Show that we can separate a regular branch of $\mathrm{Ln}(1-z^2)$ in the domain D formed from the z-plane by deleting the segments $[-1, i]$, $[1, i]$ and the ray $x = 0$, $y \geqslant 1$. Find the value at $z = 2$ of the regular branch which has the value 0 at $z = 0$.

6. Show that we can separate a regular branch of $\mathrm{Ln}[z+\sqrt{(z^2-1)}]$ in the domain D formed from the z-plane by deleting the rays $-\infty \leqslant x \leqslant -1, 1 \leqslant x \leqslant +\infty$ $(y = 0)$.

7. Defining z^z as $e^{z \ln z}$ where ln denotes the usual principal branch of the logarithm, find the values of this function at the point $z = -e$ on the upper and lower edges of the cut along the negative real axis.

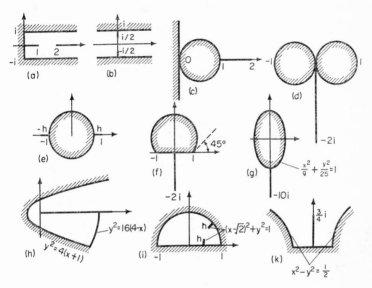

Fig. 54

8. Find the lines of equal magnification and the lines of equal angle of rotation in the mapping $w = z^2$.

9. Prove that the function $w = z^2 + 2z + 3$ gives a one–one mapping of the disc $|z| < 1$.

10. Prove that the mapping $w = \frac{1}{2}[z + (1/z)]$ is one–one in the upper half-plane $\operatorname{Im} z > 0$. What is the image of this half-plane under the mapping?

11. Find the images of

(a) the strip $0 < x < \pi/2$ under the mapping $w = \cos z$;

(b) the strip $-(\pi/4) < x < (\pi/4)$ under the mapping $w = \tan z$ (in addition, find the image of the Cartesian net in the z-plane);

(c) the strip $-\pi < y < \pi$ under the mapping $w = z + e^z$;

(d) the domain bounded by the cardioid $x = 2(1 + \cos \phi)\cos \phi$, $y = 2(1 + \cos \phi)\sin \phi$ under the mapping $w = \sqrt{z}$, where the root denotes the regular branch which is positive along the positive real axis;

(e) the domain in $\mathrm{Re}\, z < 0$ bounded by the lemniscate

$$(x^2+y^2)\{(x-4)^2+y^2\} = 16,$$

under the mapping $w = z - \frac{1}{4}z^2$ (in addition, find the conformal equivalent of the polar-coordinate net in the image domain in the w-plane).

12. Show that, in the upper half-plane, we can separate regular branches of (a) $w = \mathrm{Ln}\, \cos z$, (b) $w = \mathrm{Arc}\, \cos(\cosh \alpha \cdot \cos z)$ (α is a real constant). Find the image domain into which the upper half-plane is transformed by (a) any regular branch of $w = \mathrm{Ln}\, \cos z$, (b) the regular branch of $w = \mathrm{Arc}\, \cos(\cosh \alpha \cdot \cos z)$ which equals $\pi/2$ at $z = \pi/2$.

13. Find a conformal mapping $w = f(z)$ of

(a) the sector $0 < \arg z < \alpha$, $|z| < 1$ onto the disc $|w| < 1$;

(b) the disc $|z| < 1$ onto the strip $0 < v < 1$, such that

$$f(-1) = -\infty, \quad f(1) = +\infty, \quad f(i) = i;$$

(c) the exterior domain bounded by the ellipse $(x^2/25) + (y^2/16) = 1$ onto $|w| > 1$;

(d) the "exterior" domain bounded by the parabola $y^2 = 2px$ (that is, the domain not containing the focus) onto the half-plane $\mathrm{Im}\, w > 0$;

(e) the "exterior" domain bounded by the hyperbola

$$(x^2/\cos^2\alpha) - (y^2/\sin^2\alpha) = 1$$

(that is, the domain not containing the foci) onto the half-plane $\mathrm{Im}\, w > 0$;

(f) the domain contained between two similar logarithmic spirals $r = \alpha e^{k\phi}$, $r = \beta e^{k\phi}$ ($k > 0$, $0 < \alpha < \beta < \alpha e^{2\pi k}$) onto the strip $0 < v < 1$.

14. Find a conformal mapping, onto the half-plane or unit disc, of each of the domains shown in Fig. 54.

CHAPTER IV

APPLICATIONS TO THE THEORY OF PLANE FIELDS

34. Plane vector fields

A vector field is a region of space whose every point is associated with a certain vector (the *field vector*). The following three examples of vector fields will be of special interest to us.

(a) *The velocity field of a fluid in motion.* At any given instant, the velocity vector **V** is defined at each point of the region R occupied by the moving fluid. The association of the vector quantity **V** with each point of R constitutes the velocity field.

(b) *The electrostatic field.* In the space surrounding a charge there acts an electric force which can be detected when we introduce a "probe" charge. The force **E**q acting on a small probe charge q placed at any point of the space defines the *intensity of the field* **E** at this point. The association of the vector intensity **E** with each point in the space surrounding the original charge constitutes our electrostatic field.

(c) *The heat-flow field.* In general, the various points P in a solid material body are at different temperatures $v(P)$, and there is a flow of heat, by conduction, from the hotter parts to the cooler. At any instant, the heat flow at an interior point P in an isotropic body is given by the heat-flow vector

$$\mathbf{Q} = -k \operatorname{grad} v(P), \tag{1}$$

where k is the thermal conductivity of the body at P. This vector is directed normally to the isothermal surface through P, towards the side of lower temperature (that is, towards the side to which heat is flowing). The association of each interior point P in the body with the vector **Q** constitutes the field of thermal flow at the instant concerned.

Later we shall consider vector fields of an arbitrary physical nature; in general, however, we shall appeal to the three types listed above when giving concrete examples illustrating our theory.†

In the general case we have to consider vector fields which vary with time. The analytical specification of such fields reduces to the prescription of three scalar functions (the components of the field vector), each depending on four scalar variables (the three co-ordinates x, y, z of the field point, and the time t). We shall limit the discussion to *stationary* fields; that is, we shall assume that the field vector is independent of time and depends only on the coordinates of the field point, so that the field can be specified by means of three scalar functions of three real variables.

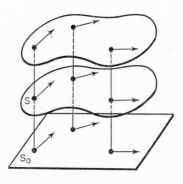

FIG. 55

We also assume in each case that the field is *plane-parallel*. This means that, at any point, the field vector is parallel to some fixed plane S, and that the field vectors at all points on any straight line perpendicular to S are identical in magnitude and direction. Such a field is called a *two-dimensional* or *plane* field; it is completely defined by the field in any plane S_0 parallel to S (Fig. 55). A stationary plane-parallel field is specified by two scalar functions (the two components of the vector giving the field in S_0), each depending on two real variables (the two coordinates of the point in S_0). The

---

† Numerous applications to the theory of elasticity can be found in the excellent books of G. V. Kolosov (*Applications of the Complex Variable to the Theory of Elasticity* [*Primeneniye kompleksnoi peremennoi k teorii uprugosti*], ONTI, 1935) and N. I. Muskhelishvili (*Certain Problems in Elasticity Theory* [*Nekotoryye zadachi teorii uprugosti*], Acad. Sci., U.S.S.R., 1949).

components of the vector **A** along the x and y axes will be denoted by A_x and A_y, so that we may consider **A** as the complex number

$$\mathbf{A} = A_x + iA_y.$$

35. Examples of plane fields

Example 1. Let us consider the electric field of a *uniformly charged infinite straight line* L bearing charge q per unit length. This field is obviously plane-parallel and we can choose any plane perpendicular to L as the plane S_0. To find the vector intensity **E** of the field at an arbitrary point P in S_0 we take rectangular Cartesian coordinates x, y, h as shown in Fig. 56. An element of L of length $\mathrm{d}h$, at height h, bears the elementary charge $q\,\mathrm{d}h$; let the intensity at P due to this charge be $\mathrm{d}\mathbf{E}$. By Coulomb's law, the magnitude of $\mathrm{d}\mathbf{E}$ is

$$|\mathrm{d}\mathbf{E}| = \frac{q\mathrm{d}h}{MP^2} = \frac{q\mathrm{d}h}{r^2 + h^2},$$

where $r = OP = \sqrt{(x^2 + y^2)}$ is the distance of P from the origin.

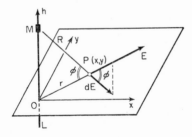

FIG. 56

By the principle of superposition, **E** is the vector sum of the intensities $\mathrm{d}\mathbf{E}$ due to all such elements. As **E** lies in the plane S_0, its magnitude is the sum of the projections on S_0 of the elementary intensities $\mathrm{d}\mathbf{E}$:

$$|\mathbf{E}| = \int \cos\phi\, |\mathrm{d}\mathbf{E}| = \int\limits_{-\infty}^{+\infty} \frac{q\cos\phi}{r^2 + h^2}\,\mathrm{d}h,$$

where ϕ is the angle between the vector $d\mathbf{E}$ and the plane S_0. From the right-angled triangle MOP we have $h = r \tan \phi$ and

$$\frac{1}{r^2 + h^2} = \frac{\cos^2\phi}{r^2},$$

so that

$$|\mathbf{E}| = \int_{-\pi/2}^{\pi/2} \frac{q \cos \phi}{r}\, d\phi = \frac{2q}{r}. \tag{2}$$

The intensity $\mathbf{E}$ is directed along the vector $\overline{OP} = z$; as the unit vector in this direction is $z/|z|$, it follows that

$$\mathbf{E} = \frac{2q}{r} \cdot \frac{z}{|z|} = \frac{2qz}{|z|^2} = \frac{2qx}{x^2 + y^2} + i\frac{2qy}{x^2 + y^2}. \tag{3}$$

The electrostatic field considered is completely specified by the distribution of the vectors $\mathbf{E}$ in the plane S_0. In what follows we

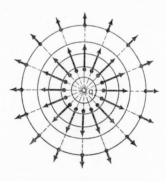

Fig. 57

shall speak of this plane field $\mathbf{E}$, which represents the field of an infinite line L bearing a uniform charge q per unit length, as the *plane field of a point-charge of strength q* located at the point where L intersects S_0. The lines of force representing the plane field (3) (lines drawn so that, at each point, they are tangential to the field vector at that point) form a pencil of straight lines with vertex at the origin of coordinates (Fig. 57); for a positive charge q the vector $\mathbf{E}$ is directed outward from O, for a negative charge $-q$ it is directed towards O.

Formula (2) shows that the magnitude of the plane field of a point charge is inversely proportional to the distance of the field point from the charge, and not to the square of the distance, as in space. Similar differences between plane fields and the corresponding spatial fields will be shown by many of the formulae given later.

Example 2. The field of a *system of point charges*, of strengths $q_1, q_2, \ldots, q_n$, situated at the respective points $z_1, z_2, \ldots, z_n$ is given by

$$\mathbf{E} = \sum_{k=1}^{n} \frac{2q_k(z-z_k)}{|z-z_k|^2}$$

$$= \sum_{k=1}^{n} \frac{2q_k(x-x_k)}{(x-x_k)^2+(y-y_k)^2} + i \sum_{k=1}^{n} \frac{2q_k(y-y_k)}{(x-x_k)^2+(y-y_k)^2}. \tag{4}$$

As the charge q_k is located at the point z_k, it will follow, as in the derivation of (3), that its field is

$$\mathbf{E}_k = \frac{2q_k(z-z_k)}{|z-z_k|^2}.$$

Formula (4), giving the field of the system of charges, follows immediately when we sum the $\mathbf{E}_k$, according to the principle of superposition.

Example 3. We consider a *uniform translatory motion of a fluid*, specified by a velocity vector $\mathbf{V}$ which is constant in magnitude and direction. We take S_0 to be any plane parallel to $\mathbf{V}$; the motion is then described by the plane field of a constant vector

$$\mathbf{V} = V_x + iV_y \tag{5}$$

($V_x = $ const., $V_y = $ const.). The stream lines ("lines of force" of the vector $\mathbf{V}$) form a pencil of parallel straight lines (Fig. 58).

Example 4. Let us consider the fluid motion represented by the vector velocity

$$\mathbf{V} = \frac{Q}{2\pi} \frac{z}{|z|^2}, \tag{6}$$

where Q is a real constant whose physical meaning will be made clear in Art. 36. The stream lines form a pencil of straight lines with vertex at the origin of coordinates (see Fig. 57). The vector **V** is directed away from the origin when $Q > 0$ and towards the origin when $Q < 0$. In both cases the magnitude of the velocity decreases in inverse proportion to the distance from the origin. Such a field is called *the plane field of a point source* (when $Q < 0$ we also speak of a *sink*). The plane field of a point source represents the plane-parallel field of flow of a fluid issuing radially into space from a source distributed uniformly along an infinite straight line.

FIG. 58

Example 5. We consider the fluid motion represented by the vector velocity

$$\mathbf{V} = \frac{\Gamma i}{2\pi} \cdot \frac{z}{|z|^2} = -\frac{\Gamma y}{2\pi(x^2+y^2)} + i\frac{\Gamma x}{2\pi(x^2+y^2)}, \qquad (7)$$

where Γ is a real constant whose physical meaning will be made clear in Art. 36. At every point $z \neq 0$ the direction of **V** is obtained by rotating the vector z through an angle $\pi/2$ (anticlockwise when $\Gamma > 0$ and clockwise when $\Gamma < 0$); consequently, the stream lines are concentric circles with centre at the origin of coordinates. The magnitude of the velocity is inversely proportional to $|z|$ (Fig. 59). Such a field is called a *plane vortex field*. The fluid rotates in the anti-clockwise sense when $\Gamma > 0$ and in the clockwise sense when $\Gamma < 0$.

Example 6. *The plane field of heat flow from a point source* (representing the flow from an infinite uniform line-source in a homogeneous isotropic medium) is given by

$$Q = \frac{q}{2\pi} \cdot \frac{z}{|z|^2}, \qquad (8)$$

where q is a real constant. The field (8) is identical in form with the field (6) representing the plane field of flow of a point source of fluid.

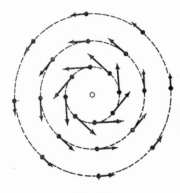

Fig. 59

36. Properties of plane vector fields

We first consider a *plane* electrostatic field arising from an arbitrary system of sources (charges) in the plane. (These sources may be considered as distributed over points, lines, and regions of the plane.) It is assumed that the reader is familiar with the fundamental concepts of vector analysis, such as flux, divergence, circulation, and curl (rotation). By Gauss's theorem the *flux of the field across any simple closed curve C* is (in general) equal to 4π times the total charge contained within C:

$$N = \oint_C (\mathbf{E}, \mathbf{n}^0)\, ds = 4\pi q. \qquad (9)$$

Here, $\mathbf{n}^0$ is the unit vector along the *outward* normal to C; and $(\mathbf{E}, \mathbf{n}^0)$ denotes the usual scalar product $\mathbf{E} \cdot \mathbf{n}^0$, so that, if $\mathbf{E} = E_x + iE_y$, $\mathbf{n}^0 = n^0{}_x + in^0{}_y$, then $(\mathbf{E}, \mathbf{n}^0) = E_x n^0{}_x + E_y n^0{}_y$. Gauss's theorem gives physical meaning to the flux of $\mathbf{E}$ across a closed contour C: if this flux is non-zero then C encloses charges giving rise to the field. The surface density of charge at a field point P is characterized by the *divergence* of the vector field at P; it is a familiar result that, under appropriate conditions,

$$\text{div } \mathbf{E} = \frac{\partial E_x}{\partial x} + \frac{\partial E_y}{\partial y} = \lim_{\Delta\sigma \to 0} \frac{1}{\Delta\sigma} \oint_C (\mathbf{E}, \mathbf{n}^0) \, ds, \qquad (10)$$

where C is a contour surrounding P, $\Delta\sigma$ is the area enclosed by C, and the limit is taken on the assumption that C shrinks up to P. By (9), the flux

$$\oint_C (\mathbf{E}, \mathbf{n}^0) \, ds$$

equals 4π times the sum Δq of the charges enclosed by C, so that

$$\text{div } \mathbf{E} = 4\pi \lim_{\Delta\sigma \to 0} \frac{\Delta q}{\Delta\sigma} = 4\pi\rho, \qquad (11)$$

where ρ is the surface density of charge at the point P. Hence, if the charge density is zero at some point of the z-plane, then, at this point,

$$\text{div } \mathbf{E} = 0. \qquad (12)$$

Any field whose divergence vanishes at every point z of a domain D is said to be (locally) *solenoidal* in this domain; thus, $\mathbf{E}$ is solenoidal in D if, and only if,

$$\text{div } \mathbf{E} = \frac{\partial E_x}{\partial x} + \frac{\partial E_y}{\partial y} = 0 \qquad (13)$$

at every point z of D.

The circulation of the vector field $\mathbf{E}$ about a closed contour C is

$$A = \oint_C (\mathbf{E}, \mathbf{s}^0) \, ds \qquad (14)$$

where $\mathbf{s}^0$ is a unit vector along the positively-directed tangent to C; it gives the work done by the field when a positive unit charge is taken around one complete circuit of C in the positive sense. As no expenditure of energy is required to maintain the electrostatic field, the work given by (14) must be zero for any closed contour C. For, otherwise, some contour C would exist such that finite positive work is done on a point charge taken around it in one sense or the other; this situation is clearly impossible as it would represent an unlimited source of energy.

It follows that, at any point of the field,

$$(\text{curl }\mathbf{E})_n = \lim_{\Delta\sigma\to 0} \frac{1}{\Delta\sigma} \oint_C (\mathbf{E}, \mathbf{s}^0)\, ds = \frac{\partial E_y}{\partial x} - \frac{\partial E_x}{\partial y} = 0. \quad (15)$$

Here, $(\text{curl }\mathbf{E})_n$ denotes the resolute of curl $\mathbf{E}$ normal to the plane (as $\mathbf{E}$ is a plane field, curl $\mathbf{E}$ has zero resolute along any direction in the plane), C is a contour surrounding the field point P concerned, $\Delta\sigma$ is the area enclosed by C, and the limit is taken on the assumption that C shrinks up to P. Any field whose curl vanishes at every point of a domain D is said to be a *potential* field in this domain. By (15), an *electrostatic field is everywhere a potential field* (or *irrotational* field).

We now turn to the other types of field. For the plane flow of an ideal incompressible fluid the *flux of the velocity vector* across a closed contour C is

$$Q = \oint_C (\mathbf{V}, \mathbf{n}^0)\, ds \quad (16)$$

and gives the quantity of fluid (per unit height) flowing in unit time from within C to the domain outside it. For example, considering the flow from a point source at the origin (see Art. 34, Example 4) across the circle $|z| = r$, we have

$$(\mathbf{V}, \mathbf{n}^0) = \pm|\mathbf{V}| = \frac{Q}{2\pi r}$$

and

$$\oint_C (\mathbf{V}, \mathbf{n}^0)\, ds = \oint_C \frac{Q}{2\pi r}\, ds = \frac{Q}{2\pi r} \cdot 2\pi r = Q.$$

This result expresses the physical meaning of the constant Q in formula (6). If the flux across C differs from zero, it follows from the assumed incompressibility of the fluid that C must enclose sources or sinks.

The *divergence of the velocity* at a point in the field, given, under appropriate conditions, by

$$\text{div }\mathbf{V} = \lim_{\Delta\sigma\to 0} \frac{1}{\Delta\sigma} \oint_C (\mathbf{V}, \mathbf{n}^0)\, ds = \frac{\partial V_x}{\partial x} + \frac{\partial V_y}{\partial y}, \quad (17)$$

determines the *density* of distribution of sources or sinks at this point. Thus, for steady plane flow, the condition that there should be no sources or sinks in some domain D is that

$$\operatorname{div} \mathbf{V} = \frac{\partial V_x}{\partial x} + \frac{\partial V_y}{\partial y} = 0 \tag{18}$$

at all points of D.

The circulation of the velocity vector $\mathbf{V}$ around the closed contour C, given by

$$\Gamma = \oint_C (\mathbf{V}, \mathbf{s}^0)\, \mathrm{d}s, \tag{19}$$

equals the integral around C of the projection of $\mathbf{V}$ along the positively-directed tangent to C. If, for some contour C, the circulation is not zero, it means that in the integral (19) the tangential projections V_s having one sign prevail over those having the other sign, so that, in a manner of speaking, the fluid whirls around C. (See Fig. 60: here the positive V_s prevail over the

Fig. 60

negative, so that $\Gamma > 0$.) For example, for the plane field of a point vortex at the origin (see Art. 35, Example 5), considering the circulation around the circle $|z| = r$, we have

$$(\mathbf{V}, \mathbf{s}^0) = \pm |\mathbf{V}| = \frac{\Gamma}{2\pi r}$$

and

$$\oint_C (\mathbf{V}, \mathbf{s}^0)\, ds = \oint_C \frac{\Gamma}{2\pi r}\, ds = \frac{\Gamma}{2\pi r} \cdot 2\pi r = \Gamma.$$

This result gives the physical meaning of the constant Γ in formula (7). The magnitude of the *curl of the velocity* at a point of the field, given, under appropriate conditions, by

$$(\operatorname{curl} \mathbf{V})_n = \lim_{\Delta\sigma \to 0} \frac{1}{\Delta\sigma} \oint_C (\mathbf{V}, \mathbf{s}^0)\, ds = \frac{\partial V_y}{\partial x} - \frac{\partial V_x}{\partial y},$$

determines the density of distribution of vortices at this point. Points of the field where $(\operatorname{curl} \mathbf{V})_n \neq 0$ are called *vortex points* or *vortices*.

Thus, *in the steady plane flow of an incompressible fluid,* the condition that there should be no vortices in a domain D is that

$$(\operatorname{curl} \mathbf{V})_n = \frac{\partial V_y}{\partial x} - \frac{\partial V_x}{\partial y} = 0 \qquad (20)$$

at all points of D.

Let us now consider a steady plane flow of heat. In the theory of heat conduction it is assumed that the quantity of heat dq flowing in unit time across a line-element of length ds is proportional to ds and to the normal derivative of the temperature $\partial v/\partial n$; that is,

$$dq = -k\frac{\partial v}{\partial n}ds = (-k\operatorname{grad} v, \mathbf{n}^0)\, ds = (\mathbf{Q}, \mathbf{n}^0)\, ds.$$

Here, k is the coefficient of thermal conductivity and the minus sign is taken because heat flows in the direction opposite to that of $\operatorname{grad} v$ (see Art. 33).

Thus, the flux of the vector $\mathbf{Q}$ across the closed contour C gives the quantity of heat flowing in unit time from within C to the domain outside it; and the divergence of $\mathbf{Q}$, given, under appropriate conditions, by

$$\operatorname{div} \mathbf{Q} = \lim_{\Delta\sigma \to 0} \frac{1}{\Delta\sigma} \oint_C (\mathbf{Q}, \mathbf{n}^0)\, ds = \frac{\partial Q_x}{\partial x} + \frac{\partial Q_y}{\partial y},$$

determines the density of distribution of the heat sources at the field point concerned.

10

In a steady plane flow of heat, the condition that there should be no sources or sinks in a domain D is that

$$\text{div } \mathbf{Q} = \frac{\partial Q_x}{\partial x} + \frac{\partial Q_y}{\partial y} = 0 \tag{21}$$

at all points of D. If k is constant, we have

$$\text{curl } \mathbf{Q} = -k \text{ curl grad } v = \mathbf{0} \tag{21'}$$

so that, at each point of the flow,

$$\frac{\partial Q_y}{\partial x} - \frac{\partial Q_x}{\partial y} = 0. \tag{22}$$

37. The force function and potential function

We consider an arbitrary electrostatic field in a simply-connected domain D which does not contain any of the charges producing the field. (A domain D in the open plane is said to be *simply-connected* if every closed contour C in D is *reducible* in D; that is, *can be continuously shrunk to a point in D without leaving D*.) By (15),

$$(\text{curl } \mathbf{E})_n = \frac{\partial E_y}{\partial x} - \frac{\partial E_x}{\partial y} = 0$$

at all points of D; accordingly, there exists a function $V = V(x, y)$ whose total differential in D is

$$\mathrm{d}V = -E_x \, \mathrm{d}x - E_y \, \mathrm{d}y;$$

that is, at all points in D,

$$E_x = -\frac{\partial V}{\partial x}, \qquad E_y = -\frac{\partial V}{\partial y}. \tag{23}$$

In this connection we recall that $P \, \mathrm{d}x + Q \, \mathrm{d}y$ (where P, Q have continuous partial derivatives) is a total differential if, and only if, $\partial P/\partial y = \partial Q/\partial x$; equation (15) shows that this condition is satisfied by the expression $-E_x \, \mathrm{d}x - E_y \, \mathrm{d}y$. The function $V(x, y)$ is given by the line integral of its total differential:

$$V(x,y) = -\int_{\substack{z_0 \\ (L)}}^{z} (E_x \, \mathrm{d}x + E_y \, \mathrm{d}y) + c, \tag{24}$$

where the integral is taken along any path L, in the domain D, connecting the fixed point z_0 with the variable point $z = x + iy$, and c is an arbitrary constant.

Equations (23) can be written as a single vector equation:

$$\mathbf{E} = -\frac{\partial V}{\partial x} - i\frac{\partial V}{\partial y} = -\operatorname{grad} V. \tag{25}$$

The function $V = V(x, y)$ is called the *potential function* or *potential* of the field, and the level lines $V(x, y) = \text{const.}$ are its *equipotential lines* or *equipotentials*. It follows from (25) that, at each point of the field, the intensity $\mathbf{E}$ is directed along the normal to the equipotential line through this point.

It is easy to express the work W done by *the field* when a unit positive point-charge is moved from the point $z_1 = x_1 + iy_1$ to the point $z_2 = x_2 + iy_2$. By (25), W is independent of the particular path C: for, $\mathbf{s}^0 \, \mathrm{d}s = \mathrm{d}x + i \, \mathrm{d}y = \mathrm{d}z$ is the vector of length $\mathrm{d}s$ directed along the tangent to C, and $\mathbf{E} = -(\partial V/\partial x) - i(\partial V/\partial y)$, so that

$$(\mathbf{E}, \mathbf{s}^0) \, \mathrm{d}s = -\frac{\partial V}{\partial x} \, \mathrm{d}x - \frac{\partial V}{\partial y} \, \mathrm{d}y = -\mathrm{d}V(x, y)$$

and

$$W = +\int_C (\mathbf{E}, \mathbf{s}^0) \, \mathrm{d}s = -\int_C \mathrm{d}V(x, y)$$

$$= V(x_1, y_1) - V(x_2, y_2); \tag{26}$$

that is, W equals the difference in potential between z_1 and z_2.

Example 1. For the *plane field of a point charge* of strength q the components of the vector intensity are

$$E_x = \frac{2qx}{x^2 + y^2}, \qquad E_y = \frac{2qy}{x^2 + y^2};$$

hence, by (24), the potential of this field is

$$V = -2q \int_{z_0}^{z} \frac{x \, \mathrm{d}x + y \, \mathrm{d}y}{x^2 + y^2} = -q \ln(x^2 + y^2) + c = 2q \ln\frac{1}{|z|} + c,$$

where L is any path which connects z_0 with z and does not pass through the origin and c is an arbitrary constant. Clearly, V becomes infinite as $z \to \infty$. The equipotential lines of the field are the concentric circles $|z| = r$ (see Fig. 57). If the charge q is situated at the point ζ then the potential of its field is obviously equal to

$$V = 2q \ln \frac{1}{|z - \zeta|} + c. \tag{27}$$

Example 2. *The potential of the plane field of a charged curvilinear arc L is given by*

$$V = \int_L 2\eta(\zeta) \cdot \ln \frac{1}{|z - \zeta|} \cdot ds \tag{28}$$

where ζ denotes a variable point on L, the real function $\eta(\zeta)$ is the linear density of charge along L at the point ζ, and ds is the element of arc. (The spatial distribution of charge giving rise to this field is that over the cylindrical surface whose generators are perpendicular to the z-plane and intersect it along the curve L, the surface density $\eta(\zeta)$ being independent of height.) To establish (28) we divide L into a large number (n) of small elements of length Δs_k $(k = 1, 2, \ldots, n)$ and suppose the charge distribution along L to be replaced by n point charges at points ζ_k on each of these sub-arcs, the charge at ζ_k being $\eta(\zeta_k) \cdot \Delta s_k$. The potential of the resulting field is

$$V' = \sum_{k=1}^{n} 2\eta(\zeta_k) \left\{ \ln \frac{1}{|z - \zeta_k|} \right\} \Delta s_k;$$

for given z this is an approximative sum for the integral (28) and tends to the integral (28) (whenever this integral exists) as

$$\max \Delta s_k \to +0.$$

Example 3. *The potential of the plane field of a charged domain D is given by*

$$V = \iint_D 2\rho(\zeta) \cdot \ln \frac{1}{|z - \zeta|} \cdot d\sigma, \tag{29}$$

where ζ is a variable point of D, $\rho(\zeta)$ is the surface density of charge at the point ζ, and $\mathrm{d}\sigma$ denotes the element of area. (The spatial system of charge producing this field is a volume distribution over the appropriate cylindrical body, the volume density $\rho(\zeta)$ being independent of height.) The proof of (29) follows similar lines to that of (28).

Let us consider the behaviour at infinity of the potential of the plane field. For definiteness we take the field of Example 2 above, and suppose that the curve L is *bounded* and that $\eta(\zeta)$ is bounded on L. For purposes of comparison we shall also consider the field of a point charge of magnitude

$$q = \int_L \eta(\zeta) \, . \, \mathrm{d}s$$

situated at the finite point ζ_0. The difference between the potentials of these two fields is

$$V - V_0 = \int_L 2\eta(\zeta) \, . \, \ln\frac{1}{|z-\zeta|} \, . \, \mathrm{d}s - 2\left\{\ln\frac{1}{|z-\zeta_0|}\right\}\int_L \eta(\zeta) \, . \, \mathrm{d}s$$

$$= \int_L 2\eta(\zeta) \, . \, \ln\left|\frac{z-\zeta_0}{z-\zeta}\right| \, . \, \mathrm{d}s = \alpha \quad \text{(say)}.$$

As ζ, ζ_0 lie in a bounded domain, it follows that, as $z \to \infty$,

$$\left|\frac{z-\zeta_0}{z-\zeta}\right| \to 1, \quad \text{and} \quad \ln\left|\frac{z-\zeta_0}{z-\zeta}\right| \to 0,$$

both limits existing *uniformly* with respect to ζ on L; accordingly, $\alpha \to 0$ as $z \to \infty$. Thus,

$$V = V_0 + \alpha = 2q\ln\frac{1}{|z-\zeta_0|} + \alpha \tag{30}$$

where q is the total charge on L, ζ_0 is any finite point in the plane, and $\alpha \to 0$ as $z \to \infty$.

In the same way we can establish the result (30) for the plane field of a bounded distribution such as that of Example 3 (or, more generally, for the field of an arbitrary bounded plane distribution of charge over a finite number of isolated points, curvilinear arcs, and domains); as in (30), q will denote the total charge of the system.

It follows from (30) that, *for* $q \neq 0$, *the potential of the field increases without limit as* $z \to \infty$, so that we cannot define the potential at a finite point as the work done by the field when a unit positive point-charge is removed from this point to $z = \infty$ (*cf.* formula 26). However, *if the total charge* $q = 0$ *it follows from* (30) *that the potential* V *tends to zero as* $z \to \infty$.

We now introduce the force function. Let D be a simply-connected domain of the open plane (so that any closed contour C in D is *reducible* in D; that is, C can be continuously shrunk to a point in D without leaving D), and suppose that D does not contain any of the charges producing the field $\mathbf{E}$. As $\mathbf{E}$ is solenoidal in D,

$$\operatorname{div} \mathbf{E} = \frac{\partial E_x}{\partial x} + \frac{\partial E_y}{\partial y} = 0 \tag{31}$$

at all points in this domain. It follows that, in D, the expression $-E_y\,\mathrm{d}x + E_x\,\mathrm{d}y$ is the total differential of some function U; that is, at all points of D we have

$$E_x = \frac{\partial U}{\partial y}, \qquad E_y = -\frac{\partial U}{\partial x}. \tag{31'}$$

The function $U(x, y)$ is given in D by the formula

$$U(x,y) = \int_{\substack{z_0 \\ (L)}}^{z} (-E_y\,\mathrm{d}x + E_x\,\mathrm{d}y) + c, \tag{32}$$

where the integral is taken along any path L in D connecting some fixed point z_0 with the variable point z, and c is an arbitrary constant.

The level lines of U in D are the curves $U(x, y) = $ const.; at any point on such a curve the gradient of the tangent is, by (31'),

$$\frac{\mathrm{d}y}{\mathrm{d}x} = -\left(\frac{\partial U}{\partial x}\right) \Big/ \left(\frac{\partial U}{\partial y}\right) = \frac{E_y}{E_x};$$

as E_y/E_x is the gradient of the line of action of $\mathbf{E}$ at the point concerned, it follows that the curves $U(x, y) = $ const. are the lines of force in this domain. For this reason $U(x, y)$ is called the *force function* of the field in D.

Suppose that the charge producing the field (including possible induced charges and dipoles) is distributed over a set of points S in the plane; the set of points *exterior* to S in the plane (the complement of $\bar{S}$) will be the union of one or more disjoint domains (the *field domains*). The general field domain D will be **multiply-connected** (in the open plane) and the function U constructed in it according to formula (32) will, in general, be infinitely many-valued; it will be clear from the above that *continuously-differentiable branches* of U can be separated in any simply-connected sub-domain D_0 of D (and, in particular, in any disc neighbourhood in D), and that *each such branch satisfies the relations* (31′) *in* D_0.

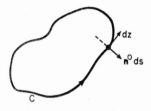

Fig. 61

We now consider a multiply-connected field domain D supporting an infinitely many-valued force function. Let C, defined by $z = z(t)$ ($\alpha \leqslant t \leqslant \beta$), be a simple closed contour (Jordan contour) in D, and suppose that C is described in the positive (anticlockwise) sense and encloses a total charge q (so that C is *not* reducible in D); let L be the Jordan arc $z = z(t)$ ($\alpha \leqslant t \leqslant \gamma$, $\alpha < \gamma < \beta$). It follows readily from the Heine–Borel covering theorem that L is contained in a *simply-connected* sub-domain D_0 of D. Let U be **any** continuously-differentiable branch of the force-function in D_0 **and** let $\mathbf{n}^0$ be the unit vector along the outward normal to C. **Then**, with the usual notation, we have, at any point on L,

$$\mathbf{n}^0 \, ds = -i \, dz = dy - i \, dx$$

and, by (31′),

$$(\mathbf{E}, \mathbf{n}^0) \, ds = \frac{\partial U}{\partial x} \, dx + \frac{\partial U}{\partial x} \, dy = \frac{\partial U}{\partial s} \, ds,$$

so that

$$\int_L (\mathbf{E}, \mathbf{n}^0) \, ds = \int_L \frac{\partial U}{\partial s} \, ds.$$

Defining

$$\oint_C \frac{\partial U}{\partial s}\, \mathrm{d}s$$

to be

$$\lim_{\gamma \to \beta - 0} \int_L \frac{\partial U}{\partial s}\, \mathrm{d}s,$$

and using Gauss's theorem, we get

$$q = \frac{1}{4\pi} \oint_C (\mathbf{E}, \mathbf{n}^0)\, \mathrm{d}s = \frac{1}{4\pi} \oint_C \frac{\partial U}{\partial s}\, \mathrm{d}s. \tag{33}$$

Example. The plane field of a point charge q at the origin has components

$$E_x = \frac{2qx}{x^2 + y^2}, \qquad E_y = \frac{2qy}{x^2 + y^2}.$$

The field domain D, obtained from the open plane by excluding the point $z = 0$, is *not* simply-connected and the function defined by (32) is *multiform*:

$$U(x, y) = 2q \int_{z_0}^{z} \frac{-y\, \mathrm{d}x + x\, \mathrm{d}y}{x^2 + y^2}$$

$$= 2q \operatorname{Arc tan} \frac{y}{x} + c = 2q \operatorname{Arg} z + c, \tag{34}$$

where L is any path which connects z_0 with z and does not pass through the point $z = 0$ (Fig. 62). In formula (34) we take $z_0 = 1$ and interpret $\operatorname{Arg} z$ as the value of the argument which is obtained from the principal value (zero) at $z = z_0$ by continuous extension along the curve L. This value of $\operatorname{Arg} z$ obviously remains unchanged if we replace the path L by any conformable path L' in D connecting z_0 and z. (We say that two paths L, L' in D, each connecting the same two points, say z_0 and z, are *conformable* in this domain if each can be continuously deformed into the other *without leaving* D.) It follows that the integral is unaltered in value if we replace L by a path l which joins $z_0 = 1$ to z and lies entirely on one or other of the half-planes $\operatorname{Im} z \geqslant 0$, $\operatorname{Im} z \leqslant 0$, together with an appropriate number (n) of circuits of the circle $C(|z| = 1)$ in the appropriate sense. (See Fig. 62; here, $n = 2$ and C is described in the negative, or clockwise, sense.) The integral

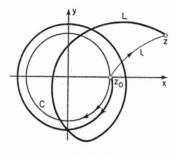

Fig. 62

along l yields the principal value $\arg z$ and that around C the value $\pm 2n\pi$, the sign being $+$ or $-$ according as whether the circuits of C are taken in the positive or negative sense. Thus, the many-valued function U is given in $|z| > 0$ by

$$U(x, y) = 2q \arg z \pm 4\pi n q + c.$$

In constructing force and potential functions for the electrostatic field we often have to take account of the multiple connectivity of the field domain concerned, for the reason that E_x and E_y generally have discontinuities at points of the set S on which the charge is distributed. The component field-domains are obtained from the open plane by cutting appropriate holes in it so as to remove the points of the set $\bar{S}$ which, in general, consists of isolated points, curvilinear arcs, and regions. A typical field domain D obtained in this way is shown in Fig. 63; in general, E_x and E_y will be discontinuous on the frontier of D, this frontier consisting of three closed curves, an arc, and a point, in the example shown. Considering a domain of this type, we see that the value given for $U(x, y)$ by formula (32) is unaltered if we replace L by a *conformable* path in D; however, if the integral

$$c_k = \oint_{C_k} (\mathbf{E}, \mathbf{n}^0)\, ds = \oint_{C_k} \frac{\partial U}{\partial s}\, ds \tag{35}$$

is not zero, where C_k is any simple positively-directed contour in D which encloses the kth component of the frontier of D (and no other component of this frontier), then we obtain a different value for $U(x, y)$ if we take the integral in (32) along a path L' which differs from L by making one or more circuits (or additional

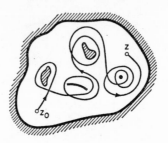

FIG. 63

circuits) about this component of the frontier. It will be clear that, in the general case, the values of $U(x, y)$ at some given point z in D will be represented by

$$U(x,y) = U_0(x,y)+n_1c_1+n_2c_2+ \ldots +n_mc_m, \qquad (36)$$

where $U_0(x, y)$ is a particular value of U at this point, $c_1, c_2, \ldots, c_m$ are the values of the integrals (35) for each of the m components of the frontier of D which are *surrounded by* D, and $n_1, n_2, \ldots, n_m$ are arbitrary integers (positive, negative, or zero) indicating the number of circuits, and the sense of these circuits, about the m components concerned. (For the example shown in Fig. 63, $m = 4$; the outer boundary-component cannot be enclosed by a contour C_k *in* D).

The integrals (35) are called the *cyclical constants* of the function $U(x, y)$ in the domain D. Formula (36) shows that $U(x, y)$ is single-valued in a multiply-connected field domain D if, and only if, all its cyclical constants in D vanish.

It will be clear that, for the potential function V, defined by (24), the cyclical constants

$$c_k' = \oint_{C_k} \frac{\partial V}{\partial s}\, \mathrm{d}s$$

are all zero, so that V is *uniform in any field domain* D; for, c_k'

equals the circulation of $\mathbf{E}$ about C_k and it has been shown (Art. 36) that this must vanish.

On the other hand, as seen from (33), the cyclical constant for the force function associated with any (bounded) hole is $4\pi q$, where q is the total charge enclosed by the contour concerned; in general, therefore, the force function is many-valued.

38. The complex potential in electrostatics

Comparing formulae (23) and (31'), we see that, in any simply-connected sub-domain D_0 of a field domain D, there exists a continuously-differentiable branch U of the force function related to the potential function by

$$\frac{\partial U}{\partial x} = \frac{\partial V}{\partial y}, \qquad \frac{\partial U}{\partial y} = -\frac{\partial V}{\partial x}. \tag{37}$$

These are the Cauchy–Riemann equations of Art. 14; as U and V are uniform in D_0 it follows immediately that

$$w = F(z) = U(x,y) + iV(x,y) \tag{38}$$

is *regular* in D_0.

The function $F(z)$ is called the *complex potential* of the field in D_0; it will be clear that $F(z)$ is defined uniquely, within an arbitrary additive constant.

If U denotes a many-valued force function then the function defined in D by (38) will be many-valued, having a multiform real part. As made clear above, we can separate a regular branch of this many-valued function $F(z)$ on any simply-connected sub-domain D_0 of D; in particular, D_0 may be the domain obtained when we make D simply-connected by introducing appropriate cuts (see Fig. 64). The complex potential of the field provides an example of a *many-valued analytic function* (for the general definition see Art. 63).

We note that the uniformity of the derivatives in (37) ensures that all branches of the complex potential $F(z)$ which are regular at the point z of a field domain D have one and the same derivative at this point. This single-valued derived function can be considered as the *derivative* $F'(z)$ of the complex potential in D.

All the fundamental quantities associated with the field can be expressed in terms of the complex potential. For example, by (37) and (23) we have

$$F'(z) = \frac{\partial U}{\partial x} + i\frac{\partial V}{\partial x} = \frac{\partial V}{\partial y} + i\frac{\partial V}{\partial x} = -E_y - iE_x = -i(E_x - iE_y)$$

whence $E_x - iE_y = iF'(z)$; accordingly, the *intensity* **E** *of the field* is given by

$$\mathbf{E} = E_x + iE_y = -i\overline{\{F'(z)\}}. \tag{39}$$

Formula (39) shows that the vector **E** can be obtained from the vector $F'(z)$ by reflecting the latter in the real axis and then rotating the image clockwise through an angle $\pi/2$ (Fig. 65). It also follows from (39) that the *magnitude of the intensity* is

$$E = |F'(z)| = \sqrt{\left\{\left(\frac{\partial V}{\partial x}\right)^2 + \left(\frac{\partial V}{\partial y}\right)^2\right\}}. \tag{40}$$

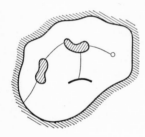

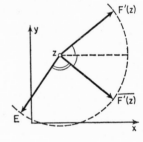

FIG. 64   FIG. 65

If D_0 is a simply-connected sub-domain of a field domain, it supports a regular branch $W = F(z)$ of the complex potential which maps D_0 onto a domain in the W-plane, the mapping being conformal at all points of D_0 at which the intensity is not zero; from the definitions it follows that the lines of force and equipotential lines in D_0 map onto straight lines parallel to the U and V axes. Thus, knowing the complex potential of the field, we can (at least, in principle) find its equipotentials and lines of force; that is, we can plot the field.

We saw above that the complex potential is defined only to within an additive constant. As this constant can be changed without affecting either the map of the field or its vector intensity, we shall omit mention of it in what follows.

At the beginning of the article we showed that a regular function $F(z)$, the complex potential of the field, exists in any simply-connected domain not intersecting the set of points over which the charge is distributed. Conversely, given any function

$$F(z) = U(x,y) + iV(x,y)$$

regular in a simply-connected domain D, there corresponds a charge distribution, over a set S not intersecting D, which produces a plane field having $F(z)$ as complex potential in D.

For, let us consider the field defined by $\mathbf{E} = -i\{\overline{F'(z)}\}$: from the Cauchy–Riemann conditions for $F(z)$ it follows that the field is solenoidal and irrotational in the domain D and hence is an electrostatic field. It is clear that $F(z)$ will be the complex potential of this field in D. In this sense, therefore, *there is a complete correspondence between plane electrostatic fields and regular functions.*

Example 1. *Consider the field of a point charge of strength q situated at the origin.* From the potential and force functions of the field (see formulae (27) and (34) of the preceding article) we immediately obtain its complex potential:

$$w = F(z) = 2q \operatorname{Arg} z + 2qi \ln \frac{1}{|z|}$$

$$= 2qi\left\{\ln\frac{1}{|z|} + i\operatorname{Arg}\frac{1}{z}\right\} = 2qi \operatorname{Ln}\frac{1}{z}.$$

The nature of this field is indicated by Fig. 57. The complex potential function maps the doubly-connected field domain

$$(0 < |z| < +\infty)$$

onto a simply connected domain (the open plane). This does not contradict the statement made in Art. 23, as the mapping function is many-valued.

If the charge is not at the origin, but at the point $z = z_0$, then the complex potential is

$$w = 2qi \operatorname{Ln}\frac{1}{z - z_0}. \tag{41}$$

Example 2. *For a system of two unlike point charges $+q$ and $-q$ situated at the points z_1 and z_2 respectively, the complex potential is*

$$w = 2qi \operatorname{Ln} \frac{1}{z - z_1} - 2qi \operatorname{Ln} \frac{1}{z - z_2} = 2qi \operatorname{Ln} \frac{z - z_2}{z - z_1}. \tag{42}$$

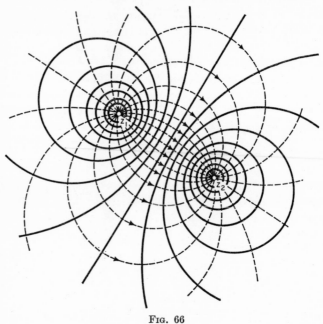

Fig. 66

The equipotential lines of the field are the curves on which

$$\operatorname{Im} w = 2q \ln \left| \frac{z - z_2}{z - z_1} \right| = \text{const.} ;$$

that is, the curves

$$\left| \frac{z - z_2}{z - z_1} \right| = \text{const.}$$

These are the circles of Apollonius having z_1 and z_2 as conjugate points (see Art. 20). The lines of force

$$\operatorname{Re} w = -2q \operatorname{Arg} \frac{z - z_2}{z - z_1} = \text{const.}$$

are the circular arcs joining the points z_1 and z_2 (see Art. 20). In Fig. 66, the equipotential lines are shown by continuous lines and the lines of force are dotted.

Example 3. *For a system of two like charges,* each of strength q, situated at z_1 and z_2, (42) is replaced by

$$w = 2qi \operatorname{Ln} \frac{1}{z-z_1} + 2qi \operatorname{Ln} \frac{1}{z-z_2}$$

$$= 2qi \operatorname{Ln} \frac{1}{(z-z_1)(z-z_2)}. \tag{43}$$

The equipotentials, given by

$$|z-z_1| \cdot |z-z_2| = \text{const.} = c,$$

are known generally as *lemniscates*; each is the locus of a point moving so that the product of its distances from z_1 and z_2 is constant

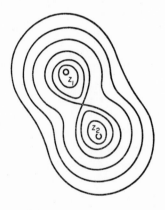

Fig. 67

(see Exercise 12c, Introduction). For $c = 0$ the curve degenerates into a pair of points; for $0 < c < \frac{1}{4}|z_1-z_2|^2$ it separates into two curves (the *ovals of Cassini*); for $c = \frac{1}{4}|z_1-z_2|^2$ it is the lemniscate of Bernoulli; and for $c > \frac{1}{4}|z_1-z_2|^2$ it is a single closed curve (Fig. 67).

Example 4. *For a system of point charges* q_1, q_2, . . .,q_n *situated at the respective points* z_1, z_2, . . ., z_n *the complex potential is*

$$w = 2i \sum_{k=1}^{n} q_k \operatorname{Ln} \frac{1}{z - z_k}. \tag{44}$$

Example 5. *The electrostatic field of a dipole.* For a system of two equal unlike charges $\pm q$ situated at the points $z_1 = 0$, $z_2 = -h$, where h is real and positive, the complex potential is, by (42),

$$w = 2qi \operatorname{Ln} \frac{z + h}{z} = 2qi \operatorname{Ln} \left(1 + \frac{h}{z}\right) = 2pi \operatorname{Ln} \left(1 + \frac{h}{z}\right)^{1/h},$$

where $p = qh$. We shall now permit the charges to approach one another infinitely closely by letting $h \to +0$, simultaneously increasing q in such a way that the product $qh = p$ remains constant. In the limit we obtain what is called a *point dipole of moment p* located at the origin of coordinates and directed along the positive x-axis. (The actual spatial distribution is one of uniform dipole moment p per unit length of an infinite line which is perpendicular to the z-plane and cuts this plane at $z = 0$.)

The complex potential for the field of this dipole is

$$w = 2pi \lim_{h \to +0} \operatorname{Ln}\left(1 + \frac{h}{z}\right)^{1/h} = 2pi \operatorname{Ln} e^{1/z} = \frac{2pi}{z}, \tag{45}$$

a simple bilinear function of z. (To obtain (45) we use the result given in Art. 8, putting $h = 1/n$, and then apply formula (31) of Chapter 3, neglecting the additive constant $2k\pi i$.)

The diagram representing the field of this dipole is the conformal equivalent, in the z-plane, of the Cartesian net in the w-plane, under the mapping $w = (2pi/z)$. The equipotential lines $V = c$ form on the w-sphere a pencil of circles touching each other at $w = \infty$; this pencil corresponds with a pencil of circles in the z-plane touching each other at $z = 0$; in particular, the real axis $V = 0$ corresponds with the imaginary axis $x = 0$ (for, by (45), w is real if, and only if, z is purely imaginary). It will thus be clear that the equipotentials (shown by continuous lines in Fig. 68) form a pencil of circles touching the y-axis at the origin. Similarly we can show that the lines of force in the z-plane (shown dotted in Fig. 68) form a pencil of circles touching the x-axis at the origin.

By (39) the intensity of the field of the dipole is

$$\mathbf{E} = i\overline{\left(\frac{2pi}{z^2}\right)} = \frac{2p}{\bar{z}^2} = \frac{2p}{r^2}e^{2i\phi},$$

where $z = re^{i\phi}$: its magnitude is inversely proportional to the square of the distance of the field point from the dipole, and its components are

$$E_x = \frac{2p\cos 2\phi}{r^2}, \qquad E_y = \frac{2p\sin 2\phi}{r^2}.$$

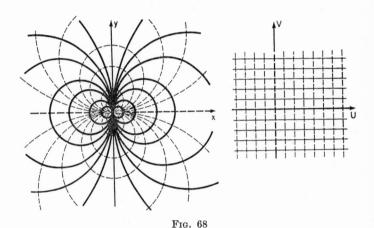

Fig. 68

39. The complex potential in hydrodynamics and heat conduction

If D is a *simply-connected* domain of steady plane flow of an ideal incompressible fluid and D contains no sources or vortices, then, at all points of this domain,

$$\frac{\partial V_x}{\partial x} + \frac{\partial V_y}{\partial y} = 0, \qquad \frac{\partial V_y}{\partial x} - \frac{\partial V_x}{\partial y} = 0,$$

so that $-V_y\,dx + V_x\,dy$ and $V_x\,dx + V_y\,dy$ are the total differentials of certain functions ψ and ϕ in D:

$$-V_y\,dx + V_x\,dy = d\psi(x,y), \qquad V_x\,dx + V_y\,dy = d\phi(x,y). \quad (46)$$

The function ϕ is called the *velocity potential*, and ψ the *stream function*. At all points z in D we have

$$V_x = \frac{\partial\phi}{\partial x}, \qquad V_y = \frac{\partial\phi}{\partial y}, \qquad \mathbf{V} = \operatorname{grad}\phi(x,y),$$

$$\phi(x,y) = \int_{\substack{z_0 \\ (L)}}^{z} (V_x\,\mathrm{d}x + V_y\,\mathrm{d}y) + c, \tag{47}$$

and

$$V_x = \frac{\partial\psi}{\partial y}, \qquad V_y = -\frac{\partial\psi}{\partial x},$$

$$\psi(x,y) = \int_{\substack{z_0 \\ (L)}}^{z} (-V_y\,\mathrm{d}x + V_x\,\mathrm{d}y) + c'; \tag{48}$$

here, L is any path in the (simply-connected) domain D connecting some fixed point z_0 with the variable point z, and c, c' denote arbitrary constants. It will be clear that the level lines of ψ in D give the trajectories of the moving particles, that is, the stream lines of the flow. The circulation Γ of the velocity vector around a closed contour C in D will be zero: with the usual notation we have

$$(\mathbf{V},\mathbf{s}^0)\,\mathrm{d}s = (\mathbf{V},\mathrm{d}z) = (V_x + iV_y, \mathrm{d}x + i\,\mathrm{d}y) = V_x\,\mathrm{d}x + V_y\,\mathrm{d}y = \frac{\partial\phi}{\partial s}\,\mathrm{d}s,$$

whence

$$\oint_C (\mathbf{V},\mathbf{s}^0)\,\mathrm{d}s = \oint_C \mathrm{d}\phi(x,y) = 0.$$

By means of ψ we can express the flow Q (that is, the volume of fluid, per unit height, passing in unit time) across a curve L', in D, joining the points z_1 and z_2: with the usual notation we have

$$(\mathbf{V}, \mathbf{n}^0)\,\mathrm{d}s = (\mathbf{V}, -i\,\mathrm{d}z) = (V_x + iV_y, \mathrm{d}y - i\,\mathrm{d}x)$$

$$= V_x\,\mathrm{d}y - V_y\,\mathrm{d}x = \frac{\partial\psi}{\partial s}\,\mathrm{d}s,$$

whence

$$Q = \int_{\substack{z_1 \\ (L')}}^{z_2} (\mathbf{V}, \mathbf{n}^0)\,\mathrm{d}s = \int_{\substack{z_1 \\ (L')}}^{z_2} \mathrm{d}\psi(x,y) = \psi(x_2,y_2) - \psi(x_1,y_1); \tag{49}$$

it will be clear that, if L' is closed, $Q = 0$.

In the general case of steady plane flow of an ideal incompressible fluid, the sources and vortices producing the flow are distributed over a set of points S; this set S, together with the moving fluid, occupies some region R of the open plane. The domains (D) of source-free irrotational flow are the (disjoint) components of the open set which remains when we remove the points of $\bar{S}$ from the interior of R by cutting appropriate holes (*cf.* Art 37). The general domain D so obtained is *multiply-connected* and the functions ϕ, ψ defined in D by the integral formulae in (47) and (48) will, in general, be multi-valued; as in Art. 37, any simply-connected sub-domain D_0 of D will support continuously-differentiable branches of these functions which satisfy equations (46), (47), (48) and enable us to define the integrals

$$\oint_C \frac{\partial \phi}{\partial s}\, ds, \qquad \oint_C \frac{\partial \psi}{\partial s}\, ds$$

around *any* positively-directed closed contour C in D (*see derivation of equation* (33)); as before, the values obtained for these integrals will not depend on the particular continuous branches chosen:

$$\left. \begin{aligned} \oint_C \frac{\partial \phi}{\partial s}\, ds &= \oint_C (\mathbf{V}, \mathbf{s}^0)\, ds = \Gamma, \\[2mm] \oint_C \frac{\partial \psi}{\partial s}\, ds &= \oint_C (\mathbf{V}, \mathbf{n}^0)\, ds = Q, \end{aligned} \right\} \tag{50}$$

where Γ (the circulation of $\mathbf{V}$ about C) is the total strength of the vortices enclosed by C, and Q (the flow across C into the surrounding domain) is the total strength of the sources enclosed by C.

Let D be a domain of free flow, of the type considered in the preceding paragraph. If D is *simply-connected* it follows immediately from (47), (48) that the *complex potential for the flow, defined in D by*

$$w = \Phi(z) = \phi(x, y) + i\psi(x, y), \tag{51}$$

is a regular function in this domain. In the more general case D is multiply-connected; and, if C is a contour in D surrounding a particular component of the frontier of D, the corresponding cyclical constants for ϕ and ψ (given by (50) and equal, respectively, to Γ and Q) will not both vanish: the cyclical constant for ϕ associated with this frontier component will differ from zero if the appropriate contour C encloses vortices whose total strength is not zero; similarly, the cyclical constant for ψ will not vanish if C encloses sources whose total strength is not zero. In general, therefore, both the real and imaginary parts of the complex potential defined in a multiply-connected domain D by (51) will be many-valued; this fact constitutes the main distinction between the complex potentials of electrostatics and hydrodynamics. It will be clear that in this case the function $\Phi(z)$ provides yet another example of a multiform analytic function defined in D: as before (see Art. 38), we can separate regular branches of Φ on any simply-connected sub-domain D_0, and every such branch which is regular at a point z in D will have the *same* derivative—denoted by $\Phi'(z)$—at this point, so that the function $\Phi'(z)$ defined in this way is *uniform* in D.

All the basic quantities connected with this plane flow can be expressed in terms of the complex potential. For example, by (47) and (48) we have

$$\Phi'(z) = \frac{\partial \phi}{\partial x} + i \frac{\partial \psi}{\partial x} = V_x - i V_y,$$

so that the velocity is

$$\mathbf{V} = V_x + i V_y = \overline{\Phi'(z)} \tag{52}$$

and has magnitude

$$V = |\Phi'(z)| = \sqrt{\left\{ \left(\frac{\partial \phi}{\partial x} \right)^2 + \left(\frac{\partial \phi}{\partial y} \right)^2 \right\}}. \tag{53}$$

On the plane representing the complex potential w, the horizontal lines Im w = const. correspond to the stream lines and the vertical straight lines Re w = const. correspond to the equipotential lines.

Example 1. For the *translatory motion* of a fluid (Example 3, Art. 35) the potential function and the stream function are linear:

$$\phi = V_x x + V_y y + c_1, \qquad \psi = -V_y x + V_x y + c_2.$$

The complex potential is a linear function of z:

$$w = \Phi(z) = \phi + i\psi = x(V_x - i V_y) + iy(V_x - i V_y) = \bar{\mathbf{V}} z, \tag{54}$$

where $\bar{\mathbf{V}} = V_x - iV_y$ is the conjugate of the velocity vector $V_x + iV_y$.

Example 2. *For a point source* (Example 4, Art. 35) the components of velocity are equal to

$$V_x = \left(\frac{Q}{2\pi}\right)\frac{x}{x^2+y^2}, \qquad V_y = \left(\frac{Q}{2\pi}\right)\frac{y}{x^2+y^2};$$

the potential function and the stream function are given by the integral formulae in (47) and (48):

$$\phi = \frac{Q}{2\pi}\ln|z|, \qquad \psi = \frac{Q}{2\pi}\operatorname{Arg} z.$$

Thus, the complex potential is

$$w = \Phi(z) = \frac{Q}{2\pi}\operatorname{Ln} z. \tag{55}$$

Example 3. *For a point vortex* (Example 5, Art. 35) it is similarly found that

$$\phi = \frac{\Gamma}{2\pi}\operatorname{Arg} z, \qquad \psi = -\frac{\Gamma}{2\pi}\ln|z|,$$

so that the complex potential is

$$w = \frac{\Gamma}{2\pi i}\operatorname{Ln} z. \tag{56}$$

This result differs from (55) by the factor $1/i$. It follows that the stream lines and equipotential lines are obtained by changing the roles of the corresponding lines in the preceding example.

Example 4. *A point dipole* in hydrodynamics is the complete analogue of the electrostatic dipole in Example 5 of Art. 38. In place of (45) we now write the complex potential as

$$w = -\frac{M}{2\pi} \cdot \frac{1}{z}, \tag{57}$$

where $M \ (= Qh)$ is the moment of the dipole, supposed directed along the positive x-axis. The stream lines for (57) coincide with the lines of force for (45) and the equipotential lines for (57) with the equipotentials for (45) (see Fig. 68).

The complex potential in the theory of heat conduction is constructed in a precisely similar way. We consider a steady plane flow of heat in a homogeneous isotropic medium. For a domain D which contains no sources of heat, it follows from (21) and (22) that

$$\frac{\partial Q_x}{\partial x} + \frac{\partial Q_y}{\partial y} = 0, \qquad \frac{\partial Q_y}{\partial x} - \frac{\partial Q_x}{\partial y} = 0 \qquad (58)$$

at each point of D. The temperature v takes the role of the potential ϕ:

$$\mathbf{Q} = -k\,\mathrm{grad}\,v; \qquad \frac{\partial v}{\partial x} = -\frac{1}{k}Q_x, \qquad \frac{\partial v}{\partial y} = -\frac{1}{k}Q_y.$$

From the first relation in (58) we deduce that, in any simply-connected sub-domain of D, $-(1/k)(Q_y\,\mathrm{d}x - Q_x\,\mathrm{d}y)$ is the total differential of a function $u = u(x, y)$ which we call the *stream function* and which is related to the temperature by the Cauchy–Riemann equations

$$\frac{\partial u}{\partial x} = \frac{\partial v}{\partial y} = -\frac{1}{k}Q_y, \qquad \frac{\partial u}{\partial y} = -\frac{\partial v}{\partial x} = \frac{1}{k}Q_x.$$

The function $u(x, y)$ assumes constant values on the lines of heat flow. It will be clear, on physical grounds, that v is uniform even when D is multiply-connected; in such a domain the stream function is, in general, multiform, as is the *complex potential* for the heat flow, defined by

$$w = \Psi(z) = u(x,y) + iv(x,y).$$

As before, regular branches of Ψ can be separated in any simply-connected sub-domain, and every branch which is regular at a point z has the same derivative $\Psi'(z)$ (say) at this point. The heat-flow vector is

$$\mathbf{Q} = -k\,\mathrm{grad}\,v = -k\frac{\partial v}{\partial x} - ik\frac{\partial v}{\partial y} = -ki\overline{[\Psi'(z)]}. \qquad (59)$$

40. The method of conformal mapping

We list four types of problems which are specially suited to solution by the method of conformal mapping. These problems are first formulated as problems in electrostatics; we then indicate the changes which are necessary when we consider problems in other physical fields.

The four types are as follows:

I. *Determination of the electrostatic field in a curvilinear strip D between two conductors represented by curves C_1, C_2 whose four end-points all lie at $z = \infty$. The potential difference between C_1 and C_2 is given.*

II. *Determination of the field in an annular domain D between two conductors represented by simple, closed, non-intersecting curves C_1, C_2 both of which are bounded. The potential difference between C_1 and C_2 is given.*

III. *Determination of the field in a domain D bounded by a conductor which is represented on the sphere as a simple closed curve C passing through the point at infinity. The magnitude of the intensity of the field at infinity is supposed given (on the understanding that the point at infinity is not an angular point of C).*

IV. *Determination of the field in the domain D exterior to a closed conductor represented by a bounded closed contour C. The intensity of the field at infinity is supposed given in magnitude and direction.*

The term *conductor* is interpreted as a curve C on which the potential function (defined, if necessary, by continuity on to the boundary from the field domain) is constant; this curve is the boundary of the region representing the intersection of the z-plane with the actual conducting cylinder whose generators are perpendicular to this plane. The problem of determining the field reduces to that of finding its complex potential, the latter being indeterminate to within an additive constant.

In hydrodynamics the corresponding problems are stated as problems of *streamlining*. They reduce to the problem of constructing the flow of an ideal incompressible fluid in a domain D containing no sources or vortices so that the flow has one or more given curves C as stream lines. In problems of types I and II the potential difference between the curves C_1 and C_2 is now replaced by the net *flow*, defined as the volume of fluid (per unit height) passing in unit time across any cross-cut joining points on C_1 and C_2 (see formula (49), Art. 39); the velocity at infinity is supposed given in magnitude in problems of type III, and in magnitude and direction in problems of type IV.

In the corresponding problems in heat conduction the electrical conductors are replaced by bodies maintained at a constant temperature; temperature plays the part of difference in potential and temperature gradient the part of field intensity.

In the following articles we illustrate the above four types by concrete examples in various physical contexts. In each of these examples we seek a solution satisfying certain given conditions. Later, in Art. 70, we show that the solution we find for any problem of type IV must be unique (apart from an additive constant) if it satisfies the given conditions. The same result holds for the other types of problem; we shall not stop to give proofs of this statement as it is considered that in the examples studied the uniqueness of the solutions is physically obvious. A solution found by any method will be the unique solution provided it satisfies the given conditions.

41. The field in a strip

We begin with problems of type I. It is supposed that the strip D (the field domain) contains none of the charges producing the field. As D is simply-connected it follows (see Art. 38) that the complex potential $w = F(z)$ is single-valued and regular in D. The potential function $V(x, y) = \operatorname{Im} F(z)$ is constant on each of the curves C_1 and C_2; the given potential difference is $V_0 = V_2 - V_1$, where V_1, V_2 are the values of V on C_1, C_2 respectively.

It follows that the function $w = F(z)$ gives a uniform mapping of the domain D onto a horizontal strip Δ in the w-plane of width $V_2 - V_1 = V_0$. Further, the two coincident boundary points of Δ which are located at infinity (*symbolized* by $w = \pm \infty$) are the images of two coincident boundary points of D which are located at infinity (and likewise symbolized by $z = \pm \infty$): for, infinitely many lines $V = \text{const.}$ in Δ pass through the points $w = \pm \infty$ so that infinitely many equipotential lines must meet at the corresponding boundary points of D; it will thus be clear from physical considerations that these boundary points of D cannot lie in the finite plane.

All the conditions enumerated above are satisfied by the one–one conformal mapping $w = F(z)$, of the domain D onto the strip $0 < \operatorname{Im} w < V_0$, which establishes a correspondence between the points at infinity (symbolized by $F(\pm \infty) = \pm \infty$). It follows from the results given in Art. 23 that this mapping exists and is determined within an additive constant; accordingly, a solution exists for any problem of type I.

Example 1. *A condenser consists of two plates in the form of half-planes as indicated in Fig.* 69. *The two plates are coplanar; their edges are parallel and separated by a distance* 2a, *and the potential difference is* $2V_0$. The problem reduces to the construction of the plane field which has the two cuts (each regarded as two-edged) along the half-lines $-\infty < x < -a$, $a < x < +\infty$, $(y = 0)$ as equipotentials, the corresponding potential difference being $2V_0$.

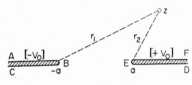

Fig. 69

This is a problem of type I: C_1 is the two-edged cut ABC and C_2 the similar cut DEF. The mapping of the field domain onto a strip of width $2V_0$ with the required normalization is given by the function (60) of Art. 33. Neglecting the irrelevant additive constant, the complex potential of the field is

$$w = \frac{2V_0}{\pi} \ln[z + \sqrt{(z^2 - a^2)}]. \qquad (60)$$

By (40) (Art. 38) the magnitude of the intensity of the field is

$$E = \left|\frac{dw}{dz}\right| = \frac{2V_0}{\pi} \cdot \frac{1}{|\sqrt{(z^2 - a^2)}|} = \frac{2V_0}{\pi} \cdot \frac{1}{\sqrt{(r_1 r_2)}},$$

where $r_1 = |z + a|$ and $r_2 = |z - a|$ are the distances of the field point z from the ends of the half-lines. From the last result it follows that, at the origin, $E = 2V_0/(\pi a)$; this value does not differ greatly from the field strength V_0/a obtained for an ordinary parallel-plate condenser with plate-separation $2a$ and potential difference $2V_0$. As z approaches the ends of the half-lines, E increases without limit (the "edge effect"); when z is removed to infinity, E tends to zero.

Example 2. *We consider the flow of an ideal fluid in a channel, of width* 2H, *which has parallel rectilinear banks and in which there* *is an obstacle in the form of a wall (Fig. 70); this wall is perpendicular to the banks and occupies half the width of the channel. The net flow Q is given.* The problem reduces to that of mapping the domain D_0 (Fig. 70) onto a strip. Under the preliminary transformation $\zeta = \pi z/(2H)$, D_0 becomes the domain of Example 4, Art. 33, with $h = \pi/2$. Formula (59) of the preceding chapter enables us to write down the mapping of D_0 onto the upper half-plane Im $\omega > 0$:

$$\omega = \sqrt{\left\{ \tanh^2 \frac{\zeta}{2} + \tan^2 \frac{\pi}{4} \right\}} = \sqrt{\left\{ \tanh^2 \frac{\pi z}{4H} + 1 \right\}};$$

the bank $ABCDE$ of the channel maps on the segment $[-\sqrt{2}, \sqrt{2}]$ and the bank FGK maps on the half-lines $[\sqrt{2}, +\infty]$ and $[-\infty, -\sqrt{2}]$. We transform this half-plane into the half-plane

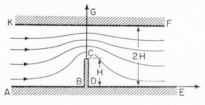

FIG. 70

Im $\omega_1 > 0$ so that the point A, K maps on $\omega_1 = 0$ and the point E, F maps on $\omega_1 = \infty$: the required mapping is

$$\omega_1 = \frac{(\sqrt{2}) + \omega}{(\sqrt{2}) - \omega} = \left\{ (\sqrt{2}) + \sqrt{\left(\tanh^2 \frac{\pi z}{4H} + 1 \right)} \right\}^2 \Big/ \left\{ 1 - \tanh^2 \frac{\pi z}{4H} \right\}$$

$$= \left\{ (\sqrt{2}) \cosh \frac{\pi z}{4H} + \sqrt{\left(\cosh^2 \frac{\pi z}{4H} + \sinh^2 \frac{\pi z}{4H} \right)} \right\}^2$$

$$= \left\{ (\sqrt{2}) \cosh \frac{\pi z}{4H} + \sqrt{\left(\cosh \frac{\pi z}{2H} \right)} \right\}^2$$

(see Chapter III, formula (45) and Exercise 3). The point C at $z = iH$ maps first onto $\omega = 0$, and then onto $\omega_1 = 1$; it follows that the bank $ABCDE$ maps on the positive real axis in the ω_1-plane, and the bank FGK on the negative real axis. It remains to transform the half-plane into a strip of width Q; this is accomplished by the logarithmic function

$$w = \frac{Q}{\pi} \ln \omega_1 = \frac{2Q}{\pi} \ln \left\{ (\sqrt{2}) \cosh \frac{\pi z}{4H} + \sqrt{\left(\cosh \frac{\pi z}{2H} \right)} \right\}. \quad (61)$$

42. The field in a ring domain

Problems of type II differ from those of type I because the conductors C_1 and C_2 have no common points and the domain D between them is doubly-connected. The method of the preceding article is not applicable, as it is not possible to give a one–one mapping of D onto a (simply-connected) strip (see Art. 23). However, it can be shown that any suitable doubly-connected domain can be mapped conformally onto an annulus $r < |\omega| < R$ in the ω-plane. If we can find such a mapping for the domain D, our problem is easily solved. It will be clear that the many-valued function

$$w = ki \operatorname{Ln} \omega, \qquad (62)$$

where k is a real constant, serves as complex potential for this annulus, since the imaginary part of w (given by $V = k \ln|\omega|$) is constant on each of the circles $|\omega| = r$ and $|\omega| = R$; by choosing k suitably we can achieve the required potential difference V_0 between the circles bounding the annulus. If $\omega = f(z)$ is the function mapping D onto $r < |\omega| < R$ we then obtain the required complex potential w in D by substituting $f(z)$ for ω in (62):

$$w = ki \operatorname{Ln} f(z).$$

This potential is multiform since its real part, $U = -k \operatorname{Arg} f(z)$ is multiform. Physically, this is permissible, because the derivative of w which defines the field is single-valued.

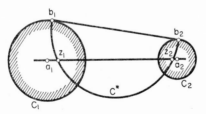

Fig. 71

Example 1. *The field of two oppositely charged parallel circular cylinders.*

Our problem is that of constructing the field in the domain D exterior to each of two circles C_1 and C_2 (Fig. 71). Let a_1 and a_2 be the centres of these circles. We construct the semi-circle C^* having their common tangent $b_1 b_2$ as diameter. The points z_1 and z_2 where

C^* intersects the line of centres a_1a_2 are conjugate points with respect to each of the given circles C_1 and C_2 since C^* and the line a_1a_2 are *both* orthogonal to each of the circles C_1 and C_2 (see Art. 20). By means of the bilinear mapping

$$\omega = \frac{z - z_1}{z - z_2}$$

we transform the points z_1, z_2 into the points $\omega = 0$, ∞; the circles C_1, C_2 become circles C_1', C_2' (in the ω-plane) for which $\omega = 0$ and $\omega = \infty$ are conjugate points. It follows that each of the circles C_1', C_2' has its centre at $\omega = 0$. Accordingly, the required complex potential is of the form

$$w = ki \operatorname{Ln} \omega = ki \operatorname{Ln} \frac{z - z_1}{z - z_2} \quad (k \text{ real}). \tag{62'}$$

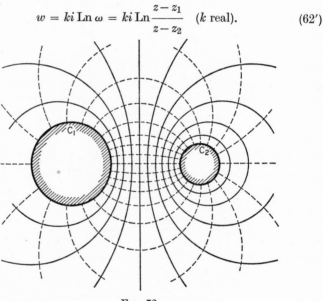

FIG. 72

By a suitable choice of the constant k we can achieve the given difference in potential between C_1 and C_2. The field is plotted in Fig. 72.

The complex potential (62') is identical with that for two unlike point charges (equation (42), Art. 38) if we take $k = 2q$. [It is easy to show that, with the potential (62'), the charge q (per unit height) associated with each of the circles C_1, C_2 is equal in magnitude to

$k/2$: for, (62′) becomes (42) when we put $k = 2q$, so that the flux of the field across any contour surrounding C_2 (but not C_1) is $4\pi(k/2) = 2\pi k$; it follows from Gauss's theorem that the charge on C_2 is $q = k/2$, and it can be shown similarly that the charge on C_1 is $-k/2$.] It will be clear that the field in D is identical with that depicted in the appropriate part of Fig. 66: the equipotentials in Fig. 66 are the circles of Apollonius and the lines of force are circular arcs joining z_1 and z_2; the circles C_1, C_2 coincide with certain equipotentials in this diagram.

It will be seen from this example that the field in the domain between two equipotentials is unchanged in form if these equipotentials are replaced by conductors. By a corresponding principle in hydrodynamics we may suppose that certain stream lines are replaced by material boundaries.

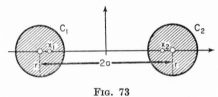

FIG. 73

Example 2. *The field of a two-conductor line* is obtained as the solution of a particular case of the preceding problem (see Fig. 73). The abscissae x_1, x_2 of the points z_1, z_2 which are conjugate with respect to each of the circles C_1 and C_2 are the roots of the equation $(a+x)(a-x) = r^2$:

$$x_1 = -\sqrt{(a^2-r^2)}, \qquad x_2 = \sqrt{(a^2-r^2)}.$$

Formula (62′) becomes

$$w = ki\,\mathrm{Ln}\,\frac{z+\sqrt{(a^2-r^2)}}{z-\sqrt{(a^2-r^2)}}. \tag{63}$$

We find the condition that the potential difference between C_1 and C_2 be equal to V_0. This potential difference is the difference of the imaginary parts of (63) at the points $a-r$ and $-a+r$:

$$V_0 = k\ln\left|\frac{a-r+\sqrt{(a^2-r^2)}}{a-r-\sqrt{(a^2-r^2)}}\right| - k\ln\left|\frac{-a+r+\sqrt{(a^2-r^2)}}{-a+r-\sqrt{(a^2-r^2)}}\right|$$

$$= 2k\ln\frac{a+\sqrt{(a^2-r^2)}}{r}.$$

This relation gives k in terms of the given quantity V_0:

$$k = V_0 \Big/ \left\{ 2 \ln \frac{a + \sqrt{(a^2 - r^2)}}{r} \right\} \approx V_0 \Big/ \left\{ 2 \ln \frac{2a}{r} \right\}$$

if r is small in comparison with a.

Example 3. *The distribution of temperature between two eccentric cylindrical surfaces maintained at temperatures t_1 and t_2* (Fig. 74). The problem reduces to that of constructing the heat flow in the ring domain between the circles C_1 and C_2. As in the preceding examples we construct the points z_1 and z_2 which are conjugate with respect to each of the circles C_1 and C_2. This construction is shown in Fig. 74: tangents are drawn to C_1, perpendicular to the line of centres, cutting C_2 at points a, b and c as shown; the points

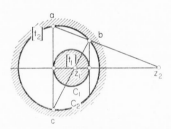

FIG. 74

z_1 and z_2 are the intersections of the line of centres with the respective lines bc and ab; the verification of this construction is left as an exercise for the reader. By means of the bilinear transformation $\omega = (z - z_1)/(z - z_2)$ we reduce the problem to that of determining the temperature in the annulus between concentric circles C_1' and C_2': for this annulus the complex potential is

$$w = \Psi(\omega) = ki \operatorname{Ln} \omega + c$$

and the temperature v is the imaginary part of w:

$$v = \operatorname{Im} \Psi(\omega) = k \ln |\omega| + l \quad \text{(say)}.$$

The constants k, l are chosen so that v has the required values t_1 and t_2 on C_1' and C_2'; the temperaturedistribu tion in the z-domain is then given by

$$v = k \ln |(z - z_1)/(z - z_2)| + l.$$

43. Streamlining an infinite curve

The problems of type III chosen to illustrate the theory will all concern fluid motion. The flow domain D is simply-connected, so that the complex potential $w = \Phi(z)$ is single-valued. The imaginary part of $\Phi(z)$ must be constant along the boundary stream line C; also, as in Art. 41, it can be shown that the point $z = \infty$ must correspond with the point at infinity in the w-plane. These conditions are satisfied if the function $w = \Phi(z)$ gives a one–one conformal mapping of the domain D onto the upper half-plane Im $w > 0$ and satisfies the normalizing condition $\Phi(\infty) = \infty$. We define $\Phi'(\infty)$ to be the limit of $\Phi'(z)$ as $z \to \infty$ through points of D, provided the limit exists uniquely (see Art. 69). If C does not have an angular point at infinity the magnitude of the velocity at infinity is supposed given ($= V_\infty$, say); we require that $|\Phi'(\infty)| = V_\infty$. It can be shown that a mapping $w = \Phi(z)$ exists satisfying *all* these conditions, Φ being determined within an additive constant. If $z = \infty$ is an angular point of C, $\Phi'(\infty)$ is zero or infinity (according as whether the *interior* angle at infinity is reflex or non-reflex; see Art. 23); in this case it is necessary to specify the magnitude of the velocity at some other, regular, point on C.

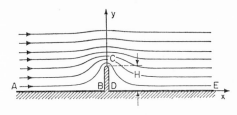

Fig. 75

Example 1. We consider the problem of streamlining *a dam of height H when the flow is infinitely deep and the velocity at infinity has the given magnitude v_∞* (Fig. 75). The function which maps the flow domain onto the half-plane Im $w > 0$ is

$$w = \sqrt{(z^2 + H^2)}$$

(see Art. 27, Example 1). It is clear that $z = \infty$ maps on $w = \infty$. The derivative of this function is

$$\frac{dw}{dz} = \frac{z}{\sqrt{(z^2 + H^2)}},$$

whence

$$\left[\left|\frac{dw}{dz}\right|\right]_{z=\infty} = \lim_{z\to\infty}\left|\frac{z}{\sqrt{(z^2+H^2)}}\right| = 1.$$

Accordingly, the required complex potential will be

$$w = v_\infty\sqrt{(z^2+H^2)}. \tag{64}$$

The stream velocity becomes infinite at the point C, where $z = iH$ (the consequence of a reflex interior angle) and zero at the points B and D, where $z = 0$ (the consequence of a non-reflex interior angle); this behaviour is quite obvious on physical grounds.

Example 2. We now consider the problem of streamlining *the parabola $y^2 = 2px$ by an "exterior" flow in which the magnitude of the velocity at $z = 0$ has the given value v_0* (Fig. 76). We seek a mapping of the flow domain D on some upper half-plane

$$\text{Im } w > \text{const.}$$

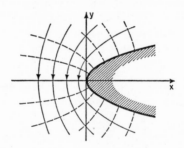

Fig. 76

As shown in Art. 25, a half-plane of this type is the image, under the mapping $w = \sqrt{z}$, of the "exterior" domain bounded by a parabola with axis along Ox and focus at $z = 0$. As the focus of our given parabola lies at $z = p/2$, we consider the function

$$w = \sqrt{\left(z - \frac{p}{2}\right)}. \tag{65}$$

Putting $w = u+iv$ and $z = x+iy$ we have

$$u^2 - v^2 = x - \frac{p}{2}, \qquad 2uv = y.$$

Substituting $u = y/(2v)$ from the second equation into the first we get

$$\frac{y^2}{4v^2} - v^2 = x - \frac{p}{2}.$$

From the last equation it is seen that the straight line $v = \sqrt{(p/2)}$ in the w-plane corresponds to the given parabola, and it follows readily that the function (65) maps D on the half-plane Im $w > p/2$ in such a way that $w = \infty$ is the image of $z = \infty$. Also, the derivative of $w = \sqrt{(z-p/2)}$ at $z = 0$ has modulus

$$\left[\left|\frac{dw}{dz}\right|\right]_{z=0} = \left[\left|\frac{1}{2\sqrt{\{z - (p/2)\}}}\right|\right]_{z=0} = \frac{1}{\sqrt{(2p)}}.$$

Accordingly, the complex potential describing the flow is

$$w = v_0\sqrt{(2pz - p^2)}. \tag{66}$$

The magnitude of the velocity at a point $z = x + iy$ on the parabolic boundary is equal to

$$\left|\frac{dw}{dz}\right| = \frac{pv_0}{\sqrt[4]{\{(2px - p^2)^2 + 4p^2y^2\}}} = \frac{v_0\sqrt{p}}{\sqrt{(2x + p)}}.$$

As z moves along the parabola $y^2 = 2px$ to infinity the velocity tends to zero; the velocity attains its maximum magnitude at the vertex of the parabola C. The stream lines are parabolas confocal with C.

Example 3. *We now consider the same parabolic boundary C and suppose that the flow approaches the boundary from the left so that it is symmetrical with respect to the real axis* (Fig. 77). It will be clear that the negative real axis is a stream line. We may consider this stream line replaced by a material boundary (see Art. 42); accordingly, the problem reduces to that of streamlining the contour ABC, the flow domain D lying above this contour. The function (65) maps D onto a quadrant: the curve BC becomes the half-line $v = \sqrt{(p/2)}$, $u > 0$ and the line AB becomes the half-line $u = 0$, $v > 0$. (It will be clear that here, as in Example 2, we choose the branch of $\sqrt{(z-p/2)}$ whose imaginary part is positive when z lies on the negative real axis.) It follows that the function

$$w = \left\{\sqrt{\left(z - \frac{p}{2}\right)} - i\sqrt{\left(\frac{p}{2}\right)}\right\}^2 = z - p - i\sqrt{(2pz - p^2)}$$

maps D on the upper half-plane Im $w > p/2$. Under this mapping, $z = \infty$ becomes the point at infinity in the w-plane; it is also easy to show that the derivative of this function is equal to unity at $z = \infty$. Accordingly, if v_∞ denotes the given velocity at infinity, the complex potential for the flow is

$$w = v_\infty\{z - p - i\sqrt{(2pz - p^2)}\}. \tag{67}$$

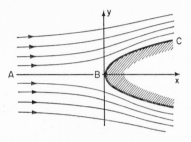

Fig. 77

We note that the derivative of (67) at the vertex of the parabola is

$$\left[\frac{dw}{dz}\right]_{z=0} = v_\infty\left[1 - i\frac{p}{\sqrt{(2pz - p^2)}}\right]_{z=0} = 0;$$

thus, the velocity at this point is zero; such points are said to be *critical* points of the flow. This last result is physically obvious.

44. The problem of complete streamlining. Chaplygin's condition

Example 1. The first problem of type IV to be considered is drawn from hydrodynamics, the contour C being the circle $|z| = R$. We begin by finding *the flow of an ideal incompressible fluid streamlining the circle $|z| = R$ and having at infinity a velocity $\mathbf{V}_\infty$ which has unit magnitude and is directed along the positive real axis* (see Fig. 78).

We impose the extra condition that the flow should be symmetrical about the real axis, so that the segments $(-\infty, -R)$ and $(R, +\infty)$ of this axis are stream lines. As these particular stream lines may be considered to be replaced by material boundaries, the problem reduces to one of type III in which we seek the flow which streamlines the infinite contour formed by these segments and the semi-circle $|z| = R$, $0 \leqslant \arg z \leqslant \pi$. By Art. 43, the complex potential representing this flow is a function $w = \Phi(z)$ which gives a one–one conformal mapping of the flow domain (the domain lying above this infinite contour) onto a half-plane, and which satisfies the normalization conditions $\Phi(\infty) = \infty$, $|\Phi'(\infty)| = 1$. From Art. 26 it will be clear that the required function is

$$w = \Phi(z) = z + \frac{R^2}{z};$$

this function maps the semi-circle $|z| = R$, $0 \leqslant \arg z \leqslant \pi$ on the segment $[-2R, 2R]$ of the u-axis, and the segments $(-\infty, -R)$, $(R, +\infty)$ of the x-axis on the respective segments $(-\infty, -2R)$,

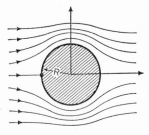

Fig. 78

$(2R, +\infty)$ of the u-axis. (The theory given in Art. 26 refers to the case $R = 1$; the modifications required to cover the case of arbitrary R are left to the reader.) It is immediately obvious that $\Phi(\infty) = \infty$ and $\Phi'(\infty) = 1$; and that Φ gives the *whole* symmetrical flow (that is, not only in D, but also in the domain D' symmetrical with D with respect to the x-axis).

We now drop the requirement that the flow be symmetrical about the x-axis. An immediate solution to the problem of streamlining the circle $|z| = R$ is the flow due to a vortex filament at $z = 0$; the corresponding complex potential is

$$w = \Phi_1(z) = \frac{\Gamma}{2\pi i} \operatorname{Ln} z,$$

where Γ is an arbitrary real constant. For this flow the velocity at infinity is zero.

It follows that the flow determined by the complex potential

$$w = \Phi(z) + \Phi_1(z) = z + \frac{R^2}{z} + \frac{\Gamma}{2\pi i} \operatorname{Ln} z \qquad (68)$$

streamlines the circle $|z| = R$ and satisfies the requirement that the velocity at infinity have unit magnitude and be directed along the positive x-axis. Later, in Art. 70, we show that the potential (68), containing the real parameter Γ, represents all possible solutions of the given problem.

For the flow given by (68), the magnitude of the velocity is

$$\left|\frac{dw}{dz}\right| = \left|1 - \frac{R^2}{z^2} + \frac{\Gamma}{2\pi i z}\right|;$$

thus, the critical points (*stagnation points*) z_s of the flow are the roots of the equation

$$z^2 + \frac{\Gamma}{2\pi i}z - R^2 = 0;$$

that is,

$$z_s = \frac{\Gamma i \pm \sqrt{(16\pi^2 R^2 - \Gamma^2)}}{4\pi}.$$

If $|\Gamma| < 4\pi R$, then

$$|z_s| = \frac{1}{4\pi}\sqrt{\{\Gamma^2 + 16\pi^2 R^2 - \Gamma^2\}} = R;$$

and if $|\Gamma| > 4\pi R$, then

$$|z_s| = \frac{1}{4\pi}|\Gamma \pm \sqrt{(\Gamma^2 - 16\pi^2 R^2)}|.$$

In the first case the stagnation points lie on the circle $|z| = R$ (Fig. 79,a); in the second case, one of these points (z_s', say) lies *outside* the circle and the other (z_s'') lies *inside* it, a result which follows immediately from the relation $z_s' z_s'' = -R^2$ connecting the roots of the above quadratic equation (Fig. 79,c). We shall limit ourselves to a discussion of the first case. At a general point $z = Re^{i\phi}$ on the circle we have

$$\left|\frac{dw}{dz}\right| = \left|1 - e^{-2i\phi} - \frac{\Gamma i}{2\pi R}e^{-i\phi}\right| = \left|2\sin\phi - \frac{\Gamma}{2\pi R}\right|;$$

thus, the arguments of the stagnation points are

$$\phi_1 = \arcsin\frac{\Gamma}{4\pi R}, \qquad \phi_2 = \pi - \arcsin\frac{\Gamma}{4\pi R}. \tag{69}$$

The stream line approaching the point $Re^{i\phi_2}$ divides in two branches: one goes round the upper arc and the other round the lower arc of the circle. At the point $Re^{i\phi_1}$ these branches coalesce (Fig. 79,a). We call $Re^{i\phi_2}$ *the point of branching* (forward stagnation point) and $Re^{i\phi_1}$ the *point of coalescence* (rear stagnation point) of the stream.

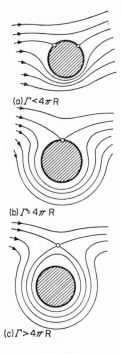

(a) $\Gamma < 4\pi R$

(b) $\Gamma = 4\pi R$

(c) $\Gamma > 4\pi R$

Fig. 79

For a symmetrical stream ($\Gamma = 0$) the critical points lie at $z = \pm R$. The effect of the vortex circulation is to draw these points together: as Γ increases from zero, both points rise and eventually merge into a single point (Fig. 79,b) when $\Gamma = 4\pi R$; further increase of Γ leads to the formation of closed stream lines (Fig. 79,c).

The determination of the flow which streamlines a given closed bounded contour C and has a prescribed (vector) velocity V_∞ at infinity and a prescribed circulation Γ about C is called the problem of *complete streamlining*. Formula (68) gives the solution of this problem for the circle $|z| = R$ when $V_\infty = 1$; for the case in which

$|\Gamma|$ is sufficiently small $(< 4\pi R)$ it suffices (see (69)) to specify *the position of the rear stagnation point* on the circle, in place of the circulation Γ.

In the general case we suppose that there is given an arbitrary closed bounded contour C, a point z_0 on C (the point of coalescence of the divided stream line) and a complex number $\mathbf{V}_\infty$ representing the (vector) velocity at infinity. As a first step in solving the problem of complete streamlining we find a one–one conformal mapping

$$\zeta = f(z) \tag{69'}$$

of the domain exterior to C onto the exterior $|\zeta| > R$ of some circle, so as to satisfy the normalizing conditions†

$$f(\infty) = \infty, \qquad f'(\infty) = \bar{\mathbf{V}}_\infty. \tag{70}$$

(Here, $\bar{\mathbf{V}}_\infty$ denotes the complex conjugate of $\mathbf{V}_\infty$.) We suppose that z_0 maps on the point $\zeta_0 = Re^{i\phi_0}$, and impose the condition that $|\phi_0| \leqslant \pi/2$. By (68), the complex potential representing the flow in the ζ-plane which has vector velocity 1 at infinity and a rear stagnation point at ζ_0 is

$$w = \Phi_1(\zeta) = \zeta + \frac{R^2}{\zeta} + \frac{\Gamma}{2\pi i} \operatorname{Ln} \zeta, \tag{71}$$

where, by (69), $\Gamma = 4\pi R \sin \phi_0$. The complex potential given by the composite function $w = \Phi_1[f(z)]$ then represents a flow in the z-plane which streamlines C, has rear stagnation point z_0 and has a velocity at infinity given in magnitude and direction by

$$\overline{\left[\frac{dw}{dz}\right]}_{z=\infty} = \overline{\Phi_1'(\infty) \cdot f'(\infty)} = \mathbf{V}_\infty;$$

it follows immediately that this complex potential gives the solution of the general problem.

Example 2. *Complete streamlining of the circle* $|z| = R_0$ *with a given velocity* $\mathbf{V}_\infty$ *at infinity.*

In this case the function (69′) is $\zeta = \bar{\mathbf{V}}_\infty z$; accordingly, the

---

† Here, we normalize the derivative $f'(\infty)$ but leave R to be determined later from the other conditions of the problem (see Example 2).

radius R in formula (71) is taken equal to $|V_\infty| \cdot R_0$, and the complex potential giving the solution is

$$w = \overline{V}_\infty z + \frac{R_0{}^2 |V_\infty|^2}{\overline{V}_\infty \cdot z} + \frac{\Gamma}{2\pi i} \operatorname{Ln} z$$

$$= \overline{V}_\infty z + \frac{V_\infty R_0{}^2}{z} + \frac{\Gamma}{2\pi i} \operatorname{Ln} z. \qquad (72)$$

(Here we have omitted the additive constant $(\Gamma/2\pi i) \operatorname{Ln} \overline{V}_\infty$.)

The reader can show for himself that, in place of (69), the equation relating the circulation and the position of the stagnation points on $|z| = R_0$ is

$$\Gamma = 4\pi v_\infty R_0 \sin(\phi_0 - \theta), \qquad (73)$$

where $v_\infty = |V_\infty|$, $\theta = \arg V_\infty$, and ϕ_0 is the argument of the rear stagnation point of the stream.

Remark. In place of (69′) and the associated conditions (70) we could choose a conformal mapping $\zeta = g(z)$ of the domain exterior to C onto the exterior $|\zeta| > R$ of some circle, with the normalization $g(\infty) = \infty$, $g'(\infty) = 1$, and then use (72) to construct the flow which has velocity V_∞ at infinity. In this way the solution of the general problem of complete streamlining is obtained in the form

$$w = \overline{V}_\infty g(z) + \frac{V_\infty R^2}{g(z)} + \frac{\Gamma}{2\pi i} \operatorname{Ln} g(z). \qquad (74)$$

Example 3. *Complete streamlining of the Joukowski profile.* We denote this contour by C; in Fig. 40, a of Art. 28 it is denoted by C^*. It is shown in Art. 28 that the function

$$\omega = \omega(z) = \tfrac{1}{2}[z + \sqrt{(z^2 - 4)}] \qquad (75)$$

gives a conformal mapping of the domain D exterior to C onto the domain Δ_1 exterior to a circle C^* in the ω-plane. We construct a bilinear mapping $\zeta = l(\omega)$ of Δ_1 onto the domain $|\zeta| > R$ which is exterior to some circle in the ζ-plane, this mapping satisfying the relations

$$l(\infty) = \infty, \qquad l'(\infty) = 1.$$

Then, the composite function $\zeta = l[\omega(z)] = g(z)$ maps D on $|\zeta| > R$ so as to satisfy the normalizing conditions $g(\infty) = \infty,$

$g'(\infty) = l'(\infty) \, . \, \omega'(\infty) = 1$. It follows that, with this function $g(z)$, (74) gives the required complex potential.

At the sharp edge A of the wing, where $z = 2$ (see Fig. 80), the derivative of $\omega(z)$ is

$$\left[\frac{\mathrm{d}w}{\mathrm{d}z}\right]_{z=2} = \left[\frac{1}{2}\left(1 + \frac{z}{\sqrt{(z^2-4)}}\right)\right]_{z=2} = \infty;$$

this is the result of the cusp at $z = 2$. As $\mathrm{d}\zeta/\mathrm{d}\omega = l'(\omega)$ is finite at all points of C^* we thus have

$$\left[\frac{\mathrm{d}\zeta}{\mathrm{d}z}\right]_{z=2} = \left[l'(\omega) \, . \, \frac{\mathrm{d}\omega}{\mathrm{d}z}\right]_{z=2} = \infty.$$

However, as was shown by S. A. Chaplygin (a well-known Russian scientist; 1869–1942), *the effect of finite viscosity and vorticity is to make the stream velocity finite* at a sharp trailing edge such as A.

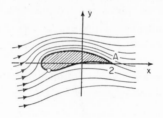

FIG. 80

As a consequence of this condition, the derivative $\mathrm{d}\omega/\mathrm{d}\zeta$ must vanish at the point on $|\zeta| = R$ corresponding to the point A, so that the vector velocity

$$\overline{\left(\frac{\mathrm{d}w}{\mathrm{d}z}\right)} = \overline{\left(\frac{\mathrm{d}w}{\mathrm{d}\zeta}\right)} \, . \, \overline{\left(\frac{\mathrm{d}\zeta}{\mathrm{d}z}\right)}$$

at A (defined by continuity) becomes finite.

This condition is called *Chaplygin's condition* (sometimes referred to in the literature as Joukowski's hypothesis). Its effect in the problem of streamlining a contour with one sharp edge is to determine the rear stagnation point in the equivalent flow in the ζ-plane about the circle $|\zeta| = R$; thus, (by (73), with $R_0 = R$) it determines the circulation Γ in formula (74). The velocity at infinity $\mathbf{V}_\infty$ remains a complex parameter at our disposal: for example, changing the direction of the vector V_∞ is equivalent to changing the angle of attack.

45. Other methods

We now give solutions of a number of applied problems in which we use methods other than those presented in the preceding articles.

Example 1. We consider *the temperature distribution in the space* (see Fig. 81) *bounded by two infinite vertical walls maintained at temperature* 0 *and a horizontal floor maintained at temperature* t. (Each wall is insulated from the floor. The space is occupied by homogeneous isotropic conducting matter.)

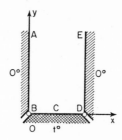

FIG. 81

The problem reduces to that of finding a suitable complex potential $\Psi(z)$ in the half-strip Δ shown in Fig. 81. We take the distance between the walls to be π.

This problem is of type III; however, it is somewhat unusual because of the insulating points B and D. We take it as physically obvious that the solution is unique. Following the usual procedure for problems of type III, we first transform the domain onto the upper half-plane Im $\omega > 0$; this is accomplished by the function

$$\omega = \sin\left(z - \frac{\pi}{2}\right) = -\cos z$$

(see Example 2, Art. 33). The insulating points 0 and π map onto the respective points -1 and 1.

We now seek a function $w = g(\omega)$ which is regular in Im $\omega > 0$ and whose imaginary part equals t on the open segment $(-1, 1)$

corresponding to the base BD and equals 0 on the rays $(-\infty, -1)$ and $(1, +\infty)$ corresponding to the walls AB and DE. If we know such a function, the required complex potential is given by the composite function $w = g(-\cos z)$.

The real variable function $\arg x$ equals 0 for $x > 0$ and π for $x < 0$. Thus, $\arg(\omega+1)$ and $\arg(\omega-1)$ have their discontinuities at the required points on the real axis in the ω-plane, and it is natural to take

$$\operatorname{Im} g(\omega) = c_1 \arg(\omega+1) + c_2 \arg(\omega-1) + c_3.$$

The real constants c_1, c_2, c_3 are determined by the following three conditions which must be satisfied when ω is *real*:

$$\operatorname{Im} g(\omega) = \begin{cases} c_1\pi + c_2\pi + c_3 = 0 & \text{for } -\infty < \omega < -1, \\ c_2\pi + c_3 = t & \text{for } -1 < \omega < 1, \\ c_3 = 0 & \text{for } 1 < \omega < +\infty. \end{cases}$$

It is easily seen that the regular function having the required imaginary part is

$$w = \frac{t}{\pi} \ln \frac{\omega-1}{\omega+1}.$$

Substituting $\omega = -\cos z$ we obtain the required complex potential:

$$w = \Psi(z) = \frac{t}{\pi} \ln \frac{\cos z+1}{\cos z-1} = \frac{2t}{\pi} \ln\left(i \cot \frac{z}{2}\right).$$

Thus,

$$\begin{aligned} \Psi(z) &= \frac{2t}{\pi} \ln\left\{ i \frac{2\cos(z/2)\sin(\bar{z}/2)}{2\sin(z/2)\sin(\bar{z}/2)} \right\} \\ &= \frac{2t}{\pi} \ln\left\{ i \frac{\sin\frac{1}{2}(z+\bar{z}) - \sin\frac{1}{2}(z-\bar{z})}{\cos\frac{1}{2}(z-\bar{z}) - \cos\frac{1}{2}(z+\bar{z})} \right\} \\ &= \frac{2t}{\pi} \ln\left\{ i \frac{\sin x - i\sinh y}{\cosh y - \cos x} \right\}; \end{aligned}$$

that is,

$$\Psi(z) = \frac{2t}{\pi} \ln\left(\frac{\sinh y + i\sin x}{\cosh y - \cos x} \right). \tag{76}$$

Accordingly, the temperature is given by

$$v(x,y) = \operatorname{Im}\Psi(z) = \frac{2t}{\pi}\arg\left(\frac{\sinh y + i\sin x}{\cosh y - \cos x}\right)$$

$$= \frac{2t}{\pi}\arctan\frac{\sin x}{\sinh y}, \qquad (77)$$

and the stream function is

$$u(x,y) = \operatorname{Re}\Psi(z) = \frac{2t}{\pi}\ln\left|\frac{\sinh y + i\sin x}{\cosh y - \cos x}\right|$$

$$= \frac{t}{\pi}\ln\left\{\frac{\sinh^2 y + \sin^2 x}{(\cosh y - \cos x)^2}\right\} = \frac{t}{\pi}\ln\left(\frac{\cosh y + \cos x}{\cosh y - \cos x}\right). \qquad (78)$$

From (77) and (78) we obtain the following equations representing the families of isothermal lines and lines of heat flow:

$$\frac{\sin x}{\sinh y} = \text{const.}, \qquad \frac{\cos x}{\cosh y} = \text{const.} \qquad (79)$$

The method just described can be applied to problems such as those given as Examples 1 and 2 of Art. 41: if we can map the field domain onto a half-plane $\operatorname{Im}\omega > 0$ then we can proceed directly by finding a function $g(\omega)$, as above, which is regular in $\operatorname{Im}\omega > 0$ and satisfies appropriate conditions on the boundary of this domain; earlier, these examples were solved by mapping the field domain onto a *strip*.

This method can often be usefully applied to the problem of constructing the field in a simply-connected domain when the real part, or the imaginary part, of the complex potential is piecewise constant on the boundary of this domain (also see Art. 57). An obvious application is to electrostatic problems in which a simply-connected field domain D has a boundary C formed by conductors at different potentials, the various conductors being separated by insulating points.

Example 2. *The electrostatic field in the sectoral domain D defined by $0 < \arg z < \pi/3$, the boundary rays being conductors at the same potential, when a charge of strength q is placed at $z_0 = ae^{i\pi/6}$.* (The spatial configuration consists of intersecting conducting planes with a uniform line-charge parallel to the line of intersection of the planes.) We begin by mapping D on the half-plane Im $\zeta > 0$ by means of the transformation

$$\zeta = z^3;$$

under this mapping, z_0 is transformed into $\zeta_0 = a^3 i$. The problem thereby reduces to that of finding the field of a point charge in this half-plane when the real axis is an equipotential. The effect of the conducting boundary on the field in Im $\zeta > 0$ can be reproduced by taking a charge of strength $-q$ at the image point $\zeta_1 = -a^3 i$: for, the combined field of the two point charges has the real axis in the ζ-plane as an equipotential; it follows that, in Im $\zeta > 0$ this field is identical with the field of the point charge at ζ_0 and the charges induced by it on the conducting boundary Im $\zeta = 0$. Thus by formula (42) of Art. 38, the complex potential giving the field in Im $\zeta > 0$ is

$$w = 2qi \operatorname{Ln} \frac{\zeta + a^3 i}{\zeta - a^3 i}.$$

The required complex potential is obtained when we substitute $\zeta = z^3$ in the last result:

$$w = 2qi \operatorname{Ln} \frac{z^3 + a^3 i}{z^3 - a^3 i}. \tag{80}$$

The family of equipotential lines of the field is given by

$$\left| \frac{z^3 + a^3 i}{z^3 - a^3 i} \right| = \text{const.} = c.$$

With polar coordinates $z = re^{i\phi}$ this equation becomes

$$r^6 + 2a^3 r^3 \sin 3\phi + a^6 = c^2(r^6 - 2a^3 r^3 \sin 3\phi + a^6)$$

whence

$$\frac{c^2 - 1}{c^2 + 1}(r^6 + a^6) = 2a^3 r^3 \sin 3\phi:$$

the last relation can be written

$$\sin 3\phi = C\left(r^3 + \frac{a^6}{r^3}\right),$$

where C is an arbitrary constant. In particular, taking $C = 0$, we obtain the equipotentials $\phi = 0$ and $\phi = \pi/3$; these rays form the conducting boundary of the field.

The procedure in the above solution, whereby we replaced a rectilinear conductor by a "point" charge, of equal magnitude but opposite sign, placed symmetrically to the given charge, is called the *method of images*. Instead of using the auxiliary mapping $\zeta = z^3$, we could have applied this method directly, replacing the conducting rays bounding the sector by a system of "point" charges $q_1 = -q$, $q_2 = +q$, $q_3 = -q$, $q_4 = +q$, $q_5 = -q$ placed at the respective points $z_1 = ai$, $z_2 = -ae^{-i\pi/6}$, $z_3 = -ae^{i\pi/6}$, $z_4 = -ai$, $z_5 = ae^{-i\pi/6}$ (see Fig. 82). It is easy to show that the complex potential obtained by this method is identical with the potential given by (80).

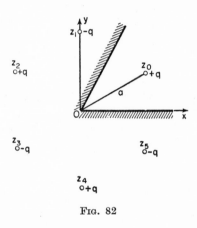

Fig. 82

The method of images can be successfully applied to many other problems in electrostatics and hydrodynamics. Thus, in hydrodynamics, when considering the field in the half-plane of a "point" vortex of strength Γ we replace the barrier bounding the half-plane by a vortex of strength $-\Gamma$ placed symmetrically to the given vortex with respect to this barrier. In solving the similar problem for the field of a "point" *source* of strength Q the wall is replaced by a symmetrical point source of the *same* strength Q (there is no change of sign as there is with a vortex or charge). The reader can discover the reason for this himself.

For further development of the subject matter of this chapter, see the books by I. M. Asnin (*Calculation of Electromagnetic Fields*

[*Raschety elektromagnitnykh polei*], VETA, 1939); V. V. Golubev (*Theory of the Aerofoil in a Plane Parallel Stream* [*Teoriya kryla aeroplana v ploskoparallel' nom potoke*], ONTI, 1935); N. E. Kochin, I. A. Kibel', and N. V. Roze (*Theoretical Hydromechanics* [*Teoreticheskaya gidromekhanika*], Gostekhizdat, 1948); H. S. Carslaw (*Introduction to the Mathematical Theory of the Conduction of Heat in Solids*, Macmillan, 1921); H. S. Carslaw and J. C. Jaeger (*Conduction of Heat in Solids*, Oxford, 1947); H. Lamb (*Hydrodynamics*, Cambridge, 1932); L. M. Milne-Thomson (*Theoretical Hydrodynamics*, Oxford, 1938); J. H. Jeans (*Electricity and Magnetism*, Cambridge, 1933); V. C. A. Ferraro (*Electromagnetic Theory*, Athlone Press, 1954); E. Weber (*Electromagnetic Fields*, Wiley, 1950); F. Ollendorff (*Berechnung Magnetischer Felder*, Springer, 1952, and *Elektronik des Einzelelektrons*, Springer, 1955).

Exercises

1. Find the equipotential lines, lines of force, and vector intensity for the field whose complex potential is $w = 1/z^2$.

2. The potential function of a field has the form

$$V = \arctan\left(\frac{\tan \pi y}{\tanh \pi x}\right).$$

Find the equation representing the lines of force and find the complex potential.

3. The equipotential lines of a field are the circles $x^2 + y^2 = 2ax$. Find the ratio of the magnitudes of the intensity of the field at the points $(2a, 0)$ and (a, a).

4. The motion of a fluid is that due to a source of strength Q and a vortex of strength Γ both situated at the coordinate origin (a "vortex source"). Prove that the stream lines are logarithmic spirals.

5. Find the equipotential lines in Example 1, Art. 41, and the stream lines in Example 1, Art. 43.

6. Find the charge distribution producing the electrostatic field whose complex potential is $w = 2qi \, \mathrm{Ln}(z^2 + z^{-2})$.

7. Sources of strength Q lie at the points $z_1 = a$, $z_2 = 1/a$ and a sink of equal strength lies at $z = 0$. Prove that the circle $|z| = 1$ is a stream line. (See the discussion of the method of images in Art. 45.)

8. The potential is V_0 along the ray $x = 0$, $y > 1$ and is zero along the x-axis. Find the density of the charge distribution along the x-axis. (The density of charge at a point on a conductor is $\sigma = \pm E/(4\pi)$, where E is the magnitude of the field intensity at this point.)

9. The cylindrical conductor represented by the circle

$$|z - 2i| = 1$$

bears a charge 2π per unit height. Find the distribution of this charge on the cylinder if the conducting sheet represented by the x-axis is earthed.

10. Find the electrostatic field in the space between two conducting cylinders which are perpendicular to the z-plane and intersect this plane in the circles $|z| = 1$ and $|z-1| = 5/2$. The potential difference between the cylinders is unity. Find the least and greatest values for the density of charge in the distribution on the cylinders.

11. On an ellipse with semi-axes of length 2 and $\sqrt{3}$ units the temperature is maintained at $0°$; on the segment between its foci it is maintained at $100°$. Find the plane heat-flow field when the included space is occupied by homogeneous isotropic conducting matter.

12. Find the temperature distribution in the sectoral domain $0 < \phi < \alpha$, $r > a$ (supposed occupied by homogeneous isotropic conducting matter) when the boundary rays are maintained at $0°$ and the boundary arc is maintained at $1°$.

13. Find the complex potential for the plane flow of a fluid flowing from the left half-plane into the right half-plane through an aperture in the imaginary axis between the points $-i$ and $+i$. The net flow across the aperture is Q.

14. Find the complex potential and the stream lines for the plane flow of a fluid in the first quadrant when there is a source of strength Q at $z = 1+i$ and a sink of equal strength at $z = 0$.

15. Find the electrostatic field in the domain $|z| < 1$, $\operatorname{Im} z > 0$ if the points i and ± 1 are insulators and the potential is $-V_0$ for $z = e^{i\phi}$ $(0 < \phi < \pi/2)$, $+V_0$ for $z = e^{i\phi}$ $(\pi/2 < \phi < \pi)$, and 0 for $y = 0$ $(-1 < x < 1)$.

16. Find the flow of a fluid in the sector $0 < \arg z < \pi/3$ produced by a source of strength Q concentrated at the point $z_0 = ae^{i\pi/6}$ (see Example 2, Art. 45).

CHAPTER V

THE INTEGRAL REPRESENTATION OF A REGULAR FUNCTION. HARMONIC FUNCTIONS

46. The integral of a function of a complex variable

WE consider a single-valued function

$$w = f(z) = u(x,y) + iv(x,y) \tag{1}$$

which is continuous in a domain D of the finite z-plane ($z = x+iy$); C, defined by $z = z(t)$ ($\alpha \leqslant t \leqslant \beta$), is any piecewise-smooth curve (see Art. 8) which [including its end points $a = z(\alpha)$, $b = z(\beta)$] is contained in D. We take any partition $\mathscr{P}$ of $[\alpha, \beta]$ by points $\alpha = t_0 < t_1 < \ldots < t_n = \beta$ and let τ_k be any point of $[t_{k-1}, t_k]$ ($k = 1, 2, \ldots, n$); we write $z_k = z(t_k)$, $\Delta z_k = z_k - z_{k-1} = \Delta x_k + i\Delta y_k$, $\zeta_k = \xi_k + i\eta_k = z(\tau_k)$. The points z_k ($k = 1, 2, \ldots, n$) occur on the (directed) curve C in the order prescribed by the mapping $z = z(t)$, ζ_k being a point on the kth sub-arc defined by $z = z(t)$, $t_{k-1} \leqslant t \leqslant t_k$.

The sum defined by

$$s(\mathscr{P}; \zeta_k) = \sum_{k=1}^{n} f(\zeta_k) \cdot \Delta z_k$$

$$= \sum_{k=1}^{n} \{u(\xi_k, \eta_k)\Delta x_k - v(\xi_k, \eta_k)\Delta y_k\} + i \sum_{k=1}^{n} \{v(\xi_k, \eta_k)\Delta x_k + u(\xi_k, \eta_k)\Delta y_k\} \tag{2}$$

is called the integral sum for $f(z)$ along C corresponding to the partition $\mathscr{P}$ and the associated points ζ_k. We call

$$\delta(\mathscr{P}) = \max_{(k=1,\ldots,n)} (t_k - t_{k-1})$$

the *norm*, or *gauge*, of the partition $\mathscr{P}$ and write

$$\Delta(\mathscr{P}) = \max_{(k=1,\ldots,n)} |\Delta z_k|.$$

Let $\{\mathscr{P}_m\}$ be a sequence of partitions of $[\alpha, \beta]$, each $\mathscr{P}_m$ being associated with auxiliary points $\zeta_k^{(m)}$ as above; we suppose that

$$\delta_m = \delta(\mathscr{P}_m) \to 0 \quad \text{as} \quad m \to +\infty. \tag{3}$$

As $z(t)$ is uniformly continuous on the finite closed interval $[\alpha, \beta]$ it follows from (3) that

$$\Delta_m = \Delta(\mathscr{P}_m) \to 0 \quad \text{as } m \to +\infty.$$

Definition. The integral of $f(z)$ along the curve C, denoted by

$$\int_C f(z)\,\mathrm{d}z,$$

is defined to be

$$\lim_{m \to +\infty} s(\mathscr{P}_m; \zeta_k^{(m)}),$$

the sequence $\{\mathscr{P}_m\}$ satisfying the condition (3):

$$\int_C f(z)\,\mathrm{d}z = \lim_{m \to +\infty} s(\mathscr{P}_m; \zeta_k^{(m)}). \tag{4}$$

The fundamental existence theorem for the integral expresses the fact that this limit *exists finitely whenever the above conditions on $f(z)$ and C are satisfied and is independent of the particular choice of the sequence of partitions $\mathscr{P}_m$ and of the associated points $\zeta_k^{(m)}$.*†

The above definition is commonly symbolized by

$$\int_C f(z)\,\mathrm{d}z = \lim_{n \to +\infty} \sum_{k=1}^{n} f(\zeta_k) \cdot \Delta z_k$$

$$= \lim_{n \to +\infty} \sum_{k=1}^{n} \{u(\xi_k, \eta_k)\Delta x_k - v(\xi_k, \eta_k)\Delta y_k\}$$

$$+ i \lim_{n \to +\infty} \sum_{k=1}^{n} \{v(\xi_k, \eta_k)\Delta x_k + u(\xi_k, \eta_k)\Delta y_k\}, \tag{4'}$$

---

† See, for example, Knopp, *Theory of Functions*, Dover, 1945 (Vol. 1). An elegant treatment of curvilinear integrals, based on the Stieltjes integral, can be found in Valiron, *Théorie des Fonctions*, Masson, 1948; or Apostol, *Mathematical Analysis*, Addison-Wesley, 1957. The last reference also includes a proof of the important result that the value obtained for $\int_C f(z)\mathrm{d}z$ is the same for any two *equivalent representations* of the same (directed) curve C. See also Estermann, *Complex Numbers and Functions*, Athlone Press, 1962.

it being understood that $\delta \to 0$ as $n \to +\infty$. These last sums are approximative sums for line integrals of real functions, and it can be shown that

$$\int_C f(z)\,\mathrm{d}z = \int_C \{u(x,y)\,\mathrm{d}x - v(x,y)\,\mathrm{d}y\} + i\int_C \{v(x,y)\,\mathrm{d}x + u(x,y)\,\mathrm{d}y\}, \quad (5)$$

so that all the usual properties of line integrals hold for the complex curvilinear integral. In particular, we have the following *fundamental inequality for curvilinear integrals*:

THEOREM 1. *As $f(z)$ is continuous on the bounded curve C, there exists a finite M such that $|f(z)| \leqslant M$ for all z on C, and*

$$\left| \int_C f(z)\mathrm{d}z \right| \leqslant Ml, \quad (6)$$

where l is the length of C.

To prove this result we consider the approximative sum (2): we have

$$|s(\mathscr{P};\zeta_k)| = \left| \sum_{k=1}^{n} f(\zeta_k)\cdot\Delta z_k \right| \leqslant \sum_{k=1}^{n} |f(\zeta_k)|\cdot|\Delta z_k|$$

$$\leqslant M\sum_{k=1}^{n} |\Delta z_k| \leqslant Ml,$$

since l is defined as the upper bound of the set of sums

$$\sum_{k=1}^{n} |\Delta z_k|$$

taken over *all* partitions $\mathscr{P}$ of $[\alpha,\beta]$; it follows immediately that

$$\left| \int_C f(z)\mathrm{d}z \right| \leqslant Ml.$$

47. Cauchy's integral theorem

We investigate the conditions under which the integral

$$\int_C f(z)\,\mathrm{d}z$$

along a path C joining any two given points a, b in a domain D is independent of the particular path C (in D) and depends on a and b only. For this it is clearly necessary and sufficient that the integral of $f(z)$ around any closed path C' in D should vanish:

$$\oint_{C'} f(z) \, \mathrm{d}z = 0. \tag{7}$$

(The circle on the integral sign indicates that C' is a closed path.) Suppose first that (7) holds for the domain D. Then, if a, b are any two points in D and C_1, C_2 are any two paths joining a to b in D,

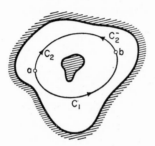

Fɪɢ. 83

we consider the closed path C' in D formed by C_1 and C_2^-, where C_2^- denotes the directed curve corresponding to a traverse of C_2 in the *reverse* sense (that is, from b to a; see Fig. 83); clearly, we have

$$0 = \oint_{C'} f(z) \, \mathrm{d}z = \int_{C_1} f(z) \, \mathrm{d}z + \int_{C_2^-} f(z) \, \mathrm{d}z = \int_{C_1} f(z) \, \mathrm{d}z - \int_{C_2} f(z) \, \mathrm{d}z,$$

whence

$$\int_{C_1} f(z) \, \mathrm{d}z = \int_{C_2} f(z) \, \mathrm{d}z,$$

and it follows that the integral along any path in D depends only on the end-points of this path. We now suppose that the integral along any path in D depends only on the end-points of the path. Let C' be any closed path in D. Choose two distinct points a, b on C', and let C_1, C_2 denote the two corresponding arcs of C' joining *a to b* (see Fig. 83); then, as before, we have

$$\oint_{C'} f(z)\, \mathrm{d}z = \int_{C_1} f(z)\, \mathrm{d}z - \int_{C_2} f(z)\, \mathrm{d}z = 0,$$

so that (7) holds for the domain D. (We remind the reader that, throughout, all paths and contours are supposed piecewise-smooth; see Art. 8.)

In this connection we have the following *fundamental integral theorem* of Cauchy:

THEOREM 2. *If $f(z)$ is regular in a simply-connected domain D, then the integral of $f(z)$ along any path in D depends only on the end-points of this path; that is, if C is any closed contour in D, then*

$$\oint_C f(z)\, \mathrm{d}z = 0.$$

As $f(z) = u(x, y) + iv(x, y)$ is regular in D, the partial derivatives $\partial u/\partial x$, $\partial u/\partial y$, $\partial v/\partial x$, $\partial v/\partial y$ exist and satisfy the Cauchy–Riemann relations (see Art. 14) at each point of D. In proving Cauchy's theorem we make the additional assumption that these partial derivatives are all continuous in D.[†] By (5), it suffices to show that each of the real line integrals

$$\oint_C (u\, \mathrm{d}x - v\, \mathrm{d}y), \qquad \oint_C (v\, \mathrm{d}x + u\, \mathrm{d}y) \tag{8}$$

vanishes. It is shown in real analysis that the integral

$$\oint_C (P\, \mathrm{d}x + Q\, \mathrm{d}y)$$

along any closed contour in a simply-connected domain D vanishes when:

(i)   the partial derivatives of the (real) functions $P(x, y)$ and $Q(x, y)$ exist and are continuous in D; and

---

[†] A full proof of Cauchy's Theorem is given by A. I. Markushevich (*A Short Course in the Theory of Analytic Functions* [Kratkii kurs teorii analiticheskikh funktsii], Gostekhizdat, Moscow, 1957). Also see Knopp (*Theory of Functions*, Dover, 1945), Apostol (*Mathematical Analysis*, Addison-Wesley, 1957) and Estermann (*Complex Numbers and Functions*, Athlone Press, 1962). A detailed proof under the so-called *Pollard conditions* is given by Valiron (*Théorie des Fonctions*, Masson, 1948); a most elegant proof under the same conditions is due to Estermann (*Math. Zeits.*, **37**, 1933, pp. 556–560).

(ii) $\partial P/\partial y = \partial Q/\partial x$ at each point of D.

(The proof of this result can be found in any standard text on real analysis; the reader should pay special attention to the significance of the requirements that D be simply-connected in the open plane and that the partial derivatives be continuous.) For the integrals (8), condition (i) is satisfied because of our assumption that the first-order derivatives of u and v are continuous, and condition (ii) is satisfied because u, v obey the Cauchy–Riemann relations

$$\frac{\partial u}{\partial y} = -\frac{\partial v}{\partial x}, \qquad \frac{\partial v}{\partial y} = \frac{\partial u}{\partial x} \qquad (9)$$

at each point of D.

We note the following converse of Cauchy's theorem (proofs can be found in the references cited above):

THEOREM. *If $f(z)$ is continuous in a simply-connected domain D and*

$$\oint_C f(z)\,\mathrm{d}z = 0$$

for every closed contour C in D, then $f(z)$ is regular in D.

Remark. We remind the reader that a domain D in the open plane is simply-connected if, and only if, any closed contour C (*closed Jordan curve*) in D is *reducible* in D. Two distinct points a, b on a *contour C* divide C into two paths, each joining a to b (say) and having only the end-points a and b in common with the other; this is not true, in general, for a *closed path C* in D, for in this case the two component paths joining a to b *may* intersect at infinitely many points and *may* separate the plane into infinitely many domains. The resulting difficulties associated with a restriction to closed *contours* (see Theorem 2, above) can be easily obviated by an appeal to the following theorem (see, e.g. Knopp, *Theory of Functions*): If $f(z)$ is *continuous* in a domain D and K is any (piecewise-smooth) path in D joining a point a to a point b, then, given any $\epsilon > 0$, there exists a *polygonal path Γ inscribed in K* which joins a to b in D and is such that

$$\left| \int_K f(z)\,\mathrm{d}z - \int_\Gamma f(z)\,\mathrm{d}z \right| < \epsilon.$$

The integrals along any two paths joining a to b can thus be approximated arbitrarily closely by integrals along two suitable inscribed *polygonal* paths; these paths together form a closed polygonal path which separates the plane into *at most a finite number* of domains. (A polygonal path is always understood as consisting of a finite number of finite line-segments.)

Cauchy's theorem and its converse enable us to give an equivalent alternative definition of a regular function: a single-valued function $f(z)$ is regular in a domain D if it is continuous in D and its integral around any closed contour C in D is equal to zero.

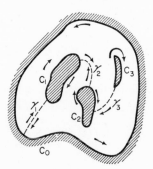

FIG. 84

Cauchy's theorem can be generalized so as to apply to multiply-connected domains. Let D be an $(n+1)$-ply connected bounded domain whose frontier consists of the $(n+1)$ disjoint contours C_0 (the external boundary component), $C_1, C_2, \ldots, C_n$ (the internal boundary components), and let $f(z)$ be regular at each point of the closed region $\overline{D}$. (See Fig. 84 showing a case in which $n = 3$.) By taking suitable (disjoint) cuts $\gamma_1, \gamma_2, \ldots, \gamma_n$ we form from D a simply-connected domain D' whose boundary we denote by C'. (We consider each cut as two-edged, as in Art. 23.) As C' is piecewise smooth and $f(z)$ is regular in a domain Δ containing $\overline{D}$ it follows from Cauchy's theorem that

$$\oint_{C'} f(z)\, \mathrm{d}z = 0.$$

Here, we adopt the usual convention that C' is traversed so that D' always remains on the left: thus C_0 is traversed in the anti-clockwise (positive) sense and $C_1, C_2, \ldots, C_n$ in the clockwise (negative) sense; each of the cuts $\gamma_1, \gamma_2, \ldots, \gamma_n$ is traversed twice, first in one sense and then in the opposite sense. As the integrals along the two edges of each cut cancel each other, it follows from the standard properties of line integrals that

$$\oint_{C'} f(z)\,\mathrm{d}z = \oint_{C_0} f(z)\,\mathrm{d}z - \sum_{k=1}^{n} \oint_{C_k} f(z)\,\mathrm{d}z = 0, \tag{10}$$

where

$$\oint_{C_k} \quad (k = 0, 1, 2, \ldots, n)$$

denotes an integral taken around C_k in the usual *positive* sense. If we denote by C_k^- the directed curve obtained by traversing C_k in the opposite, or *negative*, sense, this result can be written

$$\oint_{C'} f(z)\,\mathrm{d}z = \oint_{C_0} f(z)\,\mathrm{d}z + \sum_{k=1}^{n} \oint_{C_{\overline{k}}} f(z)\,\mathrm{d}z = 0. \tag{11}$$

Formula (11) expresses the required generalization of Cauchy's theorem:

THEOREM 3. *If $f(z)$ is regular at each point of a bounded closed region $\overline{D}$ whose frontier B consists of a finite number of disjoint contours, then the integral of $f(z)$ around the boundary of $\overline{D}$ (taken so that each component of the boundary is traversed in a sense such that the interior D of $\overline{D}$ remains on the left) is equal to zero.* (We adopt the obvious notation

$$\int_{B^+} f(z)\,\mathrm{d}z$$

for this integral.)

Remark. The above result can be established under the less stringent requirement that $f(z)$ be regular in D and continuous on $\overline{D}$. (See above references to Valiron and Estermann.)

48. Cauchy's residue theorem.   Chaplygin's formula

Assuming that the conditions under which (10) holds are satisfied, and writing C for C_0, we have

$$\oint_{C} f(z)\,\mathrm{d}z = \sum_{k=1}^{n} \oint_{C_k} f(z)\,\mathrm{d}z. \tag{12}$$

Here, all integrals are taken in the anticlockwise sense. In particular, if $n = 1$ and $f(z)$ is regular at each point of the closure of the annular domain whose frontier consists of the curves C and C_1, then

$$\oint_C f(z)\,dz = \oint_{C_1} f(z)\,dz. \tag{13}$$

Later we shall often have to deal with cases where $f(z)$ is regular everywhere in the interior domain D bounded by a closed contour C, except at a finite number of points $a_1, a_2, \ldots, a_n$. These exceptional points are called *singular points* (*singularities*) of $f(z)$. (For a full definition of this term see Art. 61.) We enclose the a_k by mutually disjoint circles c_k in D, each circle c_k enclosing no singular point other than the corresponding point a_k. It follows readily from (13) that the integral of $f(z)$ around c_k is equal to the integral around any other contour c_k' in D which also encloses a_k but does *not* enclose or pass through any other singular point of $f(z)$; the value of this integral is thus characteristic of $f(z)$ and the singular point a_k and determines what we call the *residue* of $f(z)$ at the point a_k; the residue of $f(z)$ at the singular point a_k is denoted by $\operatorname{res} f(a_k)$ and is defined to be

$$\operatorname{res} f(a_k) = \frac{1}{2\pi i} \oint_{c_k} f(z)\,dz. \tag{14}$$

Formula (12) leads immediately to the following result, known as *Cauchy's residue theorem*:

THEOREM 4. *Let D be the interior domain bounded by a closed contour C and let $f(z)$ be regular at all points of $\overline{D}$ with the exception of a finite number of singular points $a_1, a_2, \ldots, a_n$ contained in the domain D; then, the integral of $f(z)$ around C is $2\pi i$ times the sum of its residues at the points a_k:*

$$\oint_C f(z)\,dz = 2\pi i \sum_{k=1}^{n} \operatorname{res} f(a_k). \tag{15}$$

Later, in Chapter VI, we study the singularities of functions in greater detail; in particular, we shall find methods of calculating residues without integration. Knowing how to evaluate residues, we can often evaluate complex line integrals and definite integrals of real functions by means of Theorem 4 (see Chapter VII). For the present, however, we shall limit the application of the residue theorem to the derivation of certain formulae in applied mathematics.

(a) *Determination of charge enclosed by a contour, and work done on a unit charge.* We consider a plane electrostatic field. Let D be any component field-domain (see preamble to equation (33), Art. 37), and let C be any contour in D; by the equation just referred to, the total charge enclosed within C is

$$q = \frac{1}{4\pi} \oint_C (\mathbf{E}, \mathbf{n}^0)\, \mathrm{d}s = \frac{1}{4\pi} \oint_C \frac{\partial U}{\partial s}\, \mathrm{d}s, \qquad (16)$$

where $U(x, y)$ is the force function for the field. Let $F(z) = U + iV$ denote the complex potential in D. Then $F(z)$ has a regular branch in any simply-connected sub-domain of D and defines a derived function $F'(z)$ which is single-valued in D. It follows from Cauchy's integral formulae (see Arts. 51, 52) that $F'(z)$ is *regular* in D, and we have $U(x, y) = \mathrm{Re}\, F(z)$, $(\partial U/\partial s)\, \mathrm{d}s = \mathrm{Re}\,[F'(z)\, \mathrm{d}z]$, so that (16) becomes

$$q = \frac{1}{4\pi}\mathrm{Re} \oint_C F'(z)\, \mathrm{d}z. \qquad (17)$$

If, in particular, C encloses no charges other than a finite number of "point" charges concentrated at the points $a_1, a_2, \ldots, a_n$ then it follows from the residue theorem that

$$q = \frac{1}{4\pi}\mathrm{Re}\{2\pi i \sum_{k=1}^{n} \mathrm{res}\, F'(a_k)\} = -\tfrac{1}{2}\mathrm{Im} \sum_{k=1}^{n} \mathrm{res}\, F'(a_k). \qquad (18)$$

Similarly, it follows from equation (26) of Art. 37 that the work which must be done *against* the field when we move a unit positive point-charge along a path K in D is

$$A = \int_K \mathrm{d}V(x, y) = \mathrm{Im} \int_K F'(z)\, \mathrm{d}z. \qquad (19)$$

(b) *Determination of net flow across a contour, and circulation around a contour.* We consider a plane flow of an ideal incompressible fluid. Let D be a domain of source-free irrotational flow (see Art. 39) and let C be a contour in D. By equations (50) of Art.

39, the net flow Q across C and the circulation Γ about C are given by

$$Q = \oint_C (\mathbf{V}, \mathbf{n}^0)\,\mathrm{d}s = \oint_C \frac{\partial\psi}{\partial s}\,\mathrm{d}s = \operatorname{Im}\oint_C \Phi'(z)\,\mathrm{d}z, \tag{20}$$

$$\Gamma = \oint_C (\mathbf{V}, \mathbf{s}^0)\,\mathrm{d}s = \oint_C \frac{\partial\phi}{\partial s}\,\mathrm{d}s = \operatorname{Re}\oint_C \Phi'(z)\,\mathrm{d}z. \tag{21}$$

Here, ϕ is the velocity potential, ψ is the stream function, and $\Phi(z) = \phi + i\psi$ is the complex potential for the flow. Combining the last two equations, we have

$$\Gamma + iQ = \oint_C \Phi'(z)\,\mathrm{d}z. \tag{22}$$

If, in particular, C encloses only a finite number of "point" sources and "point" vortices, these being located at points $a_1, a_2 \ldots, a_n$ (say), it follows from the residue theorem that

$$\left.\begin{array}{l} Q = 2\pi\operatorname{Re}\displaystyle\sum_{k=1}^{n} \operatorname{res}\Phi'(a_k), \\[2ex] \Gamma = -2\pi\operatorname{Im}\displaystyle\sum_{k=1}^{n} \operatorname{res}\Phi'(a_k). \end{array}\right\} \tag{23}$$

(c) *Chaplygin's formula.* In a plane fluid flow, as in (b) above, the pressure is given by Bernoulli's formula

$$p = A - \tfrac{1}{2}\rho V^2, \tag{24}$$

where A is a constant, ρ is the density of the fluid, and $V = |\mathbf{V}|$ is the magnitude of the stream velocity at the point concerned.

We consider a flow around a closed contour C (Fig. 85). As the pressure on C is directed inwards along the normal, the force acting on the element $\mathrm{d}s = |\mathrm{d}z|$ of the contour C is given in magnitude and direction by

$$pi\,\mathrm{d}z = Ai\,\mathrm{d}z - \tfrac{1}{2}\rho i V^2\,\mathrm{d}z;$$

accordingly, the resultant force $\mathbf{P}$ acting on the closed contour C is

$$\mathbf{P} = X + iY = \oint_C pi\,\mathrm{d}z = -\tfrac{1}{2}\rho i\oint_C V^2\,\mathrm{d}z.$$

(The vanishing of the integral

$$\oint_C A i \, \mathrm{d}z$$

is an immediate consequence of Cauchy's theorem.) As the flow streamlines the contour C the stream velocity is directed tangentially at any point on C:

$$\mathbf{V} = \overline{\Phi'(z)} = V e^{i\phi},$$

where $\phi = \arg \mathrm{d}z$ ($\mathrm{d}z = \mathrm{d}s \, . \, e^{i\phi}$). Thus,

$$V = \overline{\Phi'(z)} e^{-i\phi},$$

and

$$\mathbf{P} = -\tfrac{1}{2}\rho i \oint_C [\overline{\Phi'(z)}]^2 e^{-2i\phi} \, \mathrm{d}z = -\tfrac{1}{2}\rho i \oint_C [\overline{\Phi'(z)}]^2 \, \overline{\mathrm{d}z},$$

since $e^{-2i\phi} \, \mathrm{d}z = e^{-i\phi} \, \mathrm{d}s = \overline{\mathrm{d}z}$. Taking conjugate quantities we obtain the conjugate of the complex number giving the resultant

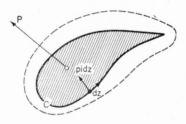

FIG. 85

thrust $\mathbf{P}$ acting per unit height on the cylinder represented by the contour C:

$$\overline{\mathbf{P}} = X - iY = \tfrac{1}{2}\rho i \oint_C [\Phi'(z)]^2 \, \mathrm{d}z. \tag{25}$$

This last result (often associated with the names of Kutta, Joukowski, and Blasius) was obtained by C. A. Chaplygin. If the flow outside C contains no sources or vortices then $\Phi'(z)$ is regular in a domain surrounding C and it follows from Cauchy's theorem that the integral in (25) can be taken around any suitable contour enclosing the original streamlined profile C.

49. The indefinite integral

We say that $F(z)$ is a primitive of $f(z)$ in a domain D if

$$F'(z) = f(z)$$

at all points of D. It will be clear that any two primitives $F_1(z)$, $F_2(z)$ of $f(z)$ differ by a constant. For, by the very definition, $F_1(z)$, $F_2(z)$, and

$$\Phi(z) = F_1(z) - F_2(z) = U(x,y) + iV(x,y)$$

are all regular in D, with

$$\Phi'(z) = F_1'(z) - F_2'(z) = \frac{\partial U}{\partial x} + i\frac{\partial V}{\partial x} = 0,$$

so that $\partial U/\partial x$ and $\partial V/\partial x$ (and hence, by the Cauchy–Riemann relations, $\partial U/\partial y$ and $\partial V/\partial y$) vanish identically in D; it follows readily that $U(x, y)$ and $V(x, y)$ are *constant* in D, so that, at all points of this domain, $\Phi(z) = C$ (= const.) and

$$F_2(z) = F_1(z) + C.$$

Conversely, if $F(z)$ is a primitive of $f(z)$ in D then so, too, is the function obtained by adding any constant to $F(z)$; thus, if $f(z)$ has a primitive in D then it has infinitely many primitives in this domain. The set of all these primitives of the function $f(z)$ is called the *indefinite integral* of $f(z)$ and is denoted by

$$\int f(z)\, dz;$$

the indefinite integral is a family of functions whose general member differs from any particular member by an arbitrary additive constant.

THEOREM 5.   *Let $f(z)$ be regular in a simply-connected domain D, and let z_0 be any fixed point of D. Then, the function $F(z)$, defined in D by*

$$F(z) = \int_{z_0}^{z} f(z)\, dz,$$
$$(L)$$

where L is any path in D joining z_0 to z, is regular in D and is a primitive function of $f(z)$ in this domain.

It follows readily from Cauchy's theorem and the result quoted in the Remark following the statement of the converse of Cauchy's theorem in Art. 47 that the function $F(z)$ defined above is single-valued in D. It remains to show that $F'(z)$ exists and equals $f(z)$ in D. Let z be any point in D and take any positive number ϵ.

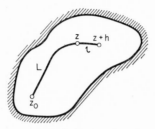

FIG. 86

Then there exists a $\delta > 0$ such that the rectilinear segment l joining z to $z+h$ lies in D whenever $|h| < \delta$, and such that

$$|f(\zeta) - f(z)| < \epsilon$$

whenever $|\zeta - z| < \delta$. Choose any complex number h such that $0 < |h| < \delta$. Then

$$\frac{F(z+h) - F(z)}{h} = \frac{1}{h} \int_{z}^{z+h} f(\zeta) \, d\zeta,$$

where we may suppose that the integral is taken along the segment l (Fig. 86). It follows immediately from the definition of a curvilinear integral that

$$\int_{z}^{z+h} d\zeta = h;$$

for, the general approximative sum for this integral is

$$\sum_{k=1}^{n} \Delta\zeta_k = (\zeta_1 - z) + (\zeta_2 - \zeta_1) + \dots + (z+h - \zeta_{n-1}) = h.$$

Accordingly,

$$\frac{F(z+h)-F(z)}{h} - f(z) = \frac{1}{h}\left\{ \int\limits_z^{z+h} f(\zeta)\,\mathrm{d}\zeta - f(z) \int\limits_z^{z+h} \mathrm{d}\zeta \right\}$$

$$= \frac{1}{h} \int\limits_z^{z+h} [f(\zeta)-f(z)]\,\mathrm{d}\zeta;$$

as $|f(\zeta)-f(z)| < \epsilon$ for all ζ on l, it follows from Theorem 1 that

$$\left| \frac{F(z+h)-F(z)}{h} - f(z) \right| \leqslant \frac{1}{|h|} \cdot \epsilon|h| = \epsilon,$$

so that

$$F'(z) = \lim_{h \to 0} \frac{F(z+h)-F(z)}{h} = f(z).$$

Accordingly, the theorem is proved.

COROLLARY 1. *If the function $f(z)$ is regular in a simply-connected domain D, then its indefinite integral in D can be represented as:*

$$\int f(z)\,\mathrm{d}z = \int_{z_0}^z f(z)\,\mathrm{d}z + C. \tag{26}$$
$$(L)$$

Here, z_0 is any fixed point of D, L is any path in D joining z_0 to the general point z in D, and C is an arbitrary constant.

This result follows directly from Theorem 5, above, and the theorem on the existence of the integral along a curve (Art. 46).

COROLLARY 2. (*The formula of Newton and Leibnitz.*) *If the function $f(z)$ is regular in a simply connected domain D, then the integral of $f(z)$, along any path which connects points z_1 and z_2 of this domain and lies within it, is equal to the difference of the values at z_2 and z_1 of any given primitive of $f(z)$:*

$$\int_{z_1}^{z_2} f(z)\,\mathrm{d}z = F(z_2)-F(z_1). \tag{27}$$
$$(L)$$

To prove (27) we note that, by Theorem 5,

$$F(z) = \int_{z_1}^{z} f(z)\,\mathrm{d}z + C,$$
$$_{(L)}$$

where C is a constant. Putting $z = z_1$, we get $F(z_1) = C$, whence

$$\int_{z_1}^{z_2} f(z)\,\mathrm{d}z = F(z_2) - C = F(z_2) - F(z_1).$$
$$_{(L)}$$

This gives the required result.

Thus, we see that the definition of a primitive and the Newton–Leibnitz formula carry over unchanged from the real domain to the complex domain. As a result, integrals of elementary functions of a complex variable are calculated by means of formulae and methods which are formally the same as those used in ordinary real analysis.

50. Integration of powers of $(z-a)$

We begin by considering integrals of the function $w = 1/z$. As this function has a singularity at $z = 0$ its integral around the circle C defined by $z = Re^{i\phi}$ $(0 \leqslant \phi \leqslant 2\pi)$ may differ from zero. We have $\mathrm{d}z = Re^{i\phi}i\,\mathrm{d}\phi$ and

$$\oint_C \frac{\mathrm{d}z}{z} = \int_0^{2\pi} \frac{Re^{i\phi}}{Re^{i\phi}}i\mathrm{d}\phi = i\int_0^{2\pi} \mathrm{d}\phi = 2\pi i. \tag{28}$$

It follows from (19) that the residue of $w = 1/z$ at the singularity $z = 0$ is equal to 1.

We now consider the integral of $1/z$ along a path l joining 1 to the point z $(\neq 0)$ it being supposed that l does not pass through the origin. Let D denote the domain formed from the open plane by deleting the origin and the negative real axis. To begin, we suppose that l lies in D. In D, the principal branch of the logarithm,

$$\ln z = \ln|z| + i\arg z, \quad -\pi < \arg z \leqslant \pi,$$

is a primitive of $1/z$, as $(d/dz) \ln z = 1/z$. Another primitive of $1/z$ is

$$\int_{1 \atop (l)}^{z} \frac{dz}{z};$$

hence, by (26),

$$\int_{1 \atop (l)}^{z} \frac{dz}{z} = \ln z + C.$$

Putting $z = 1$ in this result we find that $C = 0$, so that

$$\int_{1 \atop (l)}^{z} \frac{dz}{z} = \ln z. \qquad (29)$$

It will be clear that this result extends to include the case in which z is a point on the negative real axis, provided we take l to be a path whose every point, other than its end-points, lies in the upper half-plane $\operatorname{Im} z > 0$. We have thus obtained the *integral representation of the principal branch of the logarithm*.

Now let L denote a path connecting the point 1 with the point z; the path L may make any number of circuits about the origin but may not pass through the origin. Let c be a circle with centre at $z = 0$ which encloses no points of l or L. Such a circle always exists, as l and L do not pass through $z = 0$. Let C be a circle concentric with c which encloses all points of l and L (Fig. 87), and let us denote by L' the closed path consisting of l and L^- (the latter being traversed from z to 1). By the result expressed in (13), the value of the integral

$$\int_{L'} \frac{dz}{z}$$

does not change when L' is *continuously deformed* in any way within the closed annulus bounded by c and C. Accordingly, we may take this integral along a closed path L'' consisting of two traverses of the curve l (one in each sense) and two similar traverses, in opposite senses, of the segment l' of the real axis joining the point 1 to the circle c, together with (say) n circuits of the circle c: here, the integer n depends on the form of the path L', being reckoned positive or negative according as whether c is traversed in the anticlockwise or clockwise sense (for the case shown in Fig. 87, $n = +2$). The integrals along l cancel out, as do the integrals along the segment

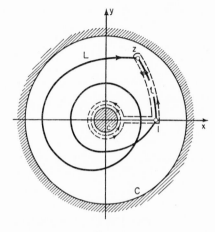

FIG. 87

l'; since the integral of $1/z$ taken around the n circuits of c contributes $2\pi n i$, it follows that

$$2\pi n i = \int_{L''} \frac{dz}{z} = \int_{l} \frac{dz}{z} - \int_{L} \frac{dz}{z},$$

whence

$$\int_{(L)}^{z} \frac{dz}{z} = \int_{(l)}^{z} \frac{dz}{z} - 2\pi n i = \ln z - 2\pi n i = \text{Ln } z. \qquad (30)$$

This result gives the value of the integral of $1/z$ along any path L which joins the point 1 to the point z and does not pass through the origin. Conversely, it is clear that, by a suitable choice of the path L, we can express any value of Ln z as the integral on the left of (30). Accordingly, (30) gives *the integral representation* of Ln z.

14

We now consider the more general case of the function $(z-a)^n$, where n is any integer, positive, negative, or zero. Let C be any contour enclosing the point a and let c be any circle which has its centre at a and which lies in the interior domain bounded by C. For all integral n, the function $(z-a)^n$ is regular at every point of the closed annular region whose boundary consists of c and C; thus, by (13),

$$\oint_C (z-a)^n \, dz = \oint_c (z-a)^n \, dz,$$

both contours being traversed in the same sense (say, the positive sense). The integral on the right is evaluated in the same way as the integral in (28): we put $z-a = re^{i\phi}$ where r is the radius of c, so that $dz = re^{i\phi} \cdot i \, d\phi$ and

$$\oint_c (z-a)^n \, dz = \int_0^{2\pi} r^n e^{in\phi} re^{i\phi} i \, d\phi = ir^{n+1} \int_0^{2\pi} e^{i(n+1)\phi} \, d\phi.$$

Now $(d/d\phi)e^{k\phi} = ke^{k\phi}$ (k constant, real or complex; see Art. 8), so that

$$\int e^{k\phi} \, d\phi = \frac{1}{k} e^{k\phi} + K \quad (k \neq 0, \quad K = \text{const.});$$

hence, if $n \neq -1$,

$$\oint_c (z-a)^n \, dz = \frac{r^{n+1}}{n+1} \left[e^{i(n+1)\phi} \right]_0^{2\pi} = \frac{r^{n+1}}{n+1} \{ e^{i2(n+1)\pi} - 1 \} = 0,$$

as $e^{i2(n+1)\pi} = 1$ for *all* integral n. It should be noted that this result follows immediately from Cauchy's theorem when n is a non-negative integer. It will be clear that, when $n = -1$,

$$\oint_c (z-a)^n \, dz = \oint_c \frac{dz}{z-a} = i \int_0^{2\pi} d\phi = 2\pi i.$$

Thus, for *integral* n we have

$$\oint_C (z-a)^n \, dz = \begin{cases} 0 \text{ for } n \neq -1, \\ 2\pi i \text{ for } n = -1. \end{cases} \tag{31}$$

This example shows that it is not necessary that a function $f(z)$ be regular in the interior domain bounded by a contour C in order that

$$\oint_C f(z)\,\mathrm{d}z$$

should vanish: for integer n, $n \leqslant -2$, the integral (31) vanishes although $(z-a)^n$ has a singularity at $z = a$. The possibility that this situation may occur more generally will be clear from Cauchy's residue theorem: assuming the conditions under which (15) holds, we see that

$$\oint_C f(z)\,\mathrm{d}z = 0,$$

not only when $f(z)$ is regular in the interior domain D, but also when the *sum* of the residues of $f(z)$ in D vanishes (and, in particular, when $f(z)$ has exactly one singular point in D, the residue of $f(z)$ being zero at this point).

51. Cauchy's integral formula

The result now to be obtained expresses a fundamental property of regular functions. We consider a bounded domain D whose frontier B consists of a finite number of disjoint closed contours and suppose that $f(z)$ is regular at each point of $\overline{D}$; it will be shown that the behaviour of $f(z)$ in D is completely determined by its behaviour on the boundary B. This result is embodied in Cauchy's (first) integral formula:

$$f(z) = \frac{1}{2\pi i} \int_{B^+} \frac{f(\zeta)}{(\zeta - z)}\,\mathrm{d}\zeta \;; \qquad (32)$$

here, z denotes any point of D (that is, any interior point of $\overline{D}$) and the symbol B^+ indicates that the integral is taken around the boundary B in the *positive* sense (that is, each component of B is traversed so that D always remains on the left; see Fig. 88).

We begin the proof by choosing an arbitrary point z of D. Then, if ϵ is any positive number there exists a $\delta > 0$ such that ζ lies in D whenever $|\zeta - z| \leqslant \delta$ and (since $f(\zeta)$ is continuous at $\zeta = z$)

$$|f(\zeta) - f(z)| < \epsilon \qquad (33)$$

whenever $|\zeta - z| \leqslant \delta$. The function $f(\zeta)/(\zeta - z)$ is regular on the closed region R formed from $\overline{D}$ by abstracting the open disc $|\zeta - z| < \delta$; thus, by Cauchy's theorem,

$$\int_{B^+} \frac{f(\zeta)}{\zeta - z}\, d\zeta = \oint_c \frac{f(\zeta)}{\zeta - z}\, d\zeta,$$

where c denotes the circle $|\zeta - z| = \delta$, supposed described positively.

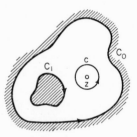

FIG. 88

From (31) (Art. 50) we have

$$f(z) = \frac{1}{2\pi i} \oint_c \frac{f(z)}{\zeta - z}\, d\zeta,$$

whence

$$\frac{1}{2\pi i} \oint_c \frac{f(\zeta)}{\zeta - z}\, d\zeta - f(z) = \frac{1}{2\pi i} \oint_c \frac{f(\zeta) - f(z)}{\zeta - z}\, d\zeta.$$

Thus, by (33) and Theorem 1 of Art. 46,

$$\left| \frac{1}{2\pi i} \int_{B^+} \frac{f(\zeta)}{\zeta - z}\, d\zeta - f(z) \right| \leqslant \frac{1}{2\pi} \cdot \frac{\epsilon}{\delta} \cdot 2\pi\delta = \epsilon;$$

as ϵ is an arbitrarily small positive number and the left-hand side of this inequality is independent of ϵ it follows that

$$f(z) = \frac{1}{2\pi i} \int_{B^+} \frac{f(\zeta)}{\zeta - z}\, d\zeta.$$

Remark 1. If the point z lies outside the region $\overline{D}$ then the function $f(\zeta)/(\zeta-z)$ is regular at all points of $\overline{D}$ and it follows from Cauchy's theorem that

$$\frac{1}{2\pi i} \int_{B^+} \frac{f(\zeta)}{\zeta-z}\,\mathrm{d}\zeta = 0. \tag{34}$$

Remark 2. Cauchy's formula also holds when $f(z)$ is regular in the domain D and is continuous on the closed region $\overline{D}$. (Above, we assumed $f(z)$ regular on $\overline{D}$.) This generalization follows from the fact that Cauchy's theorem holds under the Pollard conditions (see Valiron, *Théorie des Fonctions*); we shall use this generalized form of the integral formula in what follows.

52. The existence of higher derivatives

Cauchy's formula (32) gives a representation, in D, of a function $f(z)$ regular on $\overline{D}$, in terms of its values $f(\zeta)$ on the frontier of $\overline{D}$. The formula also has meaning when B^+ is replaced by any path, or finite collection of paths, C (not necessarily closed) and $f(\zeta)$ denotes a function which is continuous on C; the integral (which is convergent for each finite z not on C) becomes

$$F(z) = \frac{1}{2\pi i} \int_C \frac{f(\zeta)}{\zeta-z}\,\mathrm{d}\zeta \tag{35}$$

and is called an *integral of Cauchy type*.

THEOREM 6. *The function $F(z)$ defined by an integral of Cauchy type is regular at any finite point z not on C; at any such point $F(z)$ has derivatives of all orders and*

$$F^{(n)}(z) = \frac{n!}{2\pi i} \int_C \frac{f(\zeta)}{(\zeta-z)^{n+1}}\,\mathrm{d}\zeta \quad (n = 1, 2, \ldots). \tag{36}$$

We prove first that, at any point z not on C, $F'(z)$ exists finitely (so that the regularity of $F(z)$ is established) and that $F'(z)$ is given by

$$F'(z) = \frac{1}{2\pi i} \int_C \frac{f(\zeta)}{(\zeta-z)^2}\,\mathrm{d}\zeta. \tag{37}$$

Let $2d$ denote the lower bound of the distance of z from a point ζ of C as ζ traverses the complete path C; then, if

$$0 < |h| < d,$$

$F(z+h)$ and $F(z)$ both exist finitely and

$$\frac{F(z+h)-F(z)}{h} = \frac{1}{2\pi i h} \int_C \left\{ \frac{1}{\zeta-z-h} - \frac{1}{\zeta-z} \right\} f(\zeta) d\zeta$$

$$= \frac{1}{2\pi i} \int_C \frac{f(\zeta)}{(\zeta-z-h)(\zeta-z)} \, d\zeta.$$

Also, for all ζ on C we have $|\zeta-z| > d$, $|\zeta-z-h| > d$ (Fig. 89), so that $1/|\zeta-z| < 1/d$, $1/|\zeta-z-h| < 1/d$. Let M denote the

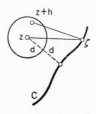

Fig. 89

upper bound of $|f(\zeta)|$ on C. For simplicity, we shall assume that C has finite total length; then, M exists finitely since $f(\zeta)$ is continuous on the bounded closed set C. By Theorem 1 of this chapter and the above results we thus have

$$\left| \frac{F(z+h)-F(z)}{h} - \frac{1}{2\pi i} \int_C \frac{f(\zeta)}{(\zeta-z)^2} \, d\zeta \right| = \frac{1}{2\pi} \left| \int_C \frac{h f(\zeta) \, d\zeta}{(\zeta-z-h)(\zeta-z)^2} \right|$$

$$\leqslant \frac{1}{2\pi} \frac{Ml|h|}{d^3}$$

where l denotes the length of the path C. As the right-hand side of this inequality tends to zero as $h \to 0$ it follows that

$$F'(z) = \lim_{h \to 0} \frac{F(z+h)-F(z)}{h} = \frac{1}{2\pi i} \int_C \frac{f(\zeta)}{(\zeta-z)^2} \, d\zeta.$$

This establishes the first part of the theorem. In exactly the same way we can prove that $F^{(2)}(z)$ exists and is given by

$$F^{(2)}(z) = \lim_{h \to 0} \frac{F'(z+h) - F'(z)}{h} = \frac{2}{2\pi i} \int_C \frac{f(\zeta)}{(\zeta - z)^3} \, d\zeta;$$

and, more generally, that, for all integers $n \geqslant 2$, $F^{(n)}(z)$ exists and equals

$$\frac{n!}{2\pi i} \int_C \frac{f(\zeta)}{(\zeta - z)^{n+1}} \, d\zeta.$$

Remark. Formula (36), giving the nth derivative of an integral of Cauchy type can be obtained by n-fold differentiation, under the integral sign, of integral (35), with respect to the parameter z. Our theorem shows that this differentiation is permissible. The above results extend to the case in which C is a suitable smooth unbounded curve when $f(\zeta)$ is bounded on C and the integral (35) is uniformly convergent with respect to z on any bounded closed region R which has no points in common with C.

From Theorem 6 it follows, in particular, that any function $f(z)$ regular on the bounded closed region $\overline{D}$ has derivatives of all orders in the domain D. The result given in the preceding article shows that $f(z)$ can be represented in D, by the Cauchy integral formula, in terms of its values on the boundary. The integral in this formula is one of Cauchy type and it follows from Theorem 6 that $f(z)$ has derivatives of all orders in D. We thus have the following result:

THEOREM 7. *If D is a bounded domain whose frontier B consists of a finite number of disjoint contours and $f(z)$ is regular in D and continuous on $\overline{D}$, then $f(z)$ has derivatives of all orders at any point z in D, with*

$$f^{(n)}(z) = \frac{n!}{2\pi i} \int_{B^+} \frac{f(\zeta)}{(\zeta - z)^{n+1}} \, d\zeta \quad (n = 1, 2, \ldots). \tag{38}$$

Remark 1. It follows from Theorem 7 that $f^{(n)}(z)$ is differentiable at every point z in D ($n = 1, 2, \ldots$), so that each $f^{(n)}(z)$ is regular in D.

Remark 2. If we adopt the usual conventions that $0! = 1$ and $f^{(0)}(z) = f(z)$, formula (38) holds for $n = 0$; it is then identical with the first integral formula (32).

Suppose now that $f(z)$ has a derivative $f'(z)$ at every point of an *arbitrary* domain D of the finite plane. (Here we place no restriction on the form of boundary of D.) Any point z of D is the centre of some closed disc $\overline{K}$ contained in D. Let B^+ denote the boundary of $\overline{K}$, described in the positive sense. It follows from (38) that $f(\zeta)$ has derivatives of *all* orders at any point ζ in the open disc K bounded by B. As z was taken to be any point in D it follows that $f(z)$ has derivatives of all orders in D, so that each of these derivatives is *regular* in D. This property draws a sharp distinction between functions regular in a domain and the functions of real analysis which are differentiable in (say) some open interval: for any function of the latter class the mere existence of the derivative does *not* ensure that this derivative is continuous in the interval concerned.

53. Properties of regular functions

We shall use Cauchy's integral formula to deduce further properties of functions $f(z)$ which are regular in some domain of the finite plane. To begin, let z denote a given point of the finite plane, and let $f(\zeta)$ be regular at all points ζ of the closed disc $|\zeta - z| \leqslant r$. Denoting the circle $|\zeta - z| = r$ by C and writing $\zeta - z = re^{i\phi}$, we have

$$f(z) = \frac{1}{2\pi i} \oint_C \frac{f(\zeta) \cdot \mathrm{d}\zeta}{\zeta - z} = \frac{1}{2\pi i} \int_0^{2\pi} \frac{f(\zeta) \cdot rie^{i\phi}}{re^{i\phi}} \, \mathrm{d}\phi$$

$$= \frac{1}{2\pi} \int_0^{2\pi} f(z + re^{i\phi}) \, \mathrm{d}\phi. \tag{39}$$

This result is called Gauss's formula: it expresses what is known as the *mean value theorem* for regular functions:

THEOREM 8. *If the function $f(z)$ is regular at all points of a closed disc then its value at the centre of this disc equals the arithmetic mean* *of its values on the circumference:*

$$f(z) = \frac{1}{2\pi} \int\limits_0^{2\pi} f(z+re^{i\phi}) \, . \, \mathrm{d}\phi. \tag{40}$$

From the theorem of the mean we deduce the *maximum modulus principle*:

THEOREM 9. *If the function f(z) is regular at each point of a bounded closed region R and is not constant on R, then $|f(z)|$ cannot attain its upper bound on R at any interior point of R.*

Let us suppose, if possible, that $|f(z)|$ attains its upper bound M on R at one or more points of the domain D which constitutes the interior of R; let E denote the set of those points of D at which $|f(z)| = M$. If E coincides with D then it follows readily from the continuity of $|f(z)|$ on $\overline{D}$ $(= R)$ that $|f(z)| = \text{const.} = M$ on R, and we can show that $f(z)$ is constant on R: this is immediately obvious if $M = 0$, for we then have $f(z) \equiv 0$ on D, so that, by continuity, $f(z) \equiv 0$ on R; if $E = D$ and $M > 0$, we have $|f(z)| > 0$ in D, so that the function

$$g(z) = \ln f(z) = \ln|f(z)| + i \arg f(z) = u + iv$$

is regular in D, being a regular function of a regular function in this domain; in this case, by the Cauchy–Riemann conditions, since $u = \text{const.} = \ln M$ in D, we have

$$\frac{\partial v}{\partial x} = -\frac{\partial u}{\partial y} = 0, \qquad \frac{\partial v}{\partial y} = \frac{\partial u}{\partial x} = 0$$

at all points of D, so that $g'(z) \equiv 0$ in D, and it follows that $g(z)$, and hence $f(z)$, is constant in D; the fact that $f(z) = \text{const.}$ $(= Me^{i\alpha}$, say) on R then follows from the continuity of $f(z)$ on R. Let us suppose now that E is *not* identical with D, so that E is a non-empty *proper* subset of D; it is then easily shown that D contains a point z_0 of the *frontier* of E (this result depends on the fact that D is a *connected* set; see, e.g., Newman, *Topology of Plane Sets*, Cambridge, 1952). It is also easily shown that z_0 belongs to E: for, suppose, if possible, that z_0 does not belong to E; then, as z_0 is a frontier point of E, *every* deleted neighbourhood of z_0 contains points of E, so that, by continuity of $|f(z)|$ in D, $|f(z_0)| = M$; accordingly, z_0 is a point of E and we have a contradiction. As z_0

belongs to D, to E, and to the frontier of E (so that every neigh-bourhood of z_0 contains points of D which do *not* belong to E) it is readily shown that there exists a finite positive r having the following properties: (i) z belongs to D whenever $|z-z_0| \leqslant r$; (ii) there exists a point z_1 on the circle $|z-z_0| = r$ which does not belong to E. We denote this circle by C. As $|f(z_1)| < M$, it follows from the continuity of $|f(z)|$ that there is an arc C_1 of C which contains z_1 and on which $|f(z)| \leqslant M-\epsilon$, where ϵ denotes some positive number. Let C_2 denote the complementary arc of C

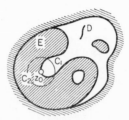

FIG. 90

(see Fig. 90); we suppose C_1, C_2 described by a point $z = z_0 + re^{i\phi}$ in a sense corresponding to a positive circuit of C. Then, by (40),

$$f(z_0) = \frac{1}{2\pi} \int_0^{2\pi} f(z) \, d\phi = \frac{1}{2\pi r} \left\{ \int_{C_1} f(z) \, ds + \int_{C_2} f(z) \, ds \right\},$$

and it follows from the fundamental inequality in Theorem 1 that

$$M = |f(z_0)| \leqslant \frac{1}{2\pi r}\{(M-\epsilon)l_1 + Ml_2\} = M - \frac{\epsilon l_1}{2\pi r},$$

where l_1 is the length of C_1 and l_2 is the length of C_2. This last inequality is impossible, so that the set E must be empty. Theorem 9 follows immediately.

Remark 1. By Theorem 2 of Art. 13, $|f(z)|$ must attain its upper bound M at some point of $R = \overline{D}$; under the conditions of Theorem 9 (namely, that $f(z)$ is regular at all points of $\overline{D}$ and is *not* constant in D) it follows that this point must belong to the boundary of D.

Remark 2. If, with the above notation, $f(z)$ is regular at all points of D, is not constant in D, and *does not vanish* at any point in D, then $|f(z)|$ cannot attain its minimum value (m, say) at any point of D (that is, at any interior point of the region $R = \overline{D}$). To prove this it suffices to apply Theorem 9 to the function $g(z) = 1/f(z)$: under the conditions stated, $g(z)$ is regular on R and not constant in D.

Remark 3. A neater proof of the maximum modulus principle is based on a formula due to Gutzmer. If $f(z)$ is regular for

$$|z-a| < R$$

then (by Taylor's theorem—see Chap. VI)

$$f(z) = \sum_{n=0}^{+\infty} a_n(z-a)^n$$

for $|z-a| < R$, where $a_n = f^{(n)}(a)/n!$ $(n = 0, 1, \ldots)$, and (Gutzmer's formula)

$$\sum_{n=0}^{+\infty} |a_n|^2 r^{2n} = \frac{1}{2\pi} \int_0^{2\pi} |f(a+re^{i\phi})|^2 \, \mathrm{d}\phi \quad (0 \leqslant r < R).$$

Thus, if $M(r)$ denotes the upper bound of $|f(z)|$ on the circle $|z-a| = r$ $(0 < r < R)$, we have

$$|a_0|^2 \leqslant \frac{1}{2\pi} \int_0^{2\pi} |f(a+re^{i\phi})|^2 \, \mathrm{d}\phi \leqslant \{M(r)\}^2,$$

so that

$$|f(a)| = |a_0| \leqslant M(r);$$

it will be clear that $|f(a)| < M(r)$ unless $a_n = 0$ for $n = 1, 2, \ldots$ (that is, unless $f(z)$ is constant for $|z-a| < R$).

By means of (38) we can obtain bounds for the *derivatives* of a function $f(z)$ at the centre of any closed disc on which $f(z)$ is regular. Let $f(z)$ be regular whenever $|z-a| \leqslant R$; then, if M denotes the upper bound of $|f(z)|$ on the circle C defined by $|z-a| = R$, we have (for $n = 1, 2, \ldots$)

$$|f^{(n)}(a)| = \frac{n!}{2\pi}\left| \oint_C \frac{f(\zeta) \cdot \mathrm{d}\zeta}{(\zeta-a)^{n+1}} \right| \leqslant \frac{n!M \cdot 2\pi R}{2\pi R^{n+1}} = \frac{n!M}{R^n}. \tag{41}$$

In particular, taking $n = 1$, we have

$$|f'(a)| \leqslant \frac{M}{R} \, . \tag{42}$$

Let us now suppose that the function $f(z)$ is regular and bounded in the whole of the open plane so that $|f(z)| \leqslant M$ (say) for *all* finite z. Then the inequality (42) can be applied to any finite point a, where R is any positive number. Letting $R \to +\infty$, it follows readily that $|f'(a)| = 0$, where a is any point of the finite plane. Thus, $f'(z) \equiv 0$ and $f(z) \equiv$ const. (See Exercise 16, Chap. I.) This result is stated formally as

THEOREM 10 (*Liouville*). *If the function $f(z)$ is regular and bounded in the whole of the open plane, then it is a constant.*

Remark 1. In formulating the fundamental theorem of Riemann on the existence of a conformal mapping of a simply connected domain D onto the unit open disc (see Art. 23), we excluded the case in which D is the whole plane (open or closed) or is obtained from the closed plane by omitting a single point. The reason for this exclusion will now be explained: if $w = f(z)$ were to map the finite plane onto the open disc $|w| < 1$, it would be regular and bounded in the whole of the finite plane, with $|f(z)| \leqslant 1$ for all finite z. It would then follow from Liouville's theorem that $f(z) \equiv$ const., which is obviously impossible. Thus, there is no conformal mapping of the open plane onto the open disc $|w| < 1$; it will be clear that the same argument shows that there is no conformal mapping of the extended plane onto $|w| < 1$. In the same way we can show that there is no conformal mapping onto $|w| < 1$ of the domain D formed from the extended plane by removing any one finite point a. To prove this it suffices to transform D into the finite ζ-plane by the mapping $\zeta = 1/(z-a)$; we then use the result just obtained.

Remark 2. Liouville's theorem can be significantly strengthened: *If the function $w = f(z)$ is regular in the whole of the open plane and does not assume the values lying on a certain curve l in the w-plane, then it is a constant.*

Here, of course, we suppose that l does not degenerate into a single point. For simplicity, let us suppose that l is an open Jordan arc. Then the set Δ of points in the extended w-plane which do not lie on l is a simply-connected doma insatisfying the conditions of the Riemann mapping theorem (Art. 23) and there exists a conformal mapping $\omega = \phi(w)$ of Δ onto the disc $|\omega| < 1$. We now consider the composite function $\omega = \phi[f(z)] = \Phi(z)$: clearly, this function is regular and bounded in the finite z-plane, with $|\Phi(z)| < 1$ for *all* finite z. By Liouville's theorem, $\Phi(z) \equiv \text{const.}$; as $\phi(w)$ is *univalent* in the domain Δ, it follows that $f(z)$ is a constant.

54. Harmonic functions

Let the function

$$f(z) = u(x, y) + iv(x, y)$$

be regular in some domain D of the finite plane. Then, at every point of D, $f'(z)$ exists and is given by

$$f'(z) = \frac{\partial u}{\partial x} + i\frac{\partial v}{\partial x} = \frac{\partial v}{\partial y} - i\frac{\partial u}{\partial y} \qquad (43)$$

(see Art. 14). Thus, the partial derivatives $\partial u/\partial x$, $\partial u/\partial y$, $\partial v/\partial x$, $\partial v/\partial y$ exist at all points of D; as $f'(z)$ is continuous in D it follows that these partial derivatives are also continuous in D. By the result proved in Art. 52, the derivative $f'(z)$ is also regular in D; hence, at all points of D, $f''(z)$ exists and is given by

$$f''(z) = \frac{\partial^2 u}{\partial x^2} + i\frac{\partial^2 v}{\partial x^2} = -\frac{\partial^2 u}{\partial y^2} - i\frac{\partial^2 v}{\partial y^2}. \qquad (44)$$

(Here we have applied formula (43): the respective functions u and v are replaced, first by $\partial u/\partial x$ and $\partial v/\partial x$, and then by $\partial v/\partial y$ and $-\partial u/\partial y$.) As $f''(z)$ is also regular in D it follows that the partial derivatives in (44) are all continuous in D. In the same way, using the Cauchy–Riemann relations where necessary, we can show that all partial derivatives, of all orders, of the functions $u(x, y)$, $v(x, y)$ exist and are continuous in D.

From (44) we have

$$\frac{\partial^2 u}{\partial x^2} = -\frac{\partial^2 u}{\partial y^2}, \qquad \frac{\partial^2 v}{\partial x^2} = -\frac{\partial^2 v}{\partial y^2};$$

thus $\phi = u$ and $\phi = v$ are both solutions (in D) of *Laplace's equation*

$$\nabla^2 \phi \equiv \frac{\partial^2 \phi}{\partial x^2} + \frac{\partial^2 \phi}{\partial y^2} = 0. \qquad (45)$$

(Here, ∇^2 denotes Laplace's differential operator in the plane.)

Definition. A real function $u(x, y)$ is said to be harmonic in the domain D, if, in this domain, it has continuous partial derivatives of the first two orders and satisfies Laplace's equation (45).

The above results are stated formally as

THEOREM 11. *If $f(z) = u(x, y) + iv(x, y)$ is regular in a domain D then the real part $u(x, y)$ and the imaginary part $v(x, y)$ are each harmonic functions in D.*

If $u(x, y)$ and $v(x, y)$ are harmonic in D and satisfy the Cauchy–Riemann relations

$$\frac{\partial u}{\partial x} = \frac{\partial v}{\partial y}, \qquad \frac{\partial u}{\partial y} = -\frac{\partial v}{\partial x} \tag{46}$$

in this domain they are said to be *conjugate* (in D).

We now show that, if $u(x, y)$ is harmonic in a simply-connected domain D, there exists a function $v(x, y)$ which is harmonic in D and is conjugate to $u(x, y)$. The problem reduces to that of constructing a function $v(x, y)$ when its first partial derivatives are given: $\partial v/\partial x = -\partial u/\partial y$, $\partial v/\partial y = \partial u/\partial x$. A solution is given by the line integral

$$\int_{z_0}^{z} \left(-\frac{\partial u}{\partial y}\,\mathrm{d}x + \frac{\partial}{\partial x}\,\mathrm{d}y \right);$$

here, z_0 is a fixed point in D, $z = x + iy$ is the general point in D. The path of integration is any piecewise-smooth curve connecting z_0 and z in D; the value of the integral is independent of the particular choice of path, since the partial derivatives of u of the first two orders are continuous in D and u satisfies Laplace's equation, so that

$$\frac{\partial}{\partial y}\left(-\frac{\partial u}{\partial y} \right) = \frac{\partial}{\partial x}\left(\frac{\partial u}{\partial x} \right).$$

In this way v is defined in D within an arbitrary additive constant; the complete solution is given by

$$v(x, y) = \int_{z_0}^{z} \left(-\frac{\partial u}{\partial y}\,\mathrm{d}x + \frac{\partial u}{\partial x}\,\mathrm{d}y \right) + C, \tag{47}$$

where C is an arbitrary constant. The function defined in D by

$$f(z) = u(x,y) + iv(x,y) \tag{48}$$

is regular in D since u and v have continuous first-order partial derivatives which satisfy the Cauchy–Riemann relations in this domain. Accordingly, the function v defined by (47) is harmonic in D.

In exactly the same way, given a function $v(x, y)$ which is harmonic in D, we can find a function $u(x, y)$ which is harmonic in D and conjugate to v in this domain. The results obtained above can be stated as

THEOREM 12. *An arbitrary function which is harmonic in the simply connected domain D can be considered as the real or imaginary part of a function regular in D.*
Remark. If the domain D is multiply connected, the function defined by the integral (47) and the function (48) may not be single-valued. This situation was discussed in Art. 37 where we solved an essentially similar problem concerning plane fields.

Theorems 11 and 12 show that many of the properties established for regular functions also hold for harmonic functions. In this connection we note the following propositions as they will be useful in what follows.

THEOREM 13. *Let the* (real) *function $u(z)$ be harmonic in a simply connected domain D, and let $z = \phi(\zeta)$ be a function which is regular in a domain Δ, each of its values in Δ lying in the domain D. Then, the composite function $u[\phi(\zeta)] = U(\zeta)$ is harmonic in Δ.* (Here, for brevity, we have written $u(z)$ for $u(x, y)$.)

To prove this we construct a function $f(z)$ which is regular in D and such that $u(z) = \operatorname{Re} f(z)$ in D. Then, clearly,

$$U(\zeta) = \operatorname{Re} f[\phi(\zeta)],$$

and the result follows, since $F(\zeta) = f[\phi(\zeta)]$ is regular in Δ.

It also follows, from Theorem 7 of Art. 52, that *if u is harmonic in some domain D then every partial derivative of u exists and is continuous in D and is itself a harmonic function in this domain.*

Separating real parts in formula (39) we obtain the corresponding *theorem of the mean for harmonic functions*:

$$u(z) = \frac{1}{2\pi} \int\limits_{0}^{2\pi} u(z + re^{i\phi}) \, . \, d\phi. \tag{49}$$

For harmonic functions we also have the following *principle of extremes*:

THEOREM 14. *Let the real function $u(z)$ be harmonic in a bounded domain D of the finite plane and let $u(z)$ be continuous on the closed region $R = \overline{D}$; then, if $u(z)$ is not constant in D, $u(z)$ cannot attain an extreme value at any interior point of R (that is, at any point of D).*

It suffices to show that $u(z)$ cannot have a maximum at any point a in D; for, if u had a minimum at a then the function $-u(z)$, which is also harmonic in D and continuous on $\overline{D}$, would have a maximum at this point. Let a be any interior point of $\overline{D}$. By means of suitable cuts (as in Art. 47) we can change D into a simply-connected domain D_1 containing a (necessarily as an interior point); it will be clear that $\overline{D}_1 = \overline{D}$. We construct the harmonic function $v(z)$ which is conjugate to $u(z)$ in D_1 and write

$$g(z) = u(z) + iv(z).$$

Then, the function $e^{g(z)}$ is regular in D_1 and its modulus is

$$\left| e^{g(z)} \right| = e^{u(z)}$$

in this domain. Suppose, if possible, that $u(z)$ has a local maximum at a: then, there exists a positive r such that D_1 contains the closed disc $|z-a| \leqslant r$ and $u(z) \leqslant u(a)$ whenever $|z-a| \leqslant r$. It follows from Theorem 9 that $e^{g(z)}$, and hence $u(z)$, is constant for $|z-a| < r$. Thus, by the *identity theorem for regular functions*, the function $e^{g(z)}$, and hence $u(z)$, is constant in D_1, so that (by continuity) $u(z)$ is constant in D; this contradicts our initial hypothesis. (The identity theorem is a simple consequence of Taylor's theorem; see Chap. VI. It can be stated as follows: if two functions f_1, f_2 are regular in a domain D of the finite plane and are equal at each point of an infinite set S of points in D which has a limit point in D, then $f_1 \equiv f_2$ in D.) Thus $u(z)$ cannot have even a local maximum at any interior point a of $\overline{D}$; it is immediately clear that $u(z)$ cannot attain its upper bound on $\overline{D}$ at any such point a.

Liouville's theorem (Art. 53) also extends to harmonic functions: *if the function $u(z)$ is harmonic in the whole of the open plane and is bounded (on one side, or on both) in this plane then it is a constant.* Suppose for definiteness that $u(z)$ is bounded above, with $u(z) \leqslant M$ for all finite z. Let $f(z)$ be a function, regular in the open plane, such that $u(z) = \operatorname{Re} f(z)$ for all points of this plane. As the values taken by $w = f(z)$ in the open plane lie in the half-plane $u \leqslant M$ it follows from the result expressed in Remark 2 to Liouville's theorem that $f(z)$ is a constant; accordingly, $u(z) = \operatorname{Re} f(z)$ is a constant in the open plane.

55. Dirichlet's problem

Many problems of mathematical physics reduce to that of constructing a function which is harmonic in some domain and has given values on the boundary of the domain. We have already met such a problem in Art. 45 where the potential function for an electrostatic field was determined from its values on the real axis.

In giving a precise formulation of this problem we limit ourselves to the case in which the domain D is simply-connected in the open plane (so that any contour in D is reducible in D), the frontier of D being a smooth curve C. (This means that D is the *interior* domain bounded by a smooth contour C in the open plane or that D is a domain whose frontier *on the sphere* is a simple smooth closed curve passing through the north pole—that is, through the point at infinity.) We also suppose that the values to be assumed by $u(z)$ on the boundary C define a function $\tilde{u}(\zeta)$ on C which is continuous on C.

Dirichlet's problem for harmonic functions, known as *the first boundary-value problem*, consists in finding a (real) function $u(z)$ satisfying the following requirements:

(1) $u(z)$ is harmonic in the domain D;

(2) $u(z)$ is continuous on the closed region $\overline{D}$;

and

(3) at each point ζ of C, $u(z)$ coincides with the function $\tilde{u}(\zeta)$ prescribed on C: $u(\zeta) = \tilde{u}(\zeta)$ at all points ζ of C.

We begin by establishing the *uniqueness theorem* for the solution of Dirichlet's problem.

THEOREM 15. *For the given domain D and the given boundary values $\tilde{u}(\zeta)$ there exists at most one solution of Dirichlet's problem.*

For, let $u_1(z)$ and $u_2(z)$ be two such solutions. Their difference $u(z) = u_1(z) - u_2(z)$ is harmonic in D and continuous on $\overline{D}$, and vanishes on C since $u_1(\zeta) = \tilde{u}(\zeta) = u_2(\zeta)$ at each point ζ on C. Suppose first that D is bounded, C being a contour in the open plane. By Theorem 14, the upper and lower bounds of $u(z)$ on D are both zero, so that $u(z) \equiv 0$ on D. Thus $u_1(z)$ and $u_2(z)$ are identical on $\overline{D}$. If D is not bounded, C being represented on the sphere as a simple smooth closed curve through the point at infinity, we choose any point a which is exterior to $\overline{D}$ and apply the transformation $w = 1/(z-a)$; this gives a one–one conformal mapping of D onto a *bounded* domain Δ in the w-plane whose frontier Γ, the image of C, is a smooth contour through $w = 0$. We write

$$U_1(w) = u_1\left(a + \frac{1}{w}\right), \qquad U_2(w) = u_2\left(a + \frac{1}{w}\right).$$

It is easily shown that U_1 and U_2 are harmonic in Δ, continuous on $\overline{\Delta}$, and equal on Γ. It follows as above that U_1 and U_2 are identically equal on $\overline{\Delta}$, whence u_1 and u_2 are identical on $\overline{D}$.

We now indicate how Dirichlet's problem is solved. (A more detailed discussion of this topic which includes proofs of certain results stated below, along with generalizations to multiply-connected domains, can be found in Nehari, *Conformal Mapping*, McGraw-Hill, 1952.) We shall assume that the region $\overline{D}$ is bounded. (If $\overline{D}$ is not bounded we make a preliminary bilinear transformation $w = 1/(z-a)$, as above, mapping $\overline{D}$ on a bounded region $\overline{\Delta}$ in the w-plane, and then, having constructed a solution of Dirichlet's problem for the domain Δ, we finally make the inverse transformation $z = a + w^{-1}$.) Let z_0 be any point in D and let

$$w = f(z; z_0) \qquad (50)$$

denote a function which is regular in D and gives a one–one conformal mapping of D onto the unit disc $|w| < 1$ so that z_0 maps on $w = 0$: thus, $f(z_0; z_0) = 0$. The fact that the function in (50) depends on the choice of z_0 is indicated by the notation used. We make the further assumption that the function (50) is regular at each point of $\overline{D}$; this is assured if the contour C is an analytic curve, for the function (50) then has a continuation which is regular in a domain D_1 containing $\overline{D}$ (see Art. 82). Let $u(z)$ be harmonic in a neighbourhood of each point of $\overline{D}$; and let $z = \phi(w)$ denote the function inverse to (50), so that $\phi(0) = z_0$. Then, by Theorem (13), the function

$$U(w) = u[\phi(w)]$$

is harmonic in a neighbourhood of every point of the closed disc

$|w| \leqslant 1$. By the theorem of the mean (Art. 54),

$$U(0) = \frac{1}{2\pi} \int\limits_0^{2\pi} U(\omega) \, d\theta \tag{51}$$

where $\omega = e^{i\theta}$ denotes the general point on the circle $|w| = 1$. Transforming to variables associated with the z-plane, we have $U(0) = u[\phi(0)] = u(z_0)$, $U(\omega) = u[\phi(\omega)] = u(\zeta)$, where ζ is the general point on the contour C. We also introduce on C the parameter s, the length of arc, measured in the positive sense from the fixed point $\zeta_0 = \phi(1)$ to the variable point ζ; then,

$$d\theta = \frac{\partial \theta}{\partial s} \, ds,$$

and (51) becomes

$$u(z_0) = \frac{1}{2\pi} \oint\limits_C u(\zeta) \frac{\partial \theta}{\partial s} \, ds. \tag{52}$$

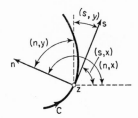

FIG. 91

We now introduce the direction n of the inward normal to C; from Fig. 91 it is clear that

$$\cos(s, x) = \cos(n, y), \qquad \cos(s, y) = -\cos(n, x),$$

whence

$$\frac{\partial \theta}{\partial s} = \frac{\partial \theta}{\partial x} \cos(s, x) + \frac{\partial \theta}{\partial y} \cos(s, y)$$

$$= \frac{\partial \theta}{\partial x} \cos(n, y) - \frac{\partial \theta}{\partial y} \cos(n, x). \tag{53}$$

Let us now consider the function

$$\ln\frac{1}{f(z;z_0)} = \ln\frac{1}{|f(z;z_0)|} + i\arg\frac{1}{f(z;z_0)} = g(z;z_0) - i\theta(z;z_s).$$

Here, the real part

$$g(z;z_0) = \ln\frac{1}{|f(z;z_0)|} \tag{54}$$

is usually called the *Green's function* for the domain D relative to the point z_0; the imaginary part is interpreted as a suitable continuous branch of $\text{Arg}\{1/f(z;z_0)\}$ on any simply-connected domain of regularity of $1/f(z;z_0)$. We note certain properties of the function g. Defining $g(z_0;z_0)$ as the limit of $g(z;z_0)$ as $z \to z_0$, we have $g(z_0;z_0) = +\infty$. Also, as $w = f(z;z_0)$ maps $\overline{D}$ on $|w| \leqslant 1$ so that $w = 0$ is the image of z_0, we have

$$g(\zeta;z_0) = \ln\{1/|f(\zeta;z_0)|\} = 0,$$

where ζ is any point on C. Further, at every point in D other than z_0, Green's function is harmonic, being the real part of a regular function:

$$\frac{\partial^2 g}{\partial x^2} + \frac{\partial^2 g}{\partial y^2} = 0.$$

It can also be shown that Green's function is symmetrical with respect to its arguments:

$$g(z;z_0) = g(z_0;z);$$

from this it follows that, for given z, the function $g(z;z_0)$ is harmonic with respect to $z_0 = x_0 + iy_0 \ (\neq z)$:

$$\frac{\partial^2 g}{\partial x_0{}^2} + \frac{\partial^2 g}{\partial y_0{}^2} = 0.$$

As the function $\ln\{1/f(z;z_0)\}$ is regular at each point of C it follows from the Cauchy–Riemann conditions that, at each such point,

$$\frac{\partial g}{\partial x} = -\frac{\partial\theta}{\partial y}, \quad \frac{\partial g}{\partial y} = \frac{\partial\theta}{\partial x};$$

by (53) we then have

$$\frac{\partial \theta}{\partial s} = \frac{\partial g}{\partial y} \cos(n, y) + \frac{\partial g}{\partial x} \cos(n, x) = \frac{\partial g}{\partial n}. \tag{55}$$

(The result expressed by (55) holds for any function

$$f(z) = u(z) + iv(z)$$

which is regular at the point $z = x + iy$, s and n denoting any pair of mutually perpendicular directions chosen as in Fig. 91: the equivalent result is

$$-\frac{\partial v}{\partial s} = \frac{\partial u}{\partial n}. \tag{55'}$$

The last formula contains the familiar Cauchy–Riemann relations; these are obtained by taking, first, $s = -y$ and $n = x$, and then, $s = x$ and $n = y$.)

By (55), formula (52) becomes

$$u(z_0) = \frac{1}{2\pi} \oint_C u(\zeta) \frac{\partial g(\zeta; z_0)}{\partial n} \, ds. \tag{56}$$

This result is known as *Green's formula*. It expresses the value of a harmonic function at *any* point z_0 in the domain D in terms of *the values taken by this function on the boundary of D*; in this sense, therefore, it represents a solution of Dirichlet's problem.

Let $\tilde{u}(\zeta)$ be any real function defined and continuous on the boundary C of D. Replacing $u(\zeta)$ by $\tilde{u}(\zeta)$ in (56) and writing z for z_0 we thereby define within D a real function

$$u(z) = \frac{1}{2\pi} \oint_C \tilde{u}(\zeta) \frac{\partial g(\zeta; z)}{\partial n} \, ds. \tag{57}$$

It does not follow from the above discussion that this function provides a solution of Dirichlet's problem: to prove this it would be necessary to show that $u(z)$ is harmonic in D and tends to $\tilde{u}(\zeta)$ as z tends to ζ through points of D. It can, however, be shown (see, e.g. Nehari, *Conformal Mapping*) that the function $u(z)$ defined in D by (57) does have these properties under the above conditions (namely, that D is a bounded domain whose frontier is a smooth contour C and that the prescribed function $\tilde{u}(\zeta)$ is real and continuous on C); thus, $u(z)$ does provide the solution of Dirichlet's problem under these conditions.

Remark 1. In applications we often consider cases in which $\tilde{u}(\zeta)$ is bounded on C but has a finite number of (finite) discontinuities on C. It can be shown that the function $u(z)$ defined in D by (57) is still harmonic in D and that $u(z)$ tends to $\tilde{u}(\zeta)$ as z tends through points of D to any boundary point ζ at which $\tilde{u}(\zeta)$ is continuous (on C); if ζ is a boundary point at which $\tilde{u}(\zeta)$ is discontinuous, the corresponding upper and lower limits being M and m, and L is any number such that $m < L < M$, then we can make $u(z)$ tend to L by letting z approach ζ through a suitable sequence of points in D.

Remark 2. It will be clear from the above that if we know the general conformal mapping of D onto the unit disc then we can, with the aid of the corresponding Green's function, solve Dirichlet's problem for this domain. The solution reduces to the quadrature (57); this integral defines the solution although its evaluation might entail the use of approximate numerical methods in any given case. We now establish the converse result: *if the general solution of Dirichlet's problem for a simply-connected domain D is known, then we can determine a conformal mapping of D onto the unit disc.* By the fundamental theorem of Art. 23, such a mapping, $w = f(z)$, exists satisfying the condition $f(z_0) = 0$. (Here, z_0 denotes an arbitrary point in D.) To begin, we suppose this mapping known, and consider the function $\phi(z)$ defined in D by

$$\phi(z) = \begin{cases} \dfrac{f(z)}{z - z_0} & \text{for } z \neq z_0, \\[2mm] \lim_{z \to z_0} \dfrac{f(z)}{z - z_0} = f'(z_0) & \text{for } z = z_0. \end{cases} \tag{58}$$

As the mapping is conformal we have $\phi(z_0) = f'(z_0) \neq 0$; it will be clear that $\phi(z) \neq 0$ at all other points in D. We show later (Art. 66) that $\phi(z)$ is *regular* in D. It follows that $g(z) = \ln|\phi(z)|$ is harmonic in D. Assuming a regular continuation of $f(z)$ onto the boundary, as above, we have

$$g(\zeta) = \ln\left|\frac{f(\zeta)}{\zeta - z_0}\right| = \ln\frac{1}{|\zeta - z_0|} \tag{59}$$

at any point ζ on C, since $w = f(z)$ maps $\overline{D}$ onto $|w| \leqslant 1$.

Now suppose we do not know the mapping $w = f(z)$. Using

the boundary values (59) in (57) we construct a real function $g(z)$ which is harmonic in D; we then construct the harmonic function $h(z)$ which is conjugate to $g(z)$ in D (this function is defined, within an arbitrary additive constant h_0, by quadratures; see Art. 54). Thus we are able to construct the function $\ln \phi(z) = g(z) + ih(z) + ih_0$, this function being determined within an imaginary additive constant ih_0. Recalling (58) we take $f(z) = (z - z_0)e^{i \ln \phi(z)}$; this function is determinate, apart from the factor e^{ih_0} corresponding to an arbitrary rotation of the disc $|w| < 1$ about its centre; it will be clear that this factor is in accordance with the full normalization requirements for the mapping (see Art. 23).

56. The integrals of Poisson and Schwarz

We begin by finding the Green's function when D is the disc $|z| < R$. By formula (25) of Art. 22,

$$w = f(z; z_0) = \frac{R(z - z_0)}{R^2 - \bar{z}_0 z} \quad (|z_0| < R)$$

so that in this case Green's function is

$$g(z; z_0) = - \ln \left| \frac{R(z - z_0)}{R^2 - \bar{z}_0 z} \right|.$$

We change to polar coordinates $z_0 = re^{i\phi}$, $\zeta = Re^{i\psi}$ (ζ is a point on the boundary $|z| = R$), and take ψ instead of s as the parameter specifying the position on the boundary; then, $ds = R\, d\psi$ and, by (55),

$$\frac{\partial g}{\partial n} = \frac{\partial \arg f(\zeta; z_0)}{\partial s} = \frac{1}{R}\frac{\partial \arg f(\zeta; z_0)}{\partial \psi};$$

here, arg denotes a branch of the argument which is continuous in a neighbourhood of the boundary point concerned. As $g(\zeta; z_0) = 0$ on C, we have

$$\frac{\partial \arg f(\zeta; z_0)}{\partial \psi} = -i\frac{\partial \ln f(\zeta; z_0)}{\partial \psi},$$

whence

$$\frac{\partial g}{\partial n} = -\frac{i}{R}\frac{\partial \ln f(\zeta; z_0)}{\partial \psi} = -\frac{i}{R}\frac{\partial}{\partial \psi}\ln \frac{Re^{i\psi} - re^{i\phi}}{R - re^{i(\psi - \phi)}}$$

$$= \frac{1}{R} \cdot \frac{R^2 - r^2}{R^2 - 2Rr\cos(\psi - \phi) + r^2}.$$

Substituting this result in (57) and writing $u(Re^{i\psi})$ for $\tilde{u}(\zeta)$ and $R\,d\psi$ for ds, we obtain

$$u(re^{i\phi}) = \frac{1}{2\pi}\int\limits_{0}^{2\pi} u(Re^{i\psi})\cdot\frac{R^2-r^2}{R^2-2Rr\cos(\psi-\phi)+r^2}\,d\psi. \qquad (60)$$

This result is called *Poisson's integral formula*; it gives the solution of Dirichlet's problem for a disc.

A similar formula can be obtained for the upper half-plane $y > 0$. Using the function (23) of Art. 22 in place of the function (25) of the same article, and proceeding as above, we obtain *Poisson's integral formula for the upper half-plane*:

$$u(x,y) = \frac{1}{\pi}\int\limits_{-\infty}^{+\infty} u(\xi)\frac{y}{(x-\xi)^2+y^2}\,d\xi. \qquad (61)$$

Here $u(\xi)$ denotes the prescribed function giving the boundary values of the harmonic function on the real axis; it is supposed that $u(\xi)$ is such as to ensure convergence of the integral (61) and has only a finite number of (finite) discontinuities of the first kind along this axis (see Remark in preceding article).

It is left to the reader to verify that the *kernel*

$$(R^2-r^2)/\{R^2-2Rr\cos(\psi-\phi)+r^2\}$$

of *Poisson's integral for the disc* is equal to $\mathrm{Re}\{(\zeta+z)/(\zeta-z)\}$, where $\zeta = Re^{i\psi}$, $z = re^{i\phi}$.

We now consider the function $f(z)$ defined in $|z| < R$ by

$$f(z) = \frac{1}{2\pi}\int\limits_{0}^{2\pi} u(Re^{i\psi})\frac{\zeta+z}{\zeta-z}\,d\psi+Ai; \qquad (62)$$

here, $\zeta = Re^{i\psi}$ and A is a real constant. As in Theorem 6 of Art. 52, on Cauchy's integral, we can show that $f(z)$ is regular for $|z| < R$. Taking real parts in (62) we obtain Poisson's integral (60). Thus, formula (62) defines a function, regular in $|z| < R$, in terms of the values $u(Re^{i\psi})$ taken by its real part on the circumference $|z| = R$. The integral on the right in this formula is called *Schwarz's integral*.

Schwarz's integral formula (62) contains an undetermined real constant A. To find A we put $z = 0$; we obtain

$$f(0) = u(0) + iv(0) = \frac{1}{2\pi} \int\limits_0^{2\pi} u(Re^{i\psi}) \, \mathrm{d}\psi + Ai.$$

By the theorem of the mean, the integral on the right is equal to $u(0)$; accordingly, $A = v(0)$, and Schwarz's integral formula becomes

$$f(z) = \frac{1}{2\pi} \int\limits_0^{2\pi} u(Re^{i\psi}) \cdot \frac{\zeta + z}{\zeta - z} \, \mathrm{d}\psi + iv(0). \tag{63}$$

It is easy to obtain the corresponding formula for the half-plane $y > 0$; for this domain the *Schwarz integral formula* is

$$f(z) = \frac{1}{\pi} \int\limits_{-\infty}^{+\infty} \frac{v(\xi) \cdot \mathrm{d}\xi}{\xi - z} + B, \tag{64}$$

where B is a real constant and $v(\xi)$ is a real function which satisfies continuity conditions similar to those for the function $u(\xi)$ in (61); for convergence we require that there exist positive constants K, C, α such that $|v(\xi)| < C/|\xi|^\alpha$ whenever $|\xi| > K$. Formula (64) defines a function, regular in $\operatorname{Im} z > 0$, in terms of the values $v(\xi)$ taken by its imaginary part along the real axis. To prove this it suffices to note that, by the identity

$$\frac{y}{(x - \xi)^2 + y^2} = \operatorname{Im} \frac{1}{\xi - z},$$

the imaginary part of the right-hand side of (64) coincides with Poisson's integral (61) when we replace $u(\xi)$ by the function $v(\xi)$. The conditions imposed on the function $v(\xi)$ ensure the existence of the integral (64).

Remark. In extending the results expressed by Cauchy's integral formulae to the function $F(z)$ defined in (35) by an integral of Cauchy type we replaced the function $f(\zeta)$, representing the continuous extension of $f(z)$ onto the boundary C, by an arbitrary continuous function defined on C. Let D be a bounded simply-connected domain whose frontier C is a smooth contour, and let

$$\tilde{f}(\zeta) = \tilde{u}(\zeta) + i\tilde{v}(\zeta)$$

denote any function which is continuous on C. Then, by Theorem 6 of Art. 52, the function

$$f(z) = \frac{1}{2\pi i} \oint_C \frac{\tilde{f}(\zeta)}{\zeta - z} \, d\zeta \qquad (65)$$

defined in D by an integral of Cauchy type is regular in D. However, unlike the function defined by Poisson's integral (60), the function (65) does not, in general, tend to $\tilde{f}(\zeta)$ as z tends to the boundary point ζ through points of D. The reason for this is easily seen. Thus, for example, as shown by Schwarz's integral for the domain $|z| < R$, a function which is regular in a disc is defined, within an additive imaginary constant, by the values of its real part on the circumference; it follows that the imaginary part of the continuous extension of $f(z)$ onto the boundary circle will be determined (within an additive constant) by the behaviour of the real part on this circle. As we have not imposed any connexion between the continuous functions $\tilde{u}(\zeta)$ and $\tilde{v}(\zeta)$ there is no reason to suppose that the continuous extension onto C of the function defined by (65) will be given by $\tilde{f}(\zeta)$. (The following *counter-example* is of interest. Let D be the domain $|z| < 1$, so that C is $|z| = 1$; and let $g(z)$ be *any* function regular for $|z| \leqslant 1$. Taking $\tilde{f}(\zeta) = \bar{g}(\zeta)$ in (65), where $\bar{g}$ denotes the complex conjugate of the function g, it is then easy to show that the function $f(z)$ defined in $|z| < 1$ by (65) is *constant* in this domain, so that its extension onto $|z| \leqslant 1$ is a constant. This result follows from a simple application of Taylor's theorem and the Cauchy integral formulae.)

57. Applications to the theory of plane fields

We shall now quote a number of results in the theory of the plane field obtained by the methods developed in this chapter.

First, the following functions are *harmonic* in the domains indicated:

(a) *The potential and force functions for a plane electrostatic field in a domain not containing charges.*

(b) *The potential and stream functions for the plane flow of an ideal incompressible fluid in a domain not containing sources and vortices.*

(c) *The stream function and temperature for a plane heat flow in a domain not containing heat sources* (the medium is supposed homogeneous and isotropic).

As the complex potential in each case has a regular branch in any simply-connected sub-domain of the domain concerned, this follows from Theorem 11. The point charges, fluid sources and vortices, and heat sources serve as singular points for these functions.

The following properties relate to the structure of the field; for definiteness we shall formulate them for the electrostatic field.

(1) *If in an electrostatic field there is a closed equipotential line C, on which $V(z) = V_0$, then either C encloses a singularity of $V(z)$, or this function is a constant everywhere within C.* (In the latter case $U(z)$, and hence $F(z)$, is constant in the domain D enclosed by C, so that the field vector $\mathbf{E}$ vanishes in D.)

This property follows directly from Theorem 15: the potential for the field solves Dirichlet's problem for the domain D bounded by C, for given, constant boundary-values $V(\zeta) = V_0$. The problem is obviously solved by the constant function $V(z) \equiv V_0$ which is clearly harmonic in D; this solution is unique.

(2) *In the electrostatic field, closed lines of force cannot exist.*

For, suppose, if possible, that there exists a closed line of force C defined by $U(z) = k$. This contour separates the field domain into two domains: adjacent to C on one "side" there are points at which $U(z) > k$, and on the other "side" there are points at which $U(z) < k$; consequently, along the direction of either the inward or outward normal we have $\partial U/\partial n \leqslant 0$ at all points of C. For definiteness, suppose this holds for the inward normal; then, by formula (55'), it follows that, along the direction s, taken as indicated in Fig. 91, we have $\partial V/\partial s = -\partial U/\partial n \geqslant 0$ at all points of C; as C is a line of force it will be clear that we must have $\partial V/\partial s > 0$ at all points of C. In this case, however, one complete circuit of our line of force would lead to a value of $V(z)$ differing from the initial value, contradicting the fact that the potential function must be single-valued (see Art. 37). Thus, no line of force can be a closed curve. (This argument can be stated otherwise: along a closed line of force C, the tangential resolute E_s would have the same sign at every point of C, and then the circulation of $\mathbf{E}$ around C would differ from zero; this is impossible (see Art. 36).)

(3) *Neither lines of force nor equipotential lines can begin or end at an interior point of any field domain.*

We establish this result for equipotential lines. Suppose, if possible, that the equipotential line $V(z) = k$ ends at some interior point z_0 of the field; then, a sufficiently small disc with centre at z_0 will not be separated by this equipotential line into two parts (Fig. 92). Thus, everywhere in this disc we must have either $V(z) \leqslant k$ or $V(z) \geqslant k$. (If there exist non-empty subsets of the disc on which, say, $V(z) > k$ and $V(z) \leqslant k$, it will be clear that these subsets must be separated by the line $V(z) = k$; this is impossible, since the line is supposed to terminate at z_0. If $V = k$ at all points of the disc it follows readily from the identity theorem that V is constant in the field domain concerned.) This would imply that $V(z)$ has a local maximum or minimum at the interior point z_0, in contradiction to Theorem 14. Note that the proof of this result applies to the level lines of any function which is harmonic in the domain.

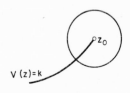

Fig. 92

From properties (2) and (3) we have:

(4) *For an electrostatic field, distinct lines of force can intersect only at boundary points of the field (for example, at charges); any line which is not terminated at both ends on the boundary must go to infinity.*

In conclusion we give examples showing how the integrals of Poisson and Schwarz can be used to find complex potentials.

Example 1. *The field in a half-plane bordered by $n+1$ electrodes represented by the open intervals $(-\infty, a_1)$, (a_1, a_2), ..., $(a_n, +\infty)$ along the real axis, these electrodes being at the respective potentials $v_0, v_1, \ldots, v_n$. (The points a_k are insulators.)*

To find the potential in $\text{Im } z > 0$ we can use Poisson's integral (61) directly:

$$V(x,y) = \frac{1}{\pi} \int\limits_{-\infty}^{+\infty} \frac{y \cdot \mathrm{d}\xi}{(x-\xi)^2 + y^2}$$

$$= \frac{v_0 y}{\pi} \int\limits_{-\infty}^{a_1} \frac{\mathrm{d}\xi}{(x-\xi)^2 + y^2} + \frac{v_1 y}{\pi} \int\limits_{a_1}^{a_2} \frac{\mathrm{d}\xi}{(x-\xi)^2 + y^2} + \dots + \frac{v_n y}{\pi} \int\limits_{a_n}^{+\infty} \frac{\mathrm{d}\xi}{(x-\xi)^2 + y^2}$$

$$= \frac{v_0}{\pi}\left(\arctan\frac{a_1 - x}{y} + \frac{\pi}{2}\right) + \frac{v_1}{\pi}\left(\arctan\frac{a_2 - x}{y} - \arctan\frac{a_1 - x}{y}\right) + \dots$$

$$+ \frac{v_n}{\pi}\left(\frac{\pi}{2} - \arctan\frac{a_n - x}{y}\right)$$

$$= \frac{v_0 + v_n}{2} + \frac{v_0 - v_1}{\pi}\arctan\frac{a_1 - x}{y} + \frac{v_1 - v_2}{\pi}\arctan\frac{a_2 - x}{y} + \dots$$

$$+ \frac{v_{n-1} - v_n}{\pi}\arctan\frac{a_n - x}{y}.$$

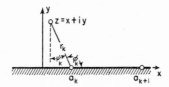

Fig. 93

As shown by Fig. 93,

$$\arctan\frac{a_k - x}{y} = \psi_k = \phi_k - \frac{\pi}{2},$$

where $\phi_k = \arg(z - a_k)$ is the angle between the vector $z - a_k$ and the positive x-axis; accordingly,

$$V(x,y) = v_n + \frac{v_0 - v_1}{\pi}\phi_1 + \ldots + \frac{v_{n-1} - v_n}{\pi}\phi_n$$

$$= v_n + \frac{v_0 - v_1}{\pi}\arg(z - a_1) + \ldots + \frac{v_{n-1} - v_n}{\pi}\arg(z - a_n). \quad (66)$$

Knowing this potential function we can easily find a complex potential $F(z)$ which is regular and has (66) as its imaginary part:

$$F(z) = v_n + \frac{v_0 - v_1}{\pi}\ln(z - a_1) + \ldots + \frac{v_{n-1} - v_n}{\pi}\ln(z - a_n). \quad (67)$$

(Here, ln denotes any regular branch of the logarithm.) By means of formula (34) of Chap. IV, we can find the vector intensity of the field:

$$\mathbf{E} = -i\,\overline{F'(z)} = -i\left\{\frac{v_0 - v_1}{\pi}\overline{\left(\frac{1}{z - a_1}\right)} + \ldots + \frac{v_{n-1} - v_n}{\pi}\overline{\left(\frac{1}{z - a_n}\right)}\right\}$$

$$= -i\left\{\frac{v_0 - v_1}{\pi}\cdot\frac{z - a_1}{|z - a_1|^2} + \ldots + \frac{v_{n-1} - v_n}{\pi}\cdot\frac{z - a_n}{|z - a_n|^2}\right\}. \quad (68)$$

Example 2. *The half-plane bordered by three electrodes* $(-\infty, -1)$, $(-1, 1)$, $(1, +\infty)$ *having the respective potentials* $2v$, v, 0. This is a particular case of the preceding problem; by formula (67) the complex potential is

$$F(z) = \frac{v}{\pi}\ln(z + 1) + \frac{v}{\pi}\ln(z - 1). \quad (69)$$

The force function for the field is

$$U = \mathrm{Re}\,F(z) = \frac{v}{\pi}\ln\{|z + 1|\cdot|z - 1|\}.$$

Thus, the lines of force are the curves

$$|z + 1|\cdot|z - 1| = C \quad (C = \mathrm{const.}).$$

These curves are lemniscates (that is, each is the locus of a point which moves so that the product of its distances from two given points ± 1 is a constant; see Exercise 12 in the Introduction and also Example 3, Art. 58). They are represented by the dotted lines in Fig. 94; the full lines represent the equipotential lines of the field.

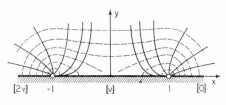

Fig. 94

Example 3. *The behaviour of the potential along the real axis is indicated by the graph in Fig. 95; it is required to find the complex potential of the field in the upper half-plane.*

Certain problems in transformer design, in which the variation of potential along the high tension winding has to be taken into account, can be reduced to problems of this type by means of conformal transformations. (In Fig. 95 the segments AB, CD of the real axis represent the earthed casing of the transformer, BO represents the low tension winding and OC represents the high tension winding.)

The given problem is solved by a direct application of Schwarz's integral formula (64):

$$F(z) = \frac{1}{\pi} \int_{-\infty}^{+\infty} V(\xi)\frac{d\xi}{\xi - z} + B$$

$$= \frac{1}{\pi} \int_{-1}^{0} v\frac{d\xi}{\xi - z} + \frac{1}{\pi} \int_{0}^{1} \{(v_2 - v_1)\xi + v_1\}\frac{d\xi}{\xi - z} + B$$

$$= \frac{v}{\pi}\ln\frac{z}{z+1} + \frac{1}{\pi}\{v_1 + (v_2 - v_1)z\}\ln\frac{z-1}{z} + \frac{v_2 - v_1}{\pi} + K.$$

The constant K is chosen so that, on the interval AB, the potential is

$$V = \operatorname{Im} F(z) = \frac{v_2 - v_1}{\pi} + K = 0$$

(on this interval, $z/(z+1) > 0$ and $(z-1)/z > 0$); the complex potential is then given by

$$F(z) = \frac{v}{\pi}\ln\frac{z}{z+1} + \frac{v_1 + (v_2 - v_1)z}{\pi}\ln\frac{z-1}{z}. \qquad (70)$$

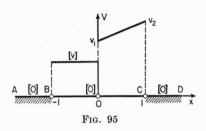

FIG. 95

Exercises

1. Evaluate

$$\int_{-i}^{i} |z|\,\mathrm{d}z$$
$$(L)$$

when L is (a) a rectilinear segment, (b) the left half of the circle $|z| = 1$, (c) the right half of the circle $|z| = 1$.

2. Evaluate

$$\oint_{(|z|=3)} \frac{2z-1}{z(z-1)}\,\mathrm{d}z.$$

3. Evaluate

$$\int_{0}^{i} z\sin z \,.\, \mathrm{d}z.$$

4. Evaluate

$$\int_{0}^{1+i} e^{\bar{z}}\,\mathrm{d}z$$
$$(L)$$

when L is the Jordan polygon with vertices at (a) $0, 1, 1+i$, (b) $0, i, 1+i$.

5. What is the geometrical meaning of the integral

$$\int_{(L)} |dz|?$$

6. Find the residue of the function $f(z) = 1/(z^2+1)$ at the point $z = i$, (a) by direct calculation, (b) by means of Cauchy's integral formula.

7. Using Cauchy's integral formula, evaluate

$$I = \oint_C \frac{\sin(\pi z/4)}{z^2-1}\, dz,$$

where C is the circle $x^2+y^2-2x = 0$.

8. Evaluate

$$I = \oint_C \frac{e^{\pi z}\, dz}{(z^2+1)^2},$$

where C is the ellipse $4x^2+y^2-2y = 0$.

9. Prove that, if $f(z)$ is regular in a bounded simply-connected domain D and continuous on $\bar{D}$, $f(z)$ *not* being identically a constant in D, then $f(z)$ vanishes at at least one point in D if $|f(z)|$ is constant on the frontier of D. Deduce that a lemniscate with n foci (that is, the locus of a point M which moves so that the product $MM_1 . MM_2 \ldots MM_n$ of its distances from n given points M_k is a constant) cannot consist of more than n components.

10. Let $f(z)$ be regular and non-constant in $|z| < R$. Let $M(r)$ denote the upper bound of $|f(z)|$ on the circle $|z| = r$ $(0 \leqslant r < R)$. Show that $M(r)$ is an increasing function of r for $0 \leqslant r < R$.

11. Under what conditions is the trinomial $u = ax^2+2bxy+cy^2$ a harmonic function (a, b, c real)?

12. The function $f(z)$ is regular and non-vanishing in the domain D. Show by direct calculation that, at each point in D,

$$\nabla^2 \ln|f(z)| = 0 \quad \text{and} \quad \nabla^2 |f(z)| > 0.$$

(∇^2 denotes Laplace's differential operator.)

13. Find the regular function $w = f(z)$ given that $f(\pi/2) = 0$ and that the real part of $f(z)$ is

$$u = \frac{\sin 2x}{\cosh 2y - \cos 2x}.$$

14. Find a function which is harmonic in $|z| < 1$ and which assumes the value 1 on the arc $\overparen{\alpha\beta}$ of the circle $|z| = 1$ and the value 0 on the complementary arc of this circle.

15. Show that the kernel of Poisson's integral for the disc $|z| < R$ is

$$\frac{R^2 - r^2}{R^2 - 2Rr\cos(\psi - \phi) + r^2} = \left| \frac{\zeta^* - z}{\zeta - z} \right|,$$

where $\zeta = R \cdot e^{i\psi}$ and ζ^* is the other end of the chord connecting the points ζ and z.

16.* Show, using the result in Exercise 15, that the integrand in Poisson's integral for the circle is

$$\frac{R^2 - r^2}{R^2 - 2Rr\cos(\psi - \phi) + r^2}\, \mathrm{d}\psi = \mathrm{d}\omega,$$

where $\omega = \arg \zeta^*$. Explain the geometrical significance of the solution of Exercise 14.

17. Prove that a function which is harmonic in the upper half-plane and assumes the value 1 on the segment ab of the real axis and vanishes at all other points on the real axis is represented at any point in this half-plane by the angle subtended by the segment ab at the point concerned.

18. Show that Schwarz's formula for the strip $-\pi/2 < y < \pi/2$ is

$$f(z) = \frac{1}{2\pi} \int\limits_{-\infty}^{+\infty} \{u_+(\xi) + u_-(\xi)\} \frac{\mathrm{d}\xi}{\cosh(\xi - z)}$$

$$- \frac{i}{2\pi}(\sinh z) \int\limits_{-\infty}^{+\infty} \{u_+(\xi) - u_-(\xi)\} \frac{\mathrm{d}\xi}{\cosh(\xi - z) \cdot \cosh \xi} ,$$

where $u_+(\xi)$ and $u_-(\xi)$ are the values of the real parts of $f(z)$ on the lines $y = +\pi/2$ and $y = -\pi/2$, respectively.

CHAPTER VI

REPRESENTATION OF REGULAR FUNCTIONS BY SERIES

58. Series in the complex domain

WE are given a sequence of complex numbers

$$a_n = \alpha_n + i\beta_n \quad (n = 0, 1, 2, \ldots)$$

from which we form the *series*

$$\sum_{n=0}^{+\infty} a_n = a_0 + a_1 + \ldots + a_n + \ldots. \tag{1}$$

We call $s_n = a_0 + a_1 + \ldots + a_n$ the *n*th *partial sum* of the series (1).

Definition. The series (1) is said to be *convergent*, if the sequence $\{s_n\}$ tends to a finite limit s as n tends to $+\infty$:

$$\lim_{n \to +\infty} s_n = s,$$

that is, given any $\epsilon > 0$ there exists an integer $N = N(\epsilon)$ such that $|s_n - s| < \epsilon$ whenever $n > N$. The number s is then called the *sum* of the series (1). If

$$\lim_{n \to +\infty} s_n$$

does not exist or is equal to ∞, we say that the series (1) *diverges*.

The following theorem enables us to reduce the study of complex series to that of real series:

THEOREM 1. *The series (1) converges if, and only if, the real series*

$$\alpha_0 + \alpha_1 + \ldots + \alpha_n + \ldots \quad \text{and} \quad \beta_0 + \beta_1 + \ldots + \beta_n + \ldots \tag{2}$$

both *converge.*

To prove this we write

$$\alpha_0 + \alpha_1 + \ldots + \alpha_n = \sigma_n, \qquad \beta_0 + \beta_1 + \ldots + \beta_n = \tau_n;$$

then, $s_n = \sigma_n + i\tau_n$ and we have

$$\lim_{n \to +\infty} s_n = \lim_{n \to +\infty} \sigma_n + i \lim_{n \to +\infty} \tau_n$$

whenever either side exists finitely. The theorem follows immediately. By means of this result it is easy to show, for example, that the nth term of any convergent series tends to zero as n tends to $+\infty$. Absolute convergence is defined as in real analysis:

Definition. The series (1) is said to be *absolutely convergent* if the series

$$|a_0| + |a_1| + \ldots + |a_n| + \ldots \tag{3}$$

converges.

We leave the reader to prove that any absolutely convergent series is convergent, and that it then has the usual properties characterizing absolutely convergent series of real terms (for example, the sum of an absolutely convergent series is not altered by an arbitrary derangement of terms).

Let us now consider the sequence $f_n(z)$ $(n = 0, 1, 2, \ldots)$ of functions of a complex variable, each function being defined in a certain domain D; from this sequence we form the series

$$\sum_{n=0}^{+\infty} f_n(z) = f_0(z) + f_1(z) + \ldots + f_n(z) + \ldots . \tag{4}$$

If the series

$$\sum_{n=0}^{+\infty} f_n(z_0)$$

converges for each z_0 in D, we say that the series (4) *converges in the domain D.* In this case its sum determines a function $F(z)$ in D.

In the theory of series certain questions arise frequently. Will $F(z)$ be continuous in D, if all the $f_n(z)$ are continuous in D? Is it possible to differentiate and integrate the function $F(z)$ by means of term by term differentiation and integration of the series (4)? As in real analysis, the answers to these questions involve the notion of uniform convergence:

Definition. We say that the series (4) is uniformly convergent to the sum $F(z)$ in the domain D if, given any $\epsilon > 0$, there exists a positive integer $N = N(\epsilon)$ (independent of z) such that, for *every* point z in D,

$$|F(z) - F_n(z)| < \epsilon \tag{5}$$

whenever $n > N$. Here we have written

$$F_n(z) = f_0(z) + f_1(z) + \ldots + f_n(z). \tag{6}$$

We emphasize that the definition refers to a set containing *several* points (in our case the set is the domain D); the idea of *uniform* convergence at a single point is of no significance.

We shall examine this definition more closely. The convergence of the series (4) at any given point z in D implies the finite existence of

$$F(z) = \lim_{n \to +\infty} F_n(z)$$

at this point: that is, given any $\epsilon > 0$, there exists a positive integer N such that the inequality (5) is satisfied at this point z whenever $n > N$. The number ϵ gives an upper bound of the error in approximating to $F(z)$ by the partial sum $F_n(z)$. As the terms in the series (4) are functions of z it may be necessary, as z ranges over D, to take a differing number of terms in order to achieve an approximation within the limits imposed by the given number ϵ. It will be clear that, in general, the least possible value of N will depend on both ϵ and z: $N = N(\epsilon, z)$.

We now suppose the positive number ϵ fixed, and consider a finite set of points $z_1, z_2, \ldots, z_k$ in D. Let the corresponding least values of N be $N_1 = N(\epsilon, z_1)$, $N_2 = N(\epsilon, z_2), \ldots, N_k = N(\epsilon, z_k)$. Then, in order to achieve the required accuracy of approximation of $F_n(z)$ to $F(z)$ at each of the points z_k simultaneously, we must take $n > N^*(\epsilon)$, where N^* denotes the greatest of the numbers $N_1, N_2, \ldots, N_k$.

If, however, we wish to guarantee the prescribed accuracy of approximation at all points of the domain D simultaneously, we encounter a new difficulty: in spite of the fact that $N(\epsilon, z)$ exists finitely at each point of D there may not exist a number $N(\epsilon)$ which exceeds all the $N(\epsilon, z)$. This difficulty arises because an infinite set of finite numbers may not be bounded above.

If, for any given $\epsilon > 0$, the set of all numbers $N(\epsilon, z)$, defined as z ranges over D, has a finite upper bound $N(\epsilon)$, we can ensure that $F_n(z)$ approximates to $F(z)$ at every point of D with an error whose modulus is less than ϵ simply by taking $n > N(\epsilon)$ for all points z in D. The series will be uniformly convergent on the set D if, and only if, this upper bound of $N(\epsilon, z)$ on D exists finitely for every given positive ϵ. In the definition above we could consider, in place of the domain D, a curve L or a closed region $\overline{D}$ or any infinite set of points S; the reader can make the appropriate restatements.

As our definition of uniform convergence is formally the same as that for real series, all the standard results for uniformly convergent series carry over unchanged to the complex domain, and we shall not stop to formulate and prove them; the most important results are those concerning continuity of the sum, termwise integration, and conditions which are sufficient for uniform convergence.

59. Weierstrass's theorem

The well-known theorem concerning termwise differentiation of series can be greatly strengthened in the complex domain. We recall that a real series

$$\sum_{n=1}^{+\infty} u_n(x)$$

of differentiable functions can be differentiated termwise on a finite interval I when

$$\sum_{n=1}^{+\infty} u_n{}'(x)$$

is uniformly convergent on this interval and

$$\sum_{n=1}^{+\infty} u_n(x)$$

is convergent for at least one point x_0 of this interval; it is easily shown that when these conditions hold the series

$$\sum_{n=1}^{+\infty} u_n(x)$$

is itself uniformly convergent on I. On the other hand, this result does not follow from the mere uniformity of convergence of

$$\sum_{n=1}^{+\infty} u_n(x)$$

on I; a simple counter-example is provided by the series

$$\sum_{n=1}^{+\infty}\left(\frac{1}{n}\sin nx\right).$$

In the complex domain, however, we have the following theorem due to Weierstrass:

THEOREM 2. *Let the series*

$$f_0(z)+f_1(z)+\ldots+f_n(z)+\ldots$$

consist of terms which are regular in some domain D, the series being convergent, with sum-function $F(z)$, in this domain. If this series is uniformly convergent on every bounded closed region $\overline{D}_1$ contained in D, then (1) *$F(z)$ is regular in D and* (2) *the derivatives $F^{(k)}(z)$ $(k = 1, 2, \ldots)$ are given at each point z in D by appropriate termwise differentiation of the original series:*

$$F^{(k)}(z) \;=\; \sum_{n=0}^{+\infty} f_n^{(k)}(z)\;,$$

the series on the right being uniformly convergent on any bounded closed region $\overline{D}_1$ contained in D.

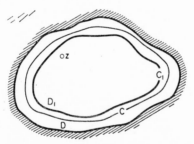

FIG. 96

First we show that $F(z)$ is regular in D. Let z be any given point of D. Let D_1, the interior domain bounded by a contour C_1, contain the point z, and let $\overline{D}_1$ be contained in D (see Fig. 96). We denote the general point on C_1 by ζ. It is easily shown that the series

$$\frac{f_0(\zeta)}{\zeta-z}+\frac{f_1(\zeta)}{\zeta-z}+\ldots+\frac{f_n(\zeta)}{\zeta-z}+\ldots$$

is uniformly convergent to $F(\zeta)/(\zeta-z)$ on C_1, and that termwise integration of this series around C_1 is permissible. Accordingly,

$$\frac{1}{2\pi i} \oint_{C_1} \frac{F(\zeta)}{\zeta-z}\,\mathrm{d}\zeta = \frac{1}{2\pi i} \oint_{C_1} \frac{f_0(\zeta)}{\zeta-z}\,\mathrm{d}\zeta + \frac{1}{2\pi i} \oint_{C_1} \frac{f_1(\zeta)}{\zeta-z}\,\mathrm{d}\zeta + \ldots$$

$$+ \frac{1}{2\pi i} \oint_{C_1} \frac{f_n(\zeta)}{\zeta-z}\,\mathrm{d}\zeta + \ldots.$$

Each $f_n(z)$ is regular in D; hence, by Cauchy's integral formula of Art. 51 and the definition of $F(z)$, we have

$$\frac{1}{2\pi i} \oint_{C_1} \frac{F(\zeta)}{\zeta-z}\,\mathrm{d}\zeta = f_0(z)+f_1(z)+ \ldots +f_n(z)+ \ldots = F(z). \qquad (7)$$

The function $F(\zeta)$ is the sum of a series which is uniformly convergent on C_1; as each term is regular, and hence continuous, on C_1, it follows that $F(\zeta)$ is continuous on C_1. Thus, the integral on the left in (7), representing $F(z)$ in D_1, is an integral of Cauchy type; it follows from the theorem in Art. 52 that $F(z)$ is regular in D_1 and, in particular, at the point z. As z was an arbitrary point in D it follows that $F(z)$ is regular in D; this gives the first part of the theorem.

To prove the second part we take any *bounded* closed region $\overline{D}_1$ in D and construct a contour C which lies in D and is such that its interior domain contains $\overline{D}_1$ (see Fig. 96). Let d be the lower bound of the distances between points of C and points of $\overline{D}_1$, let z be any given point of $\overline{D}_1$, and let ζ denote the general point on C. Then, for every integer $k \geqslant 0$, the series

$$\frac{f_0(\zeta)}{(\zeta-z)^{k+1}} + \frac{f_1(\zeta)}{(\zeta-z)^{k+1}} + \ldots + \frac{f_n(\zeta)}{(\zeta-z)^{k+1}} + \ldots$$

is uniformly convergent to $F(\zeta)/(\zeta-z)^{k+1}$ on C. Accordingly,

$$\frac{k!}{2\pi i} \oint_C \frac{F(\zeta)}{(\zeta-z)^{k+1}}\,\mathrm{d}\zeta = \frac{k!}{2\pi i} \oint_C \frac{f_0(\zeta)}{(\zeta-z)^{k+1}}\,\mathrm{d}\zeta + \frac{k!}{2\pi i} \oint_C \frac{f_1(\zeta)}{(\zeta-z)^{k+1}}\,\mathrm{d}\zeta + \ldots$$

$$+ \frac{k!}{2\pi i} \oint_C \frac{f_n(\zeta)}{(\zeta-z)^{k+1}} + \ldots;$$

it follows from the results given in Art. 53 that

$$F^{(k)}(z) = f_0^{(k)}(z) + f_1^{(k)}(z) + \ldots + f_n^{(k)}(z) + \ldots, \quad (k \geqslant 0). \qquad (8)$$

This establishes that, at any finite point z in D, the kth derivative of the sum $F(z)$ of the series (4) is given by k-fold termwise differentiation of this series. It remains to show that the series (8) is uniformly convergent on the bounded closed region $\overline{D}_1$. As the series (4) is uniformly convergent on C, then, given any $\epsilon > 0$, there exists a positive integer $N = N(\epsilon)$ such that, for all ζ on C,

$$|F(\zeta) - F_n(\zeta)| < \epsilon$$

whenever $n > N$. (Here, $F_n(\zeta)$ denotes the nth partial sum of the series (4) at the point ζ.) As $|\zeta - z| \geqslant d$ at all points ζ on C, it follows from the fundamental integral inequality of Art. 46 that, whenever $n > N$, we have

$$|F^{(k)}(z) - F_n^{(k)}(z)| = \left| \frac{k!}{2\pi i} \oint_C \frac{F(\zeta) - F_n(\zeta)}{(\zeta - z)^{k+1}} \, \mathrm{d}\zeta \right| \leqslant \frac{k!}{2\pi} \frac{\epsilon l}{\mathrm{d}^{k+1}},$$

where l is the length of C. As this inequality holds for all points of $\overline{D}_1$, and as $\epsilon_1 = (k!/2\pi)(\epsilon l/d^{k+1})$ is an arbitrary positive number, it follows that the series (8) is uniformly convergent on $\overline{D}_1$. This completes the proof of Theorem 2.

60. Power series

A *power series* is a series of the form

$$\sum_{n=0}^{+\infty} c_n(z-a)^n = c_0 + c_1(z-a) + \ldots + c_n(z-a)^n + \ldots, \qquad (9)$$

where z is a complex variable and the c_n and a are constants. The constants c_n are the *coefficients*, and a is the *centre*, of the series (9).

The fundamental result concerning power series is the following theorem:

THEOREM 3. (*Abel.*) *If the power series* (9) *converges at the point* z_0 ($\neq a$), *then it converges absolutely at each point of the disc*

$$|z-a| < |z_0-a|.$$

On every closed disc $|z-a| \leqslant q$, *where* $0 < q < |z_0-a|$, *the convergence of the series* (9) *is uniform.*

We are given that

$$\sum_{n=0}^{+\infty} c_n(z_0-a)^n$$

is convergent, so that

$$\lim_{n \to +\infty} c_n(z_0-a)^n = 0.$$

As every convergent sequence is bounded (see Art. 7), it follows that there exists a constant M such that $|c_n(z_0-a)^n| \leqslant M$ for all n. Thus, for all points of the closed disc $|z-a| \leqslant q$, we have

$$|c_n(z-a)^n| = |c_n(z_0-a)^n| \cdot \left| \frac{z-a}{z_0-a} \right|^n \leqslant M \left(\frac{q}{|z_0-a|} \right)^n.$$

Accordingly, for $|z-a| \leqslant q < |z_0-a|$, each term of (9) has modulus not exceeding the corresponding term of a geometric series of positive terms whose common ratio is $q/(|z_0-a|) < 1$. As this geometric series is then convergent, it follows from Weierstrass's M-test that the series (9) is both absolutely and uniformly convergent on the closed disc $|z-a| \leqslant q$. As q is any positive number less than $|z_0-a|$, it will be clear that the series (9) is absolutely convergent at every point of the open disc $|z-a| < |z_0-a|$. This completes the proof of our theorem.

COROLLARY. *If the series (9) diverges at the point $z = z_0$ then it also diverges at any point z for which $|z-a| > |z_0-a|$.*

For, suppose, if possible, that the series (9) converges at a point z' such that $|z'-a| > |z_0-a|$; then, by Theorem 3, this series would converge at the point z_0; this contradicts our hypothesis.

Example 1. *The geometric series*

$$1 + z + z^2 + \ldots + z^n + \ldots$$

converges absolutely in the disc $|z| < 1$. On every closed disc $|z| \leqslant q$, where $0 < q < 1$, it converges uniformly. For $|z| \geqslant 1$ the series diverges.

The result follows immediately from Theorem 3, since the series converges for all real $z = q$ where $0 \leqslant q < 1$ and diverges for $z = q > 1$. For $|z| = 1$ the series diverges, since its nth term does not then tend to zero as $n \to +\infty$.

It is left to the reader to prove that, for $|z| < 1$, the sum of the series is $1/(1-z)$.

Example 2. *The power series*

$$1 + z + 2!z^2 + \ldots + n!z^n + \ldots$$

is convergent at $z = 0$ and divergent at all other points. For, if z is any positive number,

$$\lim_{n \to +\infty} \frac{(n+1)!z^{n+1}}{n!z^n} = \lim_{n \to +\infty} (n+1)z = +\infty,$$

and it follows from D'Alembert's ratio test for series of positive terms that the given series is then divergent. By the above corollary it will be clear that the series diverges for all complex non-zero values of z.

Example 3. The power series

$$1 + z + \frac{z^2}{2!} + \ldots + \frac{z^n}{n!} + \ldots$$

is absolutely convergent for *all* finite z; this is easily proved by D'Alembert's ratio test.

Let us consider the general power series (9). There are three possibilities: (1) the series converges at its centre only; (2) the series converges for all finite z; and (3) the series converges for some values of z and diverges for other values of z. The examples given above illustrate all three cases. We examine the third case more closely. Let the series (9) converge at the point z_1 ($\neq a$) and diverge at the point z_2. By the above theorem and its corollary, the series then converges for all z such that $|z-a| < |z_1-a| = R_1$, and diverges for all z such that $|z-a| > |z_2-a| = R_2$; it will be clear that $R_1 \leqslant R_2$. If $R_1 = R_2$ we denote the common value of these quantities by R; then, the series (9) converges in the disc $|z-a| < R$ and diverges in $|z-a| > R$.

If $R_1 < R_2$, we consider the point $z_3 = a + R_3$, where

$$R_3 = \tfrac{1}{2}(R_1 + R_2)$$

(Fig. 97). Then, if the series (9) converges for $z = z_3$, it will be convergent in the disc $|z-a| < R_3$; if, on the other hand, it diverges at z_3 then it will diverge whenever $|z-a| > R_3$. In either case, the width of the annulus in which the convergence of the series is indeterminate has been halved. Continuing in this way we establish the existence of a positive number R ($R_1 \leqslant R \leqslant R_2$) such that the series (9) converges in the disc $|z-a| < R$ and diverges whenever

$|z-a| > R$; the question of the convergence of the series (9) on the circle $|z-a| = R$ remains open. This number R is called the *radius of convergence* of the series (9); the circle $|z-a| = R$ is called the *circle of convergence* of the series and $|z-a| < R$ is the *domain of convergence*.

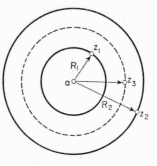

Fig. 97

In order to include the other cases, we shall consider that in case (1) the radius of convergence is $R = 0$, the circle of convergence being a degenerate point-circle; in the second case we write $R = +\infty$, the domain of convergence being the whole finite plane.

The above results are expressed in the following theorem:

THEOREM 4. *Every power series* (9) *has a definite radius of convergence* R *which is finite or* $+\infty$ $(0 \leqslant R \leqslant +\infty)$.

By Theorem 3, the series (9) is uniformly convergent on the closed disc $|z-a| \leqslant R'$ whenever $0 < R' < R$. (We suppose $R > 0$.) It follows from Weierstrass's theorem of Art. 59 that the function $f(z)$ defined in $|z-a| < R$ by

$$f(z) = c_0 + c_1(z-a) + c_2(z-a)^2 + \ldots + c_n(z-a)^n + \ldots \qquad (10)$$

is regular in $|z-a| < R$ and that, at all points of this domain,

$$\left.\begin{array}{l} f^{(1)}(z) = c_1 + 2c_2(z-a) + \ldots + nc_n(z-a)^{n-1} + \ldots, \\[4pt] f^{(2)}(z) = 2c_2 + 3 \cdot 2 \cdot c_3\,(z-a) + \ldots + n(n-1)c_n(z-a)^{n-2} + \ldots, \\[4pt] \cdot\ \cdot \\[4pt] f^{(n)}(z) = n!\,c_n + \dfrac{(n+1)!}{1!}c_{n+1}(z-a) + \dfrac{(n+2)!}{2!}c_{n+2}(z-a)^2 + \ldots, \\[4pt] \cdot\ \cdot \end{array}\right\} \qquad (11)$$

Putting $z = a$ in (10) and (11), we get

$$c_0 = f(a), \quad c_1 = f^{(1)}(a), \quad c_2 = \frac{f^{(2)}(a)}{2!}, \ldots, \quad c_n = \frac{f^{(n)}(a)}{n!}, \ldots, \qquad (12)$$

so that (10) can be written

$$f(z) = f(a) + \frac{f^{(1)}(a)}{1!}(z-a) + \frac{f^{(2)}(a)}{2!}(z-a)^2 + \ldots$$
$$+ \frac{f^{(n)}(a)}{n!}(z-a)^n + \ldots . \qquad (13)$$

The power series written in this form is called the *Taylor series* of the function $f(z)$ about the point $z = a$. We express this result as

THEOREM 5. *If the power series* (9) *has radius of convergence $R > 0$, its sum $f(z)$ is regular in the domain of convergence $|z-a| < R$ and the series* (9) *is the Taylor series of $f(z)$ about $z = a$.* On the basis of this result we can assert that if $f(z)$ can be shown in any way to be represented in a neighbourhood of some point $z = a$ by a series of powers of $(z-a)$, then this series is the Taylor series for $f(z)$ about $z = a$.

61. Representation of regular functions by Taylor series

Suppose $f(z)$ is regular for $|z-a| < R$ ($0 < R \leqslant +\infty$). Choose R_1, R_2 such that $0 < R_1 < R_2 < R$, and let C be the circle

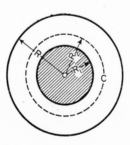

FIG. 98

$|z-a| = R_2$ (Fig. 98). By Cauchy's integral formula (Art. 51) we have

$$f(z) = \frac{1}{2\pi i} \oint_C \frac{f(\zeta)}{\zeta - z} \, d\zeta$$

for all points z of the disc $|z-a| < R_2$; thus, for such z we have

$$f(z) = \frac{1}{2\pi i} \oint_C \frac{f(\zeta) \cdot d\zeta}{(\zeta-a)-(z-a)} = \frac{1}{2\pi i} \oint_C \frac{f(\zeta)}{\zeta-a} \cdot \frac{d\zeta}{1-\left(\dfrac{z-a}{\zeta-a}\right)} . \qquad (14)$$

We may suppose R_1 chosen so that the point z lies in the disc $|z-a| < R_1$; then, as the point ζ lies on C, we have

$$\left|\frac{z-a}{\zeta-a}\right| < \frac{R_1}{R_2} < 1.$$

It follows that the series

$$1+\left(\frac{z-a}{\zeta-a}\right)+\left(\frac{z-a}{\zeta-a}\right)^2+ \ldots +\left(\frac{z-a}{\zeta-a}\right)^n + \ldots$$

is uniformly convergent on C, with sum $1/\{1-[(z-a)/(\zeta-a)]\}$, whenever $|z-a| < R_1$. Accordingly, by (14), we have, for any given z in $|z-a| < R_1$,

$$f(z) = \frac{1}{2\pi i} \oint_C \frac{f(\zeta)\, d\zeta}{\zeta-a} + \frac{(z-a)}{2\pi i} \oint_C \frac{f(\zeta)\, d\zeta}{(\zeta-a)^2} + \ldots$$

$$+ \frac{(z-a)^n}{2\pi i} \oint_C \frac{f(\zeta)\, d\zeta}{(\zeta-a)^{n+1}} + \ldots ; \qquad (15)$$

this gives the expansion of $f(z)$ in a series of powers of $(z-a)$, the coefficients being

$$c_n = \frac{1}{2\pi i} \oint_C \frac{f(\zeta)\, d\zeta}{(\zeta-a)^{n+1}} \quad (n = 0, 1, 2, \ldots). \qquad (16)$$

Using formula (38) of Art. 52 for the derivatives of a regular function we see that the series (15) is the Taylor series for $f(z)$ about the point $z = a$:

$$f(z) = f(a)+f^{(1)}(a) \cdot (z-a)+ \ldots +\frac{f^{(n)}(a)}{n!}(z-a)^n + \ldots ; \qquad (13)$$

it will be clear that (16) is the *integral formula for the Taylor coefficients*.

As the number R_1 in the above discussion can be taken as any positive number less than R it follows that the expansion (13) holds for all points z of the disc $|z-a| < R$. Moreover, we may suppose the value chosen for R to be the greatest value such that $f(z)$ is regular in $|z-a| < R$ ($0 < R \leqslant +\infty$). This result is expressed in the following theorem.

THEOREM 6.   *Any function $f(z)$ which is regular at the point a can be represented in some neighbourhood of a by the Taylor series (13). This series converges in the largest open disc $|z-a| < R$, centred on a, in which $f(z)$ is regular. (If $R = +\infty$, the "disc" is interpreted as the whole finite plane.)*

Remark. The function $f(z)$ in this theorem cannot be regular at all points of the circle $|z-a| = R$. (We suppose R finite.) For, in the contrary case, each point ζ of this circle would be the centre of some neighbourhood $|z-\zeta| < r_\zeta$ in which $f(z)$ is regular. It can then be shown that there exists a finite positive r which does not exceed the value of r_ζ for any point ζ on the circle $|z-a| = R$; from this it would follow that $f(z)$ is regular in the disc

$$|z-a| < R+r,$$

so that the series (13) would be convergent for $|z-a| < R+r$, contradicting the definition of R in the theorem.

If the point a is such that $f(z)$ is not regular at a while every neighbourhood of a contains points at which $f(z)$ is regular, we shall call a a *singular point* or *singularity* of the function $f(z)$ (see Art. 48).

We see immediately that a function $f(z)$ which is regular at the point a can be represented by the Taylor series (13) in the disc whose centre is at a and whose boundary passes through that singularity of $f(z)$ which is closest to a.

Theorems 5 and 6 show that the definition, given in Art. 14, of regularity of the function $f(z)$ at the point a is equivalent to the following definition: $f(z)$ is said to be *regular at the point a* if in some neighbourhood of a it can be represented by the Taylor series (13). From this definition it would be possible to deduce all the properties of regular functions.

In conclusion we give the Taylor expansions of certain regular functions about $z = 0$. The expansions

$$e^z = 1 + z + \frac{z^2}{2!} + \ldots + \frac{z^n}{n!} + \ldots ; \tag{17}$$

$$\left.\begin{aligned}
\sin z &= z - \frac{z^3}{3!} + \frac{z^5}{5!} - \ldots + (-1)^n \frac{z^{2n+1}}{(2n+1)!} + \ldots; \\[2mm]
\cos z &= 1 - \frac{z^2}{2!} + \ldots + (-1)^n \frac{z^{2n}}{(2n)!} + \ldots;
\end{aligned}\right\} \quad (18)$$

$$\left.\begin{aligned}
\sinh z &= z + \frac{z^3}{3!} + \frac{z^5}{5!} + \ldots + \frac{z^{2n+1}}{(2n+1)!} + \ldots; \\[2mm]
\cosh z &= 1 + \frac{z^2}{2!} + \frac{z^4}{4!} + \ldots + \frac{z^{2n}}{(2n)!} + \ldots;
\end{aligned}\right\} \quad (19)$$

hold for all finite z and the functions thus represented are regular in the whole of the finite plane. The logarithmic function $\mathrm{Ln}(1+z)$ has a regular branch in any simply-connected sub-domain of $0 < |z+1| < +\infty$; the principal branch $\ln(1+z)$ is regular in $|z| < 1$ and is represented in this unit disc by the Taylor series

$$\ln(1+z) = z - \frac{z^2}{2} + \frac{z^3}{3} - \ldots + (-1)^{n-1}\frac{z^n}{n} + \ldots. \quad (20)$$

The general power is defined with the help of the logarithmic function (see Art. 32); it can be shown that, if m is any complex number, the principal branch of $(1+z)^m$ is represented in $|z| < 1$ by the series

$$(1+z)^m = 1 + mz + \frac{m(m-1)}{2!}z^2 + \ldots$$

$$+ \frac{m(m-1)\ldots(m-n+1)}{n!}z^n + \ldots. \quad (21)$$

In general, this expansion holds only in $|z| < 1$, the function $(1+z)^m$ being regular at $z = -1$ if, and only if, m is a positive integer or zero (in which case the series in (21) contains only a finite number of terms).

The expansions (17) to (21) follow directly from Taylor's formula (13) when we take $a = 0$. They are the same as the corresponding expansions obtained in real analysis; Taylor's formula and the formulae for the derivatives of the elementary functions are formally the same in the complex domain as in the real domain.

62. The zeros of a regular function. The uniqueness theorem

Definition. If $f(a) = 0$ we call the point $z = a$ a *zero* of the function $f(z)$.

Suppose $f(z)$ is regular at $z = a$, where $f(a) = 0$ and $f(z)$ is not identically zero in any neighbourhood of $z = a$. Then, all the coefficients of the Taylor expansion of $f(z)$ about the point $z = a$ cannot vanish: for, otherwise, we would have $f(z) \equiv 0$ in some neighbourhood of a, contradicting our hypothesis. Accordingly, this expansion is of the form

$$f(z) = c_n(z-a)^n + c_{n+1}(z-a)^{n+1} + \ldots, \tag{22}$$

where $c_n \neq 0$ and $n \geqslant 1$; the number n appearing in (22) is called the *order of the zero of $f(z)$* at $z = a$.

Recalling the formulae (12) we see that *the order of this zero at $z = a$ is that of the lowest-order non-vanishing derivative $f^{(n)}(a)$ at this point.*

From (22) it follows that if $f(z)$ has a zero of order n at a then $f(z)$ is represented in some neighbourhood of a by

$$f(z) = (z-a)^n \phi(z), \tag{23}$$

where

$$\phi(z) = c_n + c_{n+1}(z-a) + \ldots, \qquad \phi(a) = c_n \neq 0.$$

The function $\phi(z)$ is continuous at the point a since the power series defining it is convergent in a neighbourhood of a. (The regularity of $\phi(z)$ at $z = a$ follows from the same reason.) We have

$$\lim_{z \to a} \phi(z) = \phi(a).$$

By hypothesis, $\phi(a) = c_n \neq 0$; thus, in some neighbourhood of a, $\phi(z) \neq 0$. To prove this, let us take $\epsilon = \frac{1}{2}|c_n|$; then, as $\phi(z)$ is continuous at a, there exists a $\delta > 0$ such that $|\phi(z) - c_n| < \frac{1}{2}|c_n|$ whenever $|z - a| < \delta$, so that, for such z,

$$|\phi(z)| \geqslant |c_n| - |\phi(z) - c_n| > \tfrac{1}{2}|c_n| > 0.$$

(If $\phi(z)$ were to vanish at some point of $|z-a| < \delta$ the inequality $|\phi(z) - c_n| < \frac{1}{2}|c_n|$ would not hold at this point.)

Thus by (23) we have the following result:

THEOREM 7. *Let the function $f(z)$ be regular at the point a and not identically equal to zero in any neighbourhood of a. Then, if a*

17

is a zero of $f(z)$, there exists a neighbourhood of this point in which $f(z)$ does not have other zeros.

From Theorem 7 we have the following:

COROLLARY. *If* (1) *$f(z)$ is regular at the point a and* (2) *$f(z)$ has a zero at each point a_n of a sequence of distinct points converging to a, then $f(z) \equiv 0$ in some neighbourhood of the point a.*

For, by the continuity of $f(z)$ at the point a, we have

$$f(a) = \lim_{n \to +\infty} f(a_n) = 0;$$

thus, a is a zero of $f(z)$. Accordingly, the supposition that $f(z) \not\equiv 0$ in some neighbourhood of a contradicts the result stated in Theorem 7.

The following important result is also deduced from Theorem 7:

THEOREM 8. (*The uniqueness theorem.*) *If the functions $f_1(z)$ and $f_2(z)$ are regular in a domain D and $f_1(a_n) = f_2(a_n)$ at each point a_n of a sequence of distinct points converging to some point a in D, then $f_1(z) \equiv f_2(z)$ in D.*

To prove this we consider the function $f(z) = f_1(z) - f_2(z)$. This is regular in D and has each point a_n as a zero ($n = 1, 2, \ldots$). It then follows from the corollary to Theorem 7 that $f(z)$ is identically zero in some neighbourhood of the point a. We wish to show that $f(z) \equiv 0$ in D. Let ζ be any point in D. We take L to be any rectifiable Jordan arc connecting a to ζ in D. As the set L is bounded and closed and consists of interior points of D, it can be shown that there exists a $\delta > 0$ such that D contains the disc $|z - b| < 2\delta$ whenever b lies on L. We take points $a = z_0, z_1, \ldots, z_{n-1}, z_n = \zeta$ in order on L so that each sub-arc $\overparen{z_{r-1}z_r}$ is of length less than δ; the disc $|z - z_r| < 2\delta$ is denoted by D_r ($r = 0, 1, \ldots, n$). We have shown that $f(z) \equiv 0$ in D_0; as D_0 contains z_1 it follows that $f(z) \equiv 0$ in some neighbourhood of z_1, so that $f(z) \equiv 0$ in D_1. Continuing in this way we show that $f(z)$ vanishes identically in D_2, in D_3, and, finally, in D_{n-1}. As D_{n-1} contains $z_n = \zeta$, it follows that $f(\zeta) = 0$. Accordingly, $f_1(\zeta) = f_2(\zeta)$; as ζ was an arbitrary point of D, the result follows.

Remark. From Theorem 8 it follows that a function which is regular in a domain D is completely determined in D by its values at a sequence $\{a_n\}$ of distinct points converging to a point a in D. In general, however, no such function can be constructed for a given, arbitrary set of values at the points a_n: for example, suppose $a_n = 1/n$ $(a = 0)$ and that

$$f(a_n) = \begin{cases} 0 \text{ for } n \text{ even,} \\ 1 \text{ for } n \text{ odd}; \end{cases}$$

no function exists which is regular at $z = 0$ and assumes the prescribed values at the points a_n, for it will be clear that $f(z)$ cannot be continuous at $z = 0$. The general problem of constructing a function when its values are given at a set of distinct points is the subject of the theory of interpolation.

63. Analytic continuation. Analytic functions

Let the domains D_1 and D_2 have a common part containing the domain Δ. (If the intersection of D_1 and D_2 consists of two or more component domains, such as Δ and Δ' in Fig. 99b, we consider any one of them.) We suppose $f_1(z)$ regular in D_1 and $f_2(z)$ regular in D_2.

Definition. If the functions $f_1(z)$ and $f_2(z)$ are identically equal in the common domain Δ we call $f_2(z)$ the (direct) analytical continuation of $f_1(z)$ into D_2 through the domain Δ.

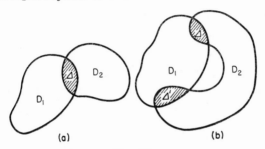

FIG. 99

For given domains D_1, D_2 (so that Δ is determined) the analytic continuation of $f_1(z)$ into D_2 through Δ is defined uniquely. For, if $f_2^{(a)}(z)$ and $f_2^{(b)}(z)$ denote two *such* continuations of $f_1(z)$ into D_2 then these functions must be identically equal in the sub-domain Δ of D_2; it would then follow from the identity theorem of the preceding article that the two continuations are identical in the whole of D_2. However, if the intersection of D_1 and D_2 consists of two or more component domains, as in Fig. 99b, then it is possible that the function defined in D_2 by continuing $f_1(z)$ into D_2 through a different component Δ' of the intersection of D_1 and D_2 may differ from the function $f_2(z)$ obtained by continuation through the original component Δ. We illustrate this later by an example based on the logarithmic function.

We now consider a given chain of domains $D_1, D_2, \ldots, D_n$ such that, for $k = 1, 2, \ldots, n-1$, the domains D_k and D_{k+1} overlap in the common sub-domain Δ_k. Let $f_k(z)$ be regular in D_k $(k = 1, 2, \ldots, n)$.

Definition. If, for $k = 1, 2, \ldots, n-1$, the functions $f_k(z)$ and $f_{k+1}(z)$ are identically equal in Δ_k, we call $f_n(z)$ the analytic continuation of $f_1(z)$ into D_n through the chain of domains $\{D_k\}$ and the associated chain $\{\Delta_k\}$.

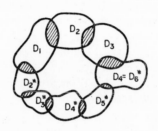

FIG. 100

We note that, in this context, for given chains $\{D_k\}$ and $\{\Delta_k\}$ the analytic continuation $f_n(z)$ of $f_1(z)$ into the domain D_n is determined uniquely. However, if we change the intermediate links of the chain $\{D_k\}$ (Fig. 100) or even change any member of the associated chain $\{\Delta_k\}$, we may arrive at a different function. It may also happen that the last link of the chain $\{D_k\}$ coincides with the first (for example, we could, in Fig. 100, consider the chain D_1, D_2, D_3, D_4, D_5^*, D_4^*, D_3^*, D_2^*, D_1); the function obtained by analytic continuation along this chain is not necessarily identical with the original function $f_1(z)$.

We shall illustrate with the following example. Let D_1 be the disc $|z-1| < \frac{1}{2}$, and suppose

$$f_1(z) = \int_{\substack{1 \\ (L)}}^{z} \frac{\mathrm{d}z}{z},$$

where L is a path connecting the points 1 and z in this disc; then,

$$f_1(z) = \ln z = \ln|z| + i \arg z,$$

where $\arg z$ denotes the usual principal branch of $\text{Arg } z$; in the upper half-disc $\arg z$ is positive and in the lower half-disc it is negative. Let D_2 and D_2^* be domains as represented in Fig. 101, and let D_3 denote their common part. The analytic continuations of $f_1(z) = \ln z$ into the domains D_2 and D_2^* are obviously given by the functions

$$f_2(z) = \int_{\substack{1 \\ (L_2)}}^{z} \frac{dz}{z} \quad \text{and} \quad f_2^*(z) = \int_{\substack{1 \\ (L_2^*)}}^{z} \frac{dz}{z};$$

here, L_2 connects the point 1 with the general point z in D_2 and lies in the union of D_2 and D_1, and L_2^* connects the point 1 with

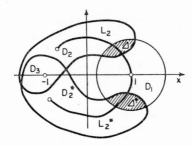

Fig. 101

the general point z in D_2^* and lies in the union of D_2^* and D_1. It will be clear that the function $f_2(z)$ defined in D_2 is equal to

$$\ln|z| + i \arg z$$

where $\arg$ now denotes a branch taking values in, say, the interval $(-\pi/2, 3\pi/2]$; and that the function $f_2^*(z)$ defined in D_2^* equals $\ln|z| + i \arg^* z$, where $\arg^*$ denotes a branch of $\text{Arg } z$ taking values in, say, the interval $(-3\pi/2, \pi/2]$. In the domain D_3 these functions define different analytic continuations of $f_1(z) = \ln z$: for example, $f_2(-1) = i\pi$ but $f_2^*(-1) = -i\pi$. Thus, the analytic continuation may depend on the choice of the chain of domains.

This same example enables us to illustrate the other remarks made above. Let the domain D consist of the points of D_2 and D_2^*; then, the intersection of D with D_1 consists of two disjoint domains Δ and Δ^* (Fig. 101). The direct analytic continuation of $f_1(z) = \ln z$ from the domain D_1 into D by way of Δ differs from the continuation into D by way of Δ^*; the first of these is represented in D by $\ln |z| + i \arg z$ where we now take $0 < \arg z < 2\pi$, and the second is given in D by $\ln |z| + i \arg^*z$ where $-2\pi < \arg^*z < 0$. Finally, we consider the analytic continuation of the function $f_1(z)$ from the domain D_1 into the same domain D_1, by way of the chain D_1, D_2, D_2^*, D_1: it will be clear that the function thus obtained differs from $f_1(z)$ by the additive constant $2\pi i$.

The process of analytic continuation leads to the concept of the general analytic function; this concept has been mentioned earlier (see, e.g. Arts. 25, 30). We suppose a function $f_2(z)$ in a domain D_2 to be the direct analytic continuation of a function $f_1(z)$ in D_1. (It is implicit that each function is regular in its domain of definition and that the domains D_1 and D_2 overlap.) Considering the domain D which is the union of D_1 and D_2 we define a function in D by

$$f(z) = \begin{cases} f_1(z) \text{ if } z \text{ lies in } D_1, \\ \\ f_2(z) \text{ if } z \text{ lies in } D_2. \end{cases}$$

If the intersection of the domains D_1, D_2 consists of a single domain then it follows from what has been said above that $f(z)$ is single-valued and regular in D. However, if this intersection consists of two or more (disjoint) domains, then the function $f_1(z)$ may have several different continuations $f_2(z)$ into D_2; in this case the function $f(z)$ may be many-valued at points of D. In all these cases we call $f(z)$ an analytic function in D.

In the more general case of the continuation of $f_1(z)$ into D_n by way of the chain D_1, D_2, . . ., D_n (and the associated chain Δ_1, Δ_2, . . ., Δ_{n-1}) we shall also consider the function $f(z)$ defined in the union D of D_1, D_2, . . ., D_n so that one of its values at the point z is given by $f(z) = f_k(z)$ if z lies in D_k ($k = 1, 2, . . ., n$).

Definition. The function $f(z)$ obtained in the domain D by any process of analytic continuation of a regular function is called an *analytic* function in the domain D.

As indicated above, this function may be single-valued or many-valued. In the first case it will be a regular function in the domain D. We shall adopt the convention that a single domain is a chain consisting of a single link; on this basis we may say that any function which is regular in some domain is analytic in this domain.

Definition. Let $f(z)$ be a regular (single-valued) function given in some domain D. Let us carry out all possible analytic continuations of this function by all possible chains of domains in the z-plane; it will be clear that the union Δ of all the domains into which $f(z)$ can be continued is itself a domain. The function $F(z)$ defined in Δ so that each of its values at any point z in Δ is the value at z of any continuation of $f(z)$ into a domain containing z is called a *complete analytic function*; in general, $F(z)$ will be many-valued (even infinitely many-valued) in Δ. The regular functions defined in various domains of the plane by continuations of $f(z)$ are called *regular branches* of $F(z)$ in these domains.

We note that each of the elementary functions discussed in Chap. III is analytic in its domain of definition.

An elegant method of constructing analytic functions which is very simple in principle is that due to Weierstrass. This method is based on the concept of a *regular element* of an analytic function, a regular element being defined as any power series

$$f(z) = \sum_{n=0}^{+\infty} c_n(z-a)^n$$

having a finite non-zero radius of convergence r. As $f(z)$ is regular in the disc $|z-a| < r$ it follows that $f(z)$ can be represented in a neighbourhood of any point a_1 of this open disc by a Taylor series

$$f_1(z) = \sum_{n=0}^{+\infty} \frac{f^{(n)}(a_1)}{n!}(z-a_1)^n.$$

This series obviously converges in the open disc whose centre is the point a_1 and whose boundary circle touches the circle $|z-a| = r$ internally; it may happen that the series converges in a larger disc centred at a_1. In the latter case the sum $f_1(z)$ will give the analytic continuation of $f(z)$ into a domain extending beyond the disc $|z-a| < r$, since $f_1(z) \equiv f(z)$ in the domain (shown shaded in Fig. 102) which is the intersection of the discs in which the series are convergent. For points of the open disc whose centre is at a_1 and whose boundary touches the circle $|z-a| = r$ internally, this equality follows directly from the definition of the function $f_1(z)$; for all other points of this shaded domain the equality of $f_1(z)$ and $f(z)$ follows from the uniqueness theorem.

This process of analytic continuation by means of power series can, in the general case, be carried on indefinitely: at each stage a point at which the current function (element) is regular is chosen as the centre for the succeeding Taylor expansion giving the next regular element. In this way, given an initial regular element, we arrive at a complete analytic function $F(z)$; in general, $F(z)$ is multi-valued and each of its elements defines a regular branch of $F(z)$ in the open disc in which the corresponding Taylor series converges (the branch concerned is, of course, given by the sum of the Taylor series in this disc).

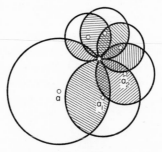

Fig. 102

In the remainder of this article we give a brief descriptive treatment of the nature of the singularities of an analytic function. Each Taylor expansion defining a regular element $f(z)$ of a complete analytic function converges in some ϵ-neighbourhood of the centre (a, say) of the expansion; we may suppose ϵ allowed to increase until the circle $|z-a| = \epsilon$ passes through a singularity of $f(z)$ (see Art. 61); it will be clear from the identity theorem that $f(z)$ cannot be continued into any neighbourhood containing this singularity. Thus, the frontier of the domain into which it is possible to continue any given regular element (*the domain of existence* of the corresponding complete analytic function) consists entirely of the singular points of the regular elements occurring in the construction. This boundary may consist of closed curves (called *natural boundaries*) together with open arcs (*cuts*) and isolated points.

With the simplest analytic functions, the boundaries of their domains of existence consist of isolated (singular) points. These isolated singular points are divided into those of *single-valued* and *many-valued* types, according as whether the function is single-valued or many-valued in a sufficiently small deleted neighbourhood of the point concerned. Thus, for example, the point $z = 0$ is a singular point of single-valued type for the function $1/z$. The nature of such singularities is examined more closely in Art. 65 and later parts of the book.

As illustrations of singular points of many-valued type we may consider the behaviour, in a deleted neighbourhood of $z = 0$, of the functions $\sqrt[n]{z}$ and Ln z: with the first, the derivative does not exist at the origin; the second has an infinite discontinuity at $z = 0$. Such points are also called *branch points*.

Finally, we note that, for a complete analytic function, the chains of overlapping discs appearing in its construction (each disc being the domain of convergence of one of its regular elements) can be used to construct a Riemann surface on which this function will be single-valued: if, in the construction, a chain of overlapping discs is such that some "link" D_q encroaches on a link D_p appearing two or more stages earlier in the chain, we may consider D_q as lying on a different sheet to that containing D_p. We shall not go more deeply into the problem of constructing the Riemann surface support for the general analytic function and shall merely advise the reader to revise the account in Chap. III of the Riemann surfaces supporting the functions $\sqrt[n]{z}$ and Ln z.

64. Laurent series

Suppose $f(z)$ regular in the annulus K defined by $r < |z-a| < R$ $(0 \leqslant r < R \leqslant +\infty)$. We construct the annular domains K', K'' defined by $r' < |z-a| < R'$, $r'' < |z-a| < R''$, where

$$r < r' < r'' < R'' < R' < R,$$

so that K contains $\overline{K}'$ and K' contains $\overline{K}''$ (Fig. 103). As $f(z)$ is regular on $\overline{K}'$ it is represented in K' by the Cauchy integral formula

$$f(z) = \frac{1}{2\pi i} \oint_{C_{R'}} \frac{f(\zeta) \cdot d\zeta}{\zeta - z} - \frac{1}{2\pi i} \oint_{C_{r'}} \frac{f(\zeta) \cdot d\zeta}{\zeta - z}, \qquad (24)$$

where $C_{R'}$ and $C_{r'}$ denote circles, of the respective radii R' and r' with centres at the point a (see Art. 51). We suppose that the point z lies in the annulus K''. Then, for all points ζ on $C_{R'}$,

$$\left| \frac{z-a}{\zeta-a} \right| < \frac{R''}{R'} = q_1 < 1;$$

accordingly, the fraction $1/(\zeta-z)$ appearing in the integrand of the first integral in (24) can be expanded as a geometric series which is uniformly convergent with respect to ζ on the circle $C_{R'}$:

$$\frac{1}{\zeta-z} = \left(\frac{1}{\zeta-a}\right)\Big/\left\{1 - \frac{z-a}{\zeta-a}\right\}$$

$$= \frac{1}{\zeta-a} + \frac{z-a}{(\zeta-a)^2} + \ldots + \frac{(z-a)^n}{(\zeta-a)^{n+1}} + \ldots .$$

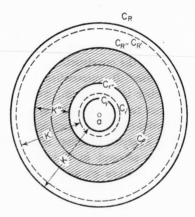

Fig. 103

Substituting this expansion in the integral concerned and integrating termwise (see Art. 61) we have

$$f_1(z) = \frac{1}{2\pi i} \oint_{C_{R'}} \frac{f(\zeta) . d\zeta}{(\zeta-z)}$$

$$= c_0 + c_1(z-a) + c_2(z-a)^2 + \ldots + c_n(z-a)^n + \ldots, \tag{25}$$

where

$$c_n = \frac{1}{2\pi i} \oint_{C_{R'}} \frac{f(\zeta) . d\zeta}{(\zeta-a)^{n+1}} \quad (n = 0, 1, 2, \ldots). \tag{26}$$

We note that, in general, it is not possible to represent the coefficient c_n in the form $[f^{(n)}(a)/n!]$ as in Art. 61, since $f(z)$ is not regular at $z = a$.

For ζ on $C_{r'}$ we have $|(\zeta-a)/(z-a)| < r'/r'' = q_2 < 1$; accordingly, the fraction $1/(\zeta-z)$ appearing in the second integral in (24) can be expanded as a geometric series which is uniformly convergent with respect to ζ on $C_{r'}$:

$$\frac{1}{\zeta-z} = -\left(\frac{1}{z-a}\right)\Big/\left\{1 - \frac{\zeta-a}{z-a}\right\}$$

$$= -\frac{1}{z-a} - \frac{\zeta-a}{(z-a)^2} - \frac{(\zeta-a)^2}{(z-a)^3} - \ldots - \frac{(\zeta-a)^{n-1}}{(z-a)^n} - \ldots .$$

Substituting this expansion in the second integral in (24) and integrating termwise we get

$$f_2(z) = -\frac{1}{2\pi i} \oint_{C_{r'}} \frac{f(\zeta) . \, d\zeta}{\zeta-z}$$

$$= \frac{c_{-1}}{z-a} + \frac{c_{-2}}{(z-a)^2} + \ldots + \frac{c_{-n}}{(z-a)^n} + \ldots, \tag{27}$$

where

$$c_{-n} = \frac{1}{2\pi i} \oint_{C_{r'}} f(\zeta) . \, (\zeta-a)^{n-1} \, d\zeta \quad (n = 1,2,3,\ldots). \tag{28}$$

Let us now replace the index $-n$, running through the values $+1$, $+2$, $\ldots$, in formulae (27) and (28) by the index n, running through the values -1, -2, $\ldots$. Then by (24), (25), and (27) we have

$$f(z) = f_1(z) + f_2(z) = \sum_{n=0}^{+\infty} c_n(z-a)^n + \sum_{n=-1}^{-\infty} \frac{c_n}{(z-a)^{-n}}$$

$$= \sum_{n=-\infty}^{+\infty} c_n(z-a)^n. \tag{29}$$

Moreover, by the result expressed in (13) of Art. 47, the path of integration in formulae (26) and (28) can be changed to any concentric circle C_ρ lying in the annulus K''. Accordingly, if we replace

n by $-n$ in (28), as above, formulae (26) and (28) can be expressed by the single formula

$$c_n = \frac{1}{2\pi i} \oint_{C_\rho} \frac{f(\zeta) \cdot d\zeta}{(\zeta-a)^{n+1}} \quad (n = 0, \pm 1, \pm 2, \ldots). \tag{30}$$

Finally, we note that, as the radii r'' and R'' can be chosen arbitrarily close to r and R $(r < r'' < R'' < R)$, and as, by (30), the coefficients c_n do not depend on the particular choice of these radii, the expansion (29) holds throughout the whole of the (open) annulus K.

Definition. The series (29) in which the coefficients c_n are defined by formula (30) is called the *Laurent series* of the function $f(z)$ in the annulus K. The series (25) and (27), the one consisting of non-negative powers of $(z-a)$ the other of negative powers of $(z-a)$, are termed the *regular* and *principal* parts, respectively, of $f(z)$ in K.

The regular part of this Laurent series is

$$f_1(z) = \sum_{n=0}^{+\infty} c_n(z-a)^n; \tag{25}$$

it is an ordinary power series. As it is convergent in the annulus K it follows that it will be convergent in the whole of the disc $|z-a| < R$. If, now we suppose R to increase, this last statement will certainly continue to hold until the circle $|z-a| = R$ passes through a singularity of $f(z)$.

The principal part of the Laurent series is

$$f_2(z) = \sum_{n=1}^{+\infty} \frac{c_{-n}}{(z-a)^n}; \tag{27}$$

it is a power series in $Z = 1/(z-a)$. By hypothesis, this series converges in the annulus $1/R < |Z| < 1/r$. Accordingly, it will be convergent in the whole of the disc $|Z| < 1/r$; that is, the series (27) will be convergent in the domain $|z-a| > r$. If, now, we suppose the radius r to decrease, this statement will certainly continue to hold until the circle $|z-a| = r$ passes through a singular point of $f(z)$.

Thus, the annulus K of convergence of the Laurent series (29) can be taken as the maximal annular domain, of the form

$$r < |z-a| < R,$$

in which the function $f(z)$ is regular; in the general case,

$$0 < r < R < +\infty,$$

and $f(z)$ will be regular in K but will have at least one singularity on each of the boundary circles $|z-a| = r$ and $|z-a| = R$. The domain K can degenerate into a disc from which the centre has been removed (it is then given by $0 < |z-a| < R$), or into the exterior of a circle $|z-a| = r$ (we usually suppose the point ∞ removed, so that K is then given by $r < |z-a| < +\infty$).

From the above discussion it will be clear that each of the series (25) and (27) is both absolutely and uniformly convergent on any closed annular region $r' \leqslant |z-a| \leqslant R'$ contained in K; with the obvious definition of convergence for the doubly-infinite series (29) it follows that the same comment holds for this series also.

The results obtained above can be formulated in the following theorem:

THEOREM 9. *Every function $f(z)$ which is regular in the annulus K defined by $r < |z-a| < R$ can be represented in this annulus by its Laurent series*

$$f(z) = \sum_{n=-\infty}^{+\infty} c_n(z-a)^n; \qquad (29)$$

here, the c_n are given by the formula (30) ($r < \rho < R$) and K may be taken as the maximal annulus, of this form, in which $f(z)$ is regular. The regular part of the Laurent series converges at all points of the disc $|z-a| < R$, and the principal part converges at all points of the domain $|z-a| > r$. The convergence of the Laurent series is uniform on any closed annular region $r' \leqslant |z-a| \leqslant R'$ contained in K.

Remark. From formula (30), using the fundamental integral inequality of Art. 46, we deduce the inequalities

$$|c_n| = \left| \frac{1}{2\pi i} \oint_{C_\rho} \frac{f(\zeta) \cdot d\zeta}{(\zeta-a)^{n+1}} \right| \leqslant \frac{M \cdot 2\pi\rho}{2\pi \cdot \rho^{n+1}} = \frac{M}{\rho^n} \quad (n = 0, \pm 1, \pm 2, \ldots)$$

where M is the upper bound of $|f(z)|$ on the circle C_ρ defined by $|z-a| = \rho$ $(r < \rho < R)$. The inequalities obtained,

$$|c_n| \leqslant \frac{M}{\rho^n} \quad (n = 0, \pm 1, \pm 2, \ldots), \tag{31}$$

are called *Cauchy's inequalities for the Laurent series* (29).

Now let there be given an arbitrary series, arranged in positive and negative powers of $(z-a)$:

$$\sum_{k=-\infty}^{+\infty} c_k(z-a)^k.$$

From the above it follows that, in general, the part of this series consisting of the non-negative powers is convergent in some disc $|z-a| < R$ and the part consisting of the negative powers is convergent in some domain $|z-a| > r$. If $r < R$ the double series will converge uniformly on any closed region contained in the annulus K defined by $r < |z-a| < R$. Assuming these conditions satisfied, let $f(z)$ denote the sum of the double series in the annulus K; it follows from Weierstrass's theorem of Art. 59 that $f(z)$ is regular in K. Let C_ρ be the circle $|z-a| = \rho$ lying in K $(r < \rho < R)$; then, on C_ρ,

$$\frac{f(\zeta)}{(\zeta-a)^{n+1}} = \sum_{k=-\infty}^{+\infty} c_k(\zeta-a)^{k-n-1},$$

where the series on the right is uniformly convergent on this circle. Accordingly the integral around C_ρ of the function on the left-hand side is given by termwise integration of this series. By formula (31) of Art. 50 it follows that the only non-zero contribution arising from the integration of the terms is that corresponding to the term for which $k-n-1 = -1$; that is, to the term for which $k = n$. Accordingly,

$$\oint_{C_\rho} \frac{f(\zeta) \cdot \mathrm{d}\zeta}{(\zeta-a)^{n+1}} = 2\pi i c_n.$$

Thus we have the following result:

THEOREM 10. *An arbitrary series of the form*

$$\sum_{k=-\infty}^{+\infty} c_k(z-a)^k$$

which is convergent, with sum $f(z)$, in an annulus $r < |z-a| < R$ is, in this annulus, the Laurent series of its sum $f(z)$.

It follows from Theorem 10 that if we can, in any way, expand a function in an appropriate annular domain as a series of powers (negative and non-negative) of $(z-a)$, then this expansion is the Laurent series representing the function in this annulus.

Example. The function

$$f(z) = \frac{1}{(z-1)(z-2)}$$

is regular in the "rings": I, $|z| < 1$; II, $1 < |z| < 2$; III, $2 < |z|$, (Fig. 104).

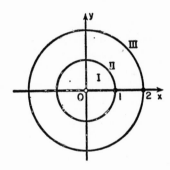

Fig. 104

In order to obtain its Laurent expansion we put

$$f(z) = \frac{1}{z-2} - \frac{1}{z-1}.$$

In the "ring" I (that is, for $|z| < 1$) the fractions are expanded as convergent geometrical series:

$$\left.\begin{array}{l}\dfrac{1}{z-2} = -\dfrac{1}{2} \cdot \dfrac{1}{1-(z/2)} = -\dfrac{1}{2}\left(1 + \dfrac{z}{2} + \dfrac{z^2}{4} + \ldots\right), \\[3mm] \dfrac{1}{z-1} = -\dfrac{1}{1-z} = -(1 + z + z^2 + \ldots),\end{array}\right\} \quad (32)$$

and the Laurent series of the function $f(z)$ becomes an ordinary power series

$$f(z) = -\frac{1}{2}\left(1 + \frac{z}{2} + \frac{z^2}{4} + \ldots\right) + (1 + z + z^2 + \ldots)$$

$$= \frac{1}{2} + \frac{3}{4}z + \frac{7}{8}z^2 + \ldots \quad . \tag{33}$$

This result is quite understandable, for the point $z = 0$ is not a singular point of $f(z)$.

In the annulus II $(1 < |z| < 2)$ the first of the expansions (32) continues to represent $1/(z-2)$ but the second must be replaced by

$$\frac{1}{z-1} = \frac{1}{z} \cdot \frac{1}{1 - (1/z)} = \frac{1}{z}\left(1 + \frac{1}{z} + \frac{1}{z^2} + \ldots\right),$$

the series on the right being convergent whenever $|z| > 1$. Accordingly, the Laurent expansion of $f(z)$ in the annulus II is given by

$$f(z) = -\frac{1}{2}\left(1 + \frac{z}{2} + \frac{z^2}{4} + \ldots\right) - \left(\frac{1}{z} + \frac{1}{z^2} + \frac{1}{z^3} + \ldots\right).$$

In the "annulus" III the last expansion for $1/(z-1)$ continues to hold but the first of the expansions (32) must now be replaced by

$$\frac{1}{z-2} = \frac{1}{z} \cdot \frac{1}{1 - (2/z)} = \frac{1}{z}\left(1 + \frac{2}{z} + \frac{4}{z^2} + \ldots\right).$$

Thus, the Laurent expansion of $f(z)$ in the "annulus" III is given by

$$f(z) = \left(\frac{1}{z} + \frac{2}{z^2} + \frac{4}{z^3} + \ldots\right) - \left(\frac{1}{z} + \frac{1}{z^2} + \frac{1}{z^3} + \ldots\right) = \frac{1}{z^2} + \frac{3}{z^3} + \ldots$$

We now indicate the connexion between Laurent series and Fourier series; it is assumed that the reader has already met Fourier series elsewhere in his mathematics courses. Let the function $f(z)$ be regular in an arbitrarily narrow annulus given by $1 - \epsilon < |z| < 1 + \epsilon$, $(0 < \epsilon < 1)$; in this annulus $f(z)$ can be represented by the Laurent series

$$f(z) = \sum_{n=-\infty}^{+\infty} c_n z^n,$$

where

$$c_n = \frac{1}{2\pi i} \oint_{(|\zeta|=1)} \frac{f(\zeta) \cdot d\zeta}{\zeta^{n+1}}$$

$$= \frac{1}{2\pi} \int_0^{2\pi} f(e^{i\theta}) \cdot e^{-in\theta} \, d\theta \quad (n = 0, \pm 1, \pm 2, \ldots).$$

In particular, at the points $z = e^{it}$ on the unit circle, $f(z)$ is represented by

$$F(t) = f(e^{it}) = \sum_{n=-\infty}^{+\infty} c_n e^{int}, \tag{34}$$

where

$$c_n = \frac{1}{2\pi} \int_0^{2\pi} F(\theta) \cdot e^{-in\theta} \, d\theta \quad (n = 0, \pm 1, \pm 2, \ldots). \tag{35}$$

The series (34) whose coefficients are given by (35) is the *complex form* of the *Fourier series* of the function $F(t)$. For, this series can be rewritten in the form

$$F(t) = c_0 + \sum_{n=1}^{+\infty} (c_n e^{int} + c_{-n} e^{-int})$$

$$= \frac{a_0}{2} + \sum_{n=1}^{+\infty} (a_n \cos nt + b_n \sin nt). \tag{36}$$

In obtaining this last form we have put $c_0 = \frac{1}{2}a_0$, applied Euler's formula, and written $c_n + c_{-n} = a_n$, $i(c_n - c_{-n}) = b_n$. It follows from (35) that the coefficients a_n and b_n are given by

$$a_0 = 2c_0 = \frac{1}{\pi} \int_0^{2\pi} F(\theta) \, d\theta, \qquad a_n = c_n + c_{-n} = \frac{1}{\pi} \int_0^{2\pi} F(\theta) \cos n\theta \, d\theta,$$

$$b_n = \frac{c_{-n} - c_n}{i} = \frac{1}{\pi} \int_0^{2\pi} F(\theta) \sin n\theta \, d\theta \quad (n = 1, 2, \ldots).$$

Thus the a_n and b_n are the usual Fourier coefficients of the function $F(t)$, and we have established that, *on the unit circle $z = e^{it}$, the Laurent series, considered as a function of the real variable t, is the Fourier series of the function $F(t) = f(e^{it})$.*

In real analysis it is shown that any real function satisfying appropriate conditions (for example, the so-called Dirichlet conditions) in the interval $0 \leqslant t \leqslant 2\pi$ can be represented in this interval by a Fourier series of the form (36). From this it follows that any complex function $F(t) = u(t) + iv(t)$, where u and v satisfy the requisite conditions can also be represented by a Fourier series in $[0, 2\pi]$. Carrying out the above transformations in the reverse sense we obtain this series in the complex form (34). Thus, *the complex form of Fourier's series holds whenever the real form does.* In the general case, however, when $F(t)$ can be represented on $0 \leqslant t \leqslant 2\pi$ by a Fourier expansion, the function $f(z)$ which is such that $f(e^{it}) \equiv F(t)$ for $0 \leqslant t \leqslant 2\pi$ is not regular at all points of $|z| = 1$ and the series

$$\sum_{n=-\infty}^{+\infty} c_n z^n,$$

where

$$c_n = \frac{1}{2\pi} \int_0^{2\pi} F(\theta) \cdot e^{-in\theta}\, d\theta \quad (n = 0, \pm 1, \pm 2, \ldots)$$

will not converge for $|z| > 1$.

65. Isolated singularities

Definition. If $f(z)$ is regular for $0 < |z - a| < R$ but is not regular at $z = a$ we say that $f(z)$ has an *isolated singularity* at $z = a$. (As $f(z)$ is regular in $0 < |z - a| < R$, it will be clear that in this case the singularity at a is of *single-valued* type. In this article we shall not consider singularities of multi-valued type.)

It follows from the Remark in the preceding article that in this case the function $f(z)$ can be represented by the Laurent series (29) in $0 < |z - a| < R$, this "annulus" being a deleted neighbourhood of the singular point a. Here R may be taken as the distance from a to the nearest other singularity of $f(z)$; the regular part of the series converges in $|z - a| < R$ and the principal part is convergent for all z other than $z = a$.

Taking $n = -1$ in formula (30) for the coefficients of the Laurent series, we get

$$c_{-1} = \frac{1}{2\pi i} \oint_{C_\rho} f(\zeta)\,d\zeta \qquad (37)$$

where C_ρ is the circle $|z - a| = \rho$ $(0 < \rho < R)$. Recalling the definition of a residue in Art. 48 we obtain the following important result:

THEOREM 11. *The residue of the function $f(z)$ at an isolated singularity a is equal to the coefficient of $(z-a)^{-1}$ in the Laurent expansion of $f(z)$ in a deleted neighbourhood of the point a.*

This theorem will find frequent application in the following chapter.

Isolated singularities are divided into three types according to the behaviour of the function in a deleted neighbourhood of the point concerned:

Definition. An isolated singularity a of the function $f(z)$ is said to be

(a) *a removable singularity*, if $\lim_{z \to a} f(z)$ exists finitely;

(b) *a pole*, if $\lim_{z \to a} f(z) = \infty$;

or

(c) *an essential singularity* if $f(z)$ does not tend to a limit (finite or infinite) as $z \to a$.

We shall discuss each of these types in greater detail and establish criteria by which they may be distinguished.

66. Removable singularities

From the above definition it follows that, if a is a removable singularity, the function $f(z)$ is bounded in some deleted neighbourhood of this point, since $f(z)$ tends to a finite limit as $z \to a$ (see Art. 12). Suppose $|f(z)| \leqslant M$ for $0 < |z - a| < \epsilon$; then, by Cauchy's inequalities (31),

$$|c_n| \leqslant \frac{M}{\rho^n} = M\rho^{-n}$$

whenever $0 < \rho < \epsilon$. Letting ρ tend to $+0$ we see that c_n vanishes for all negative integers n. Accordingly, the Laurent expansion of $f(z)$ in some deleted neighbourhood of a does not contain a principal part; thus, in this neighbourhood,

$$f(z) = c_0 + c_1(z-a) + c_2(z-a)^2 + \ldots + c_n(z-a)^n + \ldots . \quad (38)$$

Conversely, if the Laurent expansion of $f(z)$ in some deleted neighbourhood of $z = a$ does not contain a principal part, then $f(z)$ can be represented in this neighbourhood as in equation (38) and $f(z)$ tends to the finite limit c_0 as $z \to a$; thus, a is a removable singularity. We express these results as

THEOREM 12. *In order that the isolated singularity a of the function $f(z)$ should be removable, it is necessary and sufficient that the Laurent expansion of $f(z)$ in some deleted neighbourhood of a should not contain a principal part: that is,*

$$f(z) = c_0 + c_1(z-a) + c_2(z-a)^2 + \ldots + c_n(z-a)^n + \ldots$$

for $0 < |z-a| <$ some positive ϵ.

Remark 1. If equation (38) holds at the point $z = a$ also (that is, $f(a) = c_0$) then $f(z)$ is regular in some disc $|z-a| < R$, being given in this disc by the sum of the power series (38) (see Art. 61). By hypothesis, a is a singularity of $f(z)$, so that either $f(a)$ is not defined or $f(a) \neq c_0$. We can "remove" this singularity, simply by putting $f(a) = c_0$. This explains the terminology used to describe a singularity of this type.

Remark 2. If a is a removable singularity for the function $f(z)$, then $f(z)$ is bounded in some deleted neighbourhood of a. In proving Theorem 12 we have, in effect, established the following converse of this result: *if the function $f(z)$ is bounded in some deleted neighbourhood of an isolated singularity a, then a is a removable singularity for the function $f(z)$.*

Example. The function

$$f(z) = \frac{\sin z}{z}$$

is not defined for $z = 0$. For $z \neq 0$ it is represented by the series

$$\frac{\sin z}{z} = \frac{1}{z}\left(z - \frac{z^3}{3!} + \frac{z^5}{5!} - \ldots\right) = 1 - \frac{z^2}{3!} + \frac{z^4}{5!} - \ldots \ .$$

Thus $z = 0$ is a removable singularity for $f(z) = (\sin z)/z$. It is clear that

$$\lim_{z \to 0} \frac{\sin z}{z} = 1.$$

Thus, if we define $f(0)$ to be 1, the function $f(z)$ will be regular at $z = 0$ also.

Finally, we note that, by Theorem 11 of Art. 65, *the residue of* $f(z)$ *at a removable singularity is equal to zero.*

67. Poles

If $z = a$ is a pole of the function $f(z)$, it follows that, given any $M > 0$, there exists a deleted neighbourhood of a in which $|f(z)| > M$; thus $f(z)$ cannot vanish in this neighbourhood. It follows that the function $g(z) = 1/f(z)$ is regular in this same deleted neighbourhood; clearly,

$$\lim_{z \to a} g(z) = 0$$

so that $g(z)$ has a removable singularity at a. Let us put $g(a) = 0$; then, $g(z)$ is regular in some disc $|z-a| < R$ and has no zero in this disc other than the point a itself. Conversely, if the point a is a zero of a function $g(z)$ which is regular at a and is not identically zero, then (by the uniqueness theorem of Art. 62) there is some deleted neighbourhood $0 < |z-a| < R$ of this point in which $g(z)$ is regular and non-vanishing. It will be clear that the function $f(z) = 1/g(z)$ is regular for $0 < |z-a| < R$ and has a pole at $z = a$. Thus we have the following result:

THEOREM 13. *A function* $f(z)$ *which is defined in some deleted neighbourhood of* $z = a$ *has a pole at* $z = a$ *if, and only if, the function* $g(z) = 1/f(z)$ *is regular at* a *and* $g(a) = 0$ *while* $g(z) \not\equiv 0$. (*In establishing the necessity of this condition we suppose* $g(z)$ *defined by continuity at* a, *so that*

$$g(a) = \lim_{z \to a} g(z) = 0.)$$

Definition. If $f(z)$ has a pole at $z = a$, we define the *order* of this pole to be the order of the *zero* of the function $g(z) = 1/f(z)$ at $z = a$. (Here, again, we suppose $g(z)$ defined by continuity at $z = a$, so that $g(a) = 0$.)

Let $f(z)$ have a pole of order m at $z = a$. Then, by Theorem 13 and the result stated in Art. 62, the function $g(z)$ is given in some neighbourhood of $z = a$ by

$$g(z) = 1/f(z) = c_m(z-a)^m + c_{m+1}(z-a)^{m+1} + \ldots$$
$$= (z-a)^m \phi(z),$$

where $\phi(z)$ is regular in this neighbourhood and $\phi(a) = c_m \neq 0$. Thus, in some deleted neighbourhood $0 < |z-a| < R$ of the point a,

$$f(z) = \frac{1}{(z-a)^m} \cdot \frac{1}{\phi(z)} = \frac{1}{(z-a)^m}\{b_0 + b_1(z-a) + b_2(z-a)^2 + \ldots\};$$

for, the function $1/\phi(z)$ is regular at the point a and hence can be represented in a neighbourhood of this point by a Taylor series (here, $b_0 = 1/\phi(a) = 1/c_m \neq 0$). Changing the notation for the coefficients we can write the last expansion in the form

$$f(z) = \frac{c_{-m}}{(z-a)^m} + \frac{c_{-m+1}}{(z-a)^{m-1}} + \ldots + \frac{c_{-1}}{z-a} + \sum_{n=0}^{+\infty} c_n(z-a)^n, \qquad (39)$$

where $c_{-m} = b_0 \neq 0$. Thus, the principal part of the Laurent expansion of the function $f(z)$ in a deleted neighbourhood of a pole contains only a finite number of terms. Now suppose $f(z)$ has an isolated singularity at a and that its Laurent expansion in some deleted neighbourhood of a has a principal part consisting of only a finite (positive) number of terms; then $f(z)$ is represented in this deleted neighbourhood by an expansion of the form (39). Multiplying equation (39) by $(z-a)^m$ we obtain the function

$$\phi(z) = (z-a)^m f(z) = c_{-m} + c_{-m+1}(z-a) + c_{-m+2}(z-a)^2 + \ldots;$$

we define $\phi(z)$ to be equal to c_{-m} at $z = a$ so that $\phi(z)$ is regular at a. Clearly, the coefficient c_{-m} in (39) is non-zero; accordingly,

$$\lim_{z \to a} f(z) = \lim_{z \to a} \frac{\phi(z)}{(z-a)^m} = \infty,$$

so that a is a pole of $f(z)$. In some neighbourhood of a we have

$$\frac{1}{f(z)} = (z-a)^m \frac{1}{\phi(z)} = (z-a)^m\{b_{-m}+b_{-m+1}(z-a)+\ldots\},$$

where $b_{-m} = 1/c_{-m} \neq 0$; thus, $f(z)$ has a pole of order m at $z = a$. We express these results as

THEOREM 14. *If $f(z)$ has an isolated singularity at the point $z = a$, then this singularity will be a pole if, and only if, the principal part of the Laurent expansion of $f(z)$ in some deleted neighbourhood of a contains only a finite (positive) number of terms; if*

$$f(z) = \frac{c_{-m}}{(z-a)^m} + \frac{c_{-m+1}}{(z-a)^{m-1}} + \ldots + \frac{c_{-1}}{(z-a)} + \sum_{n=0}^{+\infty} c_n(z-a)^n, \quad (39)$$

for $0 < |z-a| < \epsilon$, where ϵ is some positive number, and $c_{-m} \neq 0$, then $f(z)$ has a pole of order m at a $(m \geqslant 1)$.

Theorems 13 and 14 provide convenient criteria for determining whether an isolated singularity is a pole.

Example. The function

$$f(z) = \frac{(z-1)(z-2)}{(z^2+1)(z+3)^3}$$

has three poles: two, at $z = \pm i$, are of the first order, and the third, at $z = -3$, is of the third order; the function $1/f(z)$, supposed defined by continuity at $z = i, -i, 3$, has first-order zeros at $z = \pm i$ and a third-order zero at $z = -3$.

We now give a brief discussion of the significance, in plane fluid flow, of a pole of the complex potential. The complex potential of the field formed by superposing the fields of a vortex of strength Γ and a source of strength Q, both situated at a point a (a "vortex source"), is

$$\Phi(z) = \frac{Q-i\Gamma}{2\pi} \text{Ln}(z-a)$$

(see Examples 2 and 3, Art. 39, and Exercise 4 of Chapter IV).

Thus, the logarithmic branch point at $z = a$ for a complex potential $\Phi(z) = (q/2\pi)\mathrm{Ln}(z-a)$ corresponds to a vortex source of "strength" $q = Q - i\Gamma$ (see Art. 63). We now consider two vortex sources of strengths $q' = p_2/h$ and $q'' = -p_2/h$ situated at the respective points $z_1 = a - h$ and $z_2 = a$. The limiting field obtained by combining the fields of these two vortex sources and letting $h \to 0$ (p_2 being kept constant) is called the field of a *dipole with (complex) moment* p_2. The complex potential for this field is

$$\Phi_2(z) = \lim_{h \to 0} \left\{ \frac{p_2}{2\pi h} \mathrm{Ln}(z-a+h) - \frac{p_2}{2\pi h} \mathrm{Ln}(z-a) \right\}$$

$$= \frac{p_2}{2\pi} \lim_{h \to 0} \frac{\mathrm{Ln}(z-a+h) - \mathrm{Ln}(z-a)}{h} = \frac{p_2}{2\pi} \cdot \frac{1}{z-a} \; ;$$

this has a pole of first order at $z = a$.

In exactly the same way we may consider the limiting field obtained from the combination of two dipoles with moments $p_2' = p_4/h$ and $p_2'' = -p_4/h$ situated at the respective points $z_1 = a - h$ and $z_2 = a$. This gives the field of a *quadrupole* (p_4 is a constant); its complex potential is

$$\Phi_4(z) = \lim_{h \to 0} \left\{ \frac{p_4}{2\pi h} \cdot \frac{1}{z-a+h} - \frac{p_4}{2\pi h} \cdot \frac{1}{z-a} \right\}$$

$$= \frac{p_4}{2\pi} \lim_{h \to 0} \frac{1}{h} \left\{ \frac{1}{z-a+h} - \frac{1}{z-a} \right\} = -\frac{p_4}{2\pi} \cdot \frac{1}{(z-a)^2}$$

and has a pole of second order at $z = a$. In general, the complex potential of the field of a *multipole* of multiplicity $2m$, obtained by a limiting process from the combination of two multipoles of multiplicity $2(m-1)$, is

$$\Phi_{2m}(z) = (-1)^{m-1} \frac{p_{2m} \cdot (m-1)!}{2\pi} \cdot \frac{1}{(z-a)^m} \quad (p_{2m} = \text{const.});$$

this has *a pole of order m at $z = a$.* We call p_{2m} the *moment* of this multipole.

Conversely, if a complex potential $\Phi(z)$ has a pole of order m at $z = a$ we may suppose the principal part of this potential at $z = a$ to be the field of a suitable set of multipoles located at this point; no member of this set has a multiplicity exceeding $2m$ and the moments of the component multipoles are determined by the coefficients in the principal part of the Laurent expansion of $\Phi(z)$ in some deleted neighbourhood of $z = a$.

Finally, we state a formula which enables us to determine the residue of the function $f(z)$ at a pole $z = a$. In some deleted neighbourhood of $z = a$ (supposing this pole to be of order m) we have, by (39),

$$(z-a)^m f(z) = c_{-m} + c_{-m+1}(z-a) + \ldots + c_{-1}(z-a)^{m-1} +$$
$$c_0(z-a)^m + \ldots .$$

To find c_{-1} we differentiate the last relation $(m-1)$ times:

$$\frac{\mathrm{d}^{m-1}}{\mathrm{d}z^{m-1}}\{(z-a)^m f(z)\} = (m-1)!c_{-1} + m(m-1)\ldots 3 . 2(z-a) + \ldots .$$

Letting $z \to a$ in this result we see that *the residue c_{-1} of $f(z)$ at a pole of order m is given by*

$$c_{-1} = \frac{1}{(m-1)!} \lim_{z \to a} \left[\frac{\mathrm{d}^{m-1}}{\mathrm{d}z^{m-1}}\{(z-a)^m . f(z)\} \right]. \tag{40}$$

(We cannot substitute $z = a$ in the preceding result since $f(a) = \infty$.) In particular, if $f(z)$ has a *pole of first order* at $z = a$, the corresponding residue is

$$c_{-1} = \lim_{z \to a} [(z-a) . f(z)]. \tag{41}$$

Let the function $f(z)$ be defined in some deleted neighbourhood of a as the quotient of two regular functions:

$$f(z) = \frac{\phi(z)}{\psi(z)};$$

here, we suppose $\phi(a) \neq 0$, $\psi(a) = 0$, $\psi'(a) \neq 0$. From the above it follows that $f(z)$ has a pole of the first order at $z = a$. For, by (41), we have

$$c_{-1} = \lim_{z \to a} \left[(z-a)\frac{\phi(z)}{\psi(z)} \right] = \phi(a) \lim_{z \to a} \frac{1}{\left\{\dfrac{\psi(z)-\psi(a)}{z-a}\right\}} = \frac{\phi(a)}{\psi'(a)}; \tag{42}$$

this follows from the standard results on limits and the fact that, by hypothesis, $\psi'(a) \neq 0$. Formula (42) is often very useful in the determination of residues at poles of the first order.

Example. The function

$$f(z) = \frac{1}{\sin z^2}$$

has a pole of the second order at the point $z_0 = 0$ and poles of the first order at the points $z_k = \pm \sqrt{(k\pi)}$, $(k = \pm 1, \pm 2, \ldots)$: for, writing $g(z) = \sin z^2$, we have $g(z_k) = 0$, $g'(z_k) = 2z_k \cos z_k^2 \neq 0$ for $k \neq 0$, and $g'(z_0) = 0$, $g''(z_0) \neq 0$. The residues at the points z_k $(k \neq 0)$ are given by formula (42):

$$c_{-1}^{(k)} = \frac{1}{g'(z_k)} = \frac{1}{2z_k \cos z_k^2} = \frac{(-1)^k}{2z_k};$$

the residue at the point $z_0 = 0$ is given by formula (40):

$$c_{-1}^{(0)} = \lim_{z \to 0} \left[\frac{\mathrm{d}}{\mathrm{d}z}\left(\frac{z^2}{\sin z^2} \right) \right] = \lim_{z \to 0} \frac{2z \sin z^2 - 2z^3 \cos z^2}{(\sin z^2)^2}$$

$$= \lim_{z \to 0} \frac{2z[z^2 - (z^6/3!) + \ldots] - 2z^3[1 - (z^4/2!) + \ldots]}{[z^2 - (z^6/3!) + \ldots]^2}$$

$$= \lim_{z \to 0} \frac{\frac{2}{3}z^7 + \ldots}{z^4 + \ldots} = 0.$$

The last result can be deduced directly from the fact that $f(z)$ is a regular function of z^2 in $0 < |z| < \sqrt{\pi}$ so that its Laurent expansion in this domain contains only even powers of z.

68. Essential singularities

By definition, if $f(z)$ has an (isolated) essential singularity at $z = a$ then $f(z)$ does not tend to a limit (finite or infinite) as $z \to a$. In this case it can be shown that there exist at least two sequences $\{z_n'\}$, $\{z_n''\}$ $(z_n' \neq a \neq z_n'')$, each converging to a, such that the corresponding sequences $\{f(z_n')\}$, $\{f(z_n'')\}$ tend to different limits as $n \to +\infty$. A rather sharper result is the following:

THEOREM 15. (Sokhotsky.) *If $f(z)$ has an (isolated) essential singularity at $z = a$, then, given any complex number (finite or infinite), there exists a sequence of points $\{z_n\}$ which converges to a and is such that*

$$\lim_{n \to +\infty} f(z_n) = A.$$

We shall prove this result first for $A = \infty$. The function $f(z)$ cannot be bounded in any deleted neighbourhood of a; for, by the result expressed in Remark 2 in Art. 66 the point a would then be a removable singularity. Thus, given any positive integer n, a point z_n can be found in the neighbourhood $0 < |z-a| < 1/n$ such that $|f(z_n)| > n$. It will be clear that

$$\lim_{n \to +\infty} z_n = a$$

and

$$\lim_{n \to +\infty} f(z_n) = \infty.$$

Accordingly, the theorem is proved for the case $A = \infty$.

Now suppose A is finite. Then either (i) there exists a point z_n in *every* deleted neighbourhood $0 < |z-a| < 1/n$ $(n = 1, 2, \ldots)$ such that $f(z_n) = A$, or (ii) there exists some positive integer N such that $f(z) \neq A$, and $f(z)$ is regular, for *all* points z in

$$0 < |z-a| < \frac{1}{N}.$$

In case (i) the result we are seeking to prove follows immediately, for the sequence $\{z_n\}$ then satisfies the required conditions. In case (ii) the function

$$g(z) = \frac{1}{f(z)-A}$$

is regular in $0 < |z-a| < 1/N$. The point $z = a$ must be an isolated *essential* singularity of the function $g(z)$. For, otherwise,

$$\lim_{z \to a} g(z)$$

would exist, finitely or infinitely, and this would imply the existence (finite or infinite) of

$$\lim_{z \to a} f(z) = \lim_{z \to a} \left[A + \frac{1}{g(z)} \right],$$

contradicting the hypothesis that $z = a$ is an essential singularity of $f(z)$. Accordingly, as shown in the first part of the proof, there exists a sequence of points $\{z_n\}$ $(z_n \neq a)$ such that $z_n \to a$ and

$g(z_n) \to \infty$ as $n \to +\infty$; for this sequence it will be clear that

$$\lim_{n\to+\infty} f(z_n) = A + \lim_{n\to+\infty} \{1/g(z)\} = A.$$

This completes the proof.

Remark. The real function $y = \sin(1/x)$ has a similar property in any deleted neighbourhood of $x = 0$. Thus, taking $x_n = (1/n\pi)$, we have

$$\lim_{n\to+\infty} \sin\frac{1}{x_n} = \lim_{n\to+\infty} \sin n\pi = 0;$$

and taking $x_n = 2/[(4n+1)\pi]$, we have

$$\lim_{n\to+\infty} \sin\frac{1}{x_n} = \lim_{n\to+\infty} \sin(4n+1)\frac{\pi}{2} = 1.$$

Given any number A in the interval $[-1, 1]$ we can find a real sequence $\{x_n\}$ such that $x_n \to 0$ and $\sin(1/x_n) \to A$ as $n \to +\infty$. The above theorem (given by Weierstrass) shows that we can make the sequence $\{\sin(1/z_n)\}$ tend to *any* complex number A as $n \to +\infty$ by choosing an appropriate sequence of points $\{z_n\}$ converging to zero.

If $f(z)$ has an isolated singularity at a, it follows from Theorems 12 and 14 that this singularity will be a removable singularity or a pole if the principal part of the Laurent expansion of $f(z)$ in some deleted neighbourhood of $z = a$ is zero or contains only a finite number of non-zero terms. Accordingly, we have the following result:

THEOREM 16. *If $f(z)$ has an isolated singularity at $z = a$ then this point will be an essential singularity if, and only if, the principal part of the Laurent expansion of $f(z)$ in some deleted ϵ-neighbourhood of a contains an infinite number of terms; that is,*

$$f(z) = \sum_{n=1}^{+\infty} \frac{c_{-n}}{(z-a)^n} + \sum_{n=0}^{+\infty} c_n(z-a)^n \tag{43}$$

for $0 < |z-a| < \epsilon$, where $c_{-n} \neq 0$ for infinitely many (positive) values of n.

Finally we note that the residue of the function $f(z)$ at an (isolated) essential singularity $z = a$ is the coefficient c_{-1} in the expansion (43).

Example 1. The function

$$f(z) = e^{1/z}$$

has an essential singularity at $z = 0$ and is regular for all other z. Even for real x,

$$\lim_{x \to 0} e^{1/x}$$

does not exist: we have

$$\lim_{x \to -0} e^{1/x} = 0, \qquad \lim_{x \to +0} e^{1/x} = +\infty.$$

The Laurent expansion holding for $|z| > 0$ is

$$e^{1/z} = 1 + \frac{1}{z} + \frac{1}{2!z^2} + \ldots + \frac{1}{n!z^n} + \ldots;$$

this is obtained by writing $1/z$ instead of z in equation (17) of Art. 61. Thus,

$$\operatorname{res} f(0) = 1.$$

Example 2. The function

$$f(z) = e^{a(z-z^{-1})/2} \quad (0 < |z| < +\infty),$$

where a is a non-zero complex constant, also has an essential singularity at $z = 0$. We have

$$f(z) = e^{az/2} \cdot e^{-a/(2z)}$$

$$= \left\{ 1 + \frac{a}{2}z + \frac{1}{2!}\left(\frac{a}{2}\right)^2 z^2 + \frac{1}{3!}\left(\frac{a}{2}\right)^3 z^3 + \frac{1}{4!}\left(\frac{a}{2}\right)^4 z^4 + \ldots \right\}$$

$$\times \left\{ 1 - \frac{a}{2} \cdot \frac{1}{z} + \frac{1}{2!}\left(\frac{a}{2}\right)^2 \frac{1}{z^2} - \frac{1}{3!}\left(\frac{a}{2}\right)^3 \frac{1}{z^3} + \frac{1}{4!}\left(\frac{a}{2}\right)^4 \frac{1}{z^4} - \ldots \right\};$$

thus, the coefficient of $1/z$ in the Laurent expansion of $f(z)$ in $0 < |z| < +\infty$ is

$$\operatorname{res} f(0) = -\frac{a}{2} + \frac{1}{2!}\left(\frac{a}{2}\right)^3 - \frac{1}{2!3!}\left(\frac{a}{2}\right)^5 + \frac{1}{3!4!}\left(\frac{a}{2}\right)^7 + \ldots$$

$$= -\sum_{n=0}^{+\infty} \frac{(-1)^n}{n!(n+1)!}\left(\frac{a}{2}\right)^{2n+1}.$$

Here, $\operatorname{res} f(0) = -J_1(a)$, where J_1 denotes the Bessel function of first kind and first order. (See, e.g., R. O. Kuzmin, *Bessel Functions* ("Besselevy funktsii"), ONTI, 1935; R. V. Churchill, *Fourier Series and Boundary Value Problems*, McGraw-Hill, 1941. Also see Exercise 10 at end of this chapter.)

69. The behaviour of a function at infinity

Suppose $f(z)$ to be regular in some neighbourhood

$$R < |z| < +\infty$$

of the point at infinity. The fundamental definitions of Art. 65 extend immediately to this case since the concept of the limit of $f(z)$ as $z \to \infty$ is formulated in the same way as that of the limit as $z \to a$ (finite). However, the criteria used to distinguish the three types of singularity (Theorems 12, 14, and 16) now assume a different form, as will be seen from the following discussion.

We write $z = 1/Z$ and

$$f(z) = f(1/Z) = F(Z); \tag{44}$$

then $F(Z)$ is regular in the deleted neighbourhood $0 < |Z| < 1/R$ of the point $Z = 0$. As

$$\lim_{z \to \infty} f(z) = \lim_{Z \to 0} F(Z)$$

whenever either limit exists (finite or infinite) it will be clear that the character of the singularity of $f(z)$ at $z = \infty$ will be the same as that of the singularity of $F(Z)$ at $Z = 0$. Thus, for a *removable singularity*, it follows from (38) that, for $R < |z| < +\infty$,

$$f(z) = F(Z) = c_0 + c_1 Z + c_2 Z^2 + \ldots = c_0 + \frac{c_1}{z} + \frac{c_2}{z^2} + \ldots . \tag{45}$$

For a *pole of order* m, it follows from (39) that, for $R < |z| < +\infty$,

$$f(z) = F(Z) = \frac{c_{-m}{}'}{Z^m} + \frac{c_{-m+1}{}'}{Z^{m-1}} + \ldots + \frac{c_{-1}{}'}{Z} + \sum_{n=0}^{+\infty} c_n{}' Z^n$$

$$= c_m z^m + c_{m-1} z^{m-1} + \ldots + c_1 z + \sum_{n=0}^{+\infty} \frac{c_{-n}}{z^n} , \tag{46}$$

where $c_n = c_{-n}'$ for $n \leqslant m$, and $c_m \neq 0$; finally, for an *essential* singularity it follows from (43) that, for $R < |z| < +\infty$,

$$f(z) = F(Z) = \sum_{n=1}^{+\infty} \frac{c_{-n}'}{Z^n} + \sum_{n=0}^{+\infty} c_n' Z^n = \sum_{n=1}^{+\infty} c_n z^n + \sum_{n=0}^{+\infty} \frac{c_{-n}}{z^n}, \quad (47)$$

where $c_n = c_{-n}'$ and infinitely many of the coefficients c_n ($n \geqslant 1$) are non-zero.

We see that in the Laurent expansions (45), (46), (47), of the function $f(z)$ in some deleted neighbourhood of the point at infinity, *the principal part is represented by the sum of the positive powers of z and the regular part is represented by the sum of the non-positive powers of z.*

Remark 1. If the function $f(z)$ has a removable singularity at infinity we usually put

$$f(\infty) = \lim_{z \to \infty} f(z)$$

and then say that $f(z)$ is regular at infinity.

Remark 2. Liouville's theorem of Art. 53 can now be stated in the following form: *if the function $f(z)$ is regular in the closed plane then it is a constant.* For, if $f(z)$ is regular at infinity, there exists a positive R such that the series on the right in (45) is absolutely convergent whenever $|z| \geqslant R$ and it follows immediately that

$$|f(z)| \leqslant \sum_{n=0}^{+\infty} |c_n| \cdot R^{-n} = M_1$$

(say) whenever $|z| \geqslant R$. Also, $f(z)$ is regular for $|z| \leqslant R$, whence there exists a positive M_2 such that $|f(z)| \leqslant M_2$ for $|z| \leqslant R$ (see Art. 13); taking $M = \max.(M_1, M_2)$, we have $|f(z)| \leqslant M$ for *all* z, and it follows from Liouville's theorem that $f(z)$ is constant.

Example 1. The rational function

$$f(z) = \frac{a_n z^n + a_{n-1} z^{n-1} + \ldots + a_0}{b_m z^m + b_{m-1} z^{m-1} + \ldots + b_0},$$

where $a_n \neq 0$, and $b_m \neq 0$, is regular at infinity if $n \leqslant m$ (more precisely, $f(z)$ has a zero of order $m-n$ at infinity if $n < m$) and has a pole of order $n-m$ at infinity if $n > m$. We can easily verify this by considering the function $F(Z) = f(1/Z)$. In particular, taking $m = 0$, $n \geqslant 1$ $(a_n \neq 0 \neq b_0)$ we see that the polynomial

$$f(z) = a_n z^n + a_{n-1} z^{n-1} + \ldots + a_0,$$

of degree n, has a pole of order n at infinity.

Example 2. The familiar expansions of the functions e^z, $\cos z$, $\sin z$, $\cosh z$, $\sinh z$ in powers of z (see Art. 62) can be considered as Laurent expansions in the neighbourhood of $z = \infty$. As all these expansions contain an infinite number of positive powers, it follows that these functions have essential singularities at $z = \infty$.

On the other hand, the function $e^{1/z}$ is regular at infinity, since its Laurent expansion in the neighbourhood of $z = \infty$ (see Example 1, Art. 68) does not contain positive powers of z.

Example 3. The function $f(z) = 1/\sin z$ has a non-isolated singularity at infinity. For, $f(z)$ has poles at the points $z_k = k\pi$ $(k = 0, \pm 1, \pm 2, \ldots)$ and any neighbourhood of $z = \infty$ contains infinitely many of these points (that is, the points z_k, considered as a set of points on the sphere, have a point of accumulation, or limit point, at $z = \infty$).

In conclusion we define what is meant by the residue of a function at infinity:

Definition. Let the function $f(z)$ be regular for $R < |z| < +\infty$. The *residue of $f(z)$ at the point at infinity* is defined by

$$\operatorname{res} f(\infty) = \frac{1}{2\pi i} \oint_{C^-} f(z) \, \mathrm{d}z, \tag{48}$$

where C^- is a circle $|z| = \rho$ $(R < \rho < +\infty)$ traversed in the *negative* (clockwise) sense (so that the neighbourhood $|z| > \rho$ of the point $z = \infty$ remains on the left). The value of the integral (48) does not depend on ρ for $\rho > R$ (see Art. 47).

From this definition we have the following result:

THEOREM 17. *If a function $f(z)$ is regular in the closed plane except at a finite number of (isolated) singularities, then the sum of its residues (including the residue at $z = \infty$) is equal to zero.*

For, let $z_1, z_2, \ldots, z_p$ be the finite singularities of $f(z)$, and let C be the circle $|z| = \rho$ bounding an open disc containing all these points. Here, C is described in the anti-clockwise sense. Then, by Cauchy's residue theorem of Art. 48, and the relation (48), we have:

$$0 = \frac{1}{2\pi i} \oint_C f(z)\, dz + \frac{1}{2\pi i} \oint_{C-} f(z)\, dz$$

$$= \operatorname{res} f(z_1) + \operatorname{res} f(z_2) + \ldots + \operatorname{res} f(z_p) + \operatorname{res} f(\infty). \quad (49)$$

The theorem is proved.

As the final proposition in this article we have:

THEOREM 18. *If $f(z)$ is regular in some deleted neighbourhood of $z = \infty$, the residue of $f(z)$ at $z = \infty$ is $-c_{-1}$, where c_{-1} is the coefficient of $1/z$ in the Laurent expansion of $f(z)$ in this neighbourhood.*

Suppose $f(z)$ regular for $R < |z| < +\infty$. Then, its Laurent expansion (47) in this domain is uniformly convergent on the circle C defined by $|z| = \rho$ whenever $R < \rho < +\infty$ (see Art. 64). Integrating this series termwise around C in the anticlockwise sense we see that

$$\operatorname{res} f(\infty) = -\frac{1}{2\pi i} \oint_C f(z)\, dz = -\frac{1}{2\pi i} \sum_{n=-\infty}^{+\infty} \left(c_n \oint_C z^n\, dz \right).$$

By the result given in Art. 50, the only non-vanishing integral on the right is

$$\oint_C \frac{dz}{z},$$

and it follows immediately that

$$\operatorname{res} f(\infty) = -c_{-1}. \quad (50)$$

This is the required result.

Remark. In spite of the apparent similarity between this theorem and Theorem 11 of Art. 65 there is a substantial difference between them. This is because the term in $1/z$ now belongs to the regular (and not to the principal) part of the Laurent series, so that $\operatorname{res} f(\infty)$ *may be different from zero even if $f(z)$ is regular at infinity.*

Example. Consider the integral

$$I = \oint\limits_{(|z|=4)} \frac{z^{15}}{(z^2+1)^2(z^4+2)^3} \, dz.$$

It is difficult to calculate the residues of the integrand $f(z)$ at its finite singularities. As these singularities all lie in the domain $|z| < 4$ it follows from (48) that $I = -2\pi i \operatorname{res} f(\infty)$. At infinity, $f(z)$ has a zero of first order. It is easily seen that the regular part of its Laurent expansion in a deleted neighbourhood of infinity begins with the term $1/z$. Thus $c_{-1} = -\operatorname{res} f(\infty) = 1$, and we have $I = 2\pi i$.

70. Joukowski's theorem on the thrust on an aerofoil

We return to the problem of complete streamlining considered in Art. 44. This problem entailed our finding the complex potential $\Phi(z)$ for a plane flow streamlining a closed (finite) contour C, the magnitude Γ of the circulation around C and the (vector) velocity $\mathbf{V}_\infty$ at infinity being given. We showed that a solution of this problem is that given in formula (74) of Art. 44:

$$w = \Phi(z) = \overline{\mathbf{V}}_\infty g(z) + \frac{\mathbf{V}_\infty R^2}{g(z)} + \frac{\Gamma}{2\pi i} \operatorname{Ln} g(z); \tag{51}$$

here, $\zeta = g(z)$ is the function giving a simple conformal mapping of the exterior domain whose frontier is C onto the domain $|\zeta| > R$, subject to the normalization conditions

$$g(\infty) = \infty, \qquad g'(\infty) = 1.$$

We shall now prove that this solution is unique, apart from an arbitrary additive constant. To begin we suppose the contour C to be the circle $|\zeta| = R$ of the ζ-plane. We show that, apart from an additive constant, the only solution of the problem of complete streamlining is that given by the formula

$$w = \phi(\zeta) = \overline{\mathbf{V}}_\infty \zeta + \frac{\mathbf{V}_\infty R^2}{\zeta} + \frac{\Gamma}{2\pi i} \operatorname{Ln} \zeta. \tag{52}$$

Let $w = \phi_1(\zeta)$ be any complex potential giving a solution of this problem. As the derived function $\phi_1'(\zeta)$ determines the vector velocity of the flow, according to the relation $\mathbf{V} = \overline{\phi_1'(\zeta)}$ (see

Art. 39), this function must be single-valued and regular in

$$R < |z| < +\infty.$$

By hypothesis, $\phi_1'(\zeta)$ tends to the finite limit $\overline{\mathbf{V}}_\infty$ as $\zeta \to \infty$; accordingly, $\phi_1'(\zeta)$ has a removable singularity at $\zeta = \infty$, and its Laurent expansion in a deleted neighbourhood of this point is of the form

$$\phi_1'(\zeta) = \overline{\mathbf{V}}_\infty + \frac{c_{-1}}{\zeta} + \frac{c_{-2}}{\zeta^2} + \frac{c_{-3}}{\zeta^3} + \dots . \tag{53}$$

As $\phi_1'(\zeta)$ is regular in the domain $R < |\zeta| < +\infty$, it follows from Theorem 9 that this expansion must hold for $R < |\zeta| < +\infty$. Let C^* be any contour enclosing the circle $|\zeta| = R$; then, the stream velocity determined by the potential $w = \phi_1(\zeta)$ must have a circulation Γ around C^* and the net flow across C^* must be zero. Thus, by formula (22) of Art. 48, putting $Q = 0$, we have

$$\Gamma = \oint_{C^*} \phi_1'(\zeta)\, d\zeta = 2\pi i c_{-1},$$

so that $c_{-1} = \Gamma/(2\pi i)$. Integrating (53) and neglecting the additive constant we get

$$\phi_1(\zeta) = \overline{\mathbf{V}}_\infty \zeta + \frac{\Gamma}{2\pi i} \operatorname{Ln} \zeta - \frac{c_{-2}}{\zeta} - \frac{c_{-3}}{2\zeta^2} - \dots . \tag{54}$$

As the flow streamlines the circle $|\zeta| = R$ we require that $\operatorname{Im} \phi_1(\zeta)$ be constant on this circle: putting

$$\zeta = Re^{it} = R\cos t + iR\sin t \quad (0 \leqslant t \leqslant 2\pi), \qquad c_k = \alpha_k + i\beta_k,$$
$$\mathbf{V}_\infty = V_x + iV_y,$$

we thus have

$$RV_x \sin t - RV_y \cos t - \frac{\Gamma}{2\pi}\ln R - \frac{\beta_{-2}\cos t - \alpha_{-2}\sin t}{R}$$
$$- \frac{\beta_{-3}\cos 2t - \alpha_{-3}\sin 2t}{2R^2} - \dots \equiv \text{const.} \quad (0 \leqslant t \leqslant 2\pi);$$

that is,

$$A - \left(\frac{\beta_{-2}}{R} + RV_y\right)\cos t + \left(\frac{\alpha_{-2}}{R} + RV_x\right)\sin t - \frac{\beta_{-3}}{2R^2}\cos 2t$$
$$+ \frac{\alpha_{-3}}{2R^2}\sin 2t - \dots \equiv 0 \quad (0 \leqslant t \leqslant 2\pi)$$

where A is some real constant. This relation holds identically for $0 \leqslant t \leqslant 2\pi$; as its left side is the Fourier expansion of a function which is identically zero, it follows from the uniqueness theorem for such expansions that all the Fourier coefficients must vanish; accordingly,

$$A = 0, \quad \frac{\beta_{-2}}{R} + RV_y = 0, \quad \frac{\alpha_{-2}}{R} + RV_x = 0, \quad \beta_{-k} = \alpha_{-k} = 0 \ (k \geqslant 3),$$

whence

$$c_{-2} = \alpha_{-2} + i\beta_{-2} = -R^2(V_x + iV_y) = -R^2 \mathbf{V}_\infty,$$

$$c_{-k} = \alpha_{-k} + i\beta_{-k} = 0 \qquad (k \geqslant 3),$$

and it follows that the function (54) is identical with the function (52). Thus $\phi_1(\zeta) \equiv \phi(\zeta)$ and we have established the required result for the particular case in which C is a circle.

We now return to the general case of an arbitrary contour C. Let $w = \Phi_1(z)$ be any solution of the problem of complete streamlining. We denote by $z = h(\zeta)$ the function inverse to $\zeta = g(z)$. Then, $z = h(\zeta)$ gives a one–one conformal mapping of $|\zeta| > R$ onto the exterior domain whose frontier is C, and the corresponding normalization conditions are

$$h(\infty) = \infty, \qquad h'(\infty) = \frac{1}{g'(\infty)} = 1.$$

As pointed out earlier, the function g, and hence the function h, is determined uniquely. We now construct the function

$$w = \Phi_1[h(\zeta)] = \phi_1(\zeta);$$

it will be clear that this function is analytic for $R < |\zeta| < +\infty$ so that it can be considered as the complex potential of a certain flow in the ζ-plane. On the circle $|\zeta| = R$,

$$\mathrm{Im}\,\phi_1(\zeta) = \mathrm{Im}\,\Phi_1(z) = \mathrm{const.},$$

since $z = h(\zeta)$ maps the circle $|\zeta| = R$ onto the contour C and, by hypothesis, the potential $\Phi_1(z)$ gives the flow which streamlines C. Thus, the potential $w = \phi_1(\zeta)$ gives the flow which streamlines the circle $|\zeta| = R$. The circulation of this flow around $|\zeta| = R$ is

$$\Gamma_1 = \oint_{C_1^*} \phi_1'(\zeta)\, \mathrm{d}\zeta = \oint_{C_1^*} \Phi_1'[h(\zeta)] \cdot h'(\zeta)\, \mathrm{d}\zeta = \oint_{C^*} \Phi_1'(z)\, \mathrm{d}z,$$

where $C_1{}^*$ is any contour in the ζ-plane enclosing the circle $|\zeta| = R$ and C^*, the image of $C_1{}^*$ under the mapping $z = h(\zeta)$ is a contour in the z-plane enclosing C. By hypothesis, the integral on the right equals Γ, whence $\Gamma_1 = \Gamma$. Also, the stream velocity at infinity in the ζ-plane is

$$\overline{\phi_1'(\infty)} = \overline{\Phi_1'(\infty) \cdot h'(\infty)} = \mathbf{V}_\infty.$$

Thus the function $w = \phi_1(\zeta)$ gives the solution of the problem of complete streamlining for the circle $|\zeta| = R$; by what has been proved above it follows that $\phi_1(\zeta)$ is identical with the function $w = \phi(\zeta)$ of (52), so that $\Phi_1(z) = \phi(\zeta) = \phi[g(z)]$ is identical with the function of (51). (As before, we have neglected a possible additive constant.) This completes the proof.

We now consider the *thrust* (or *lifting force*) $\mathbf{P}$, acting on the streamlined contour C. By Chaplygin's formula (25) of Art. 48 the complex conjugate of $\mathbf{P}$ is given by

$$\overline{\mathbf{P}} = \frac{i\rho}{2} \oint_{C^*} [\Phi'(z)]^2 \, dz,$$

where C^* is any contour enclosing C. We evaluate the integral on the right by finding the residue of $[\Phi'(z)]^2$ at infinity. The derivative of the complex potential determining the flow which streamlines C is regular in the exterior domain defined by C and has a Laurent expansion of the form

$$\Phi'(z) = \overline{\mathbf{V}}_\infty + \frac{c_{-1}}{z} + \frac{c_{-2}}{z^2} + \cdots$$

in some neighbourhood of $z = \infty$. (We establish this result in the same way as (53), above.) To find the coefficient c_{-1} we note that the circulation of the stream velocity around C^* is

$$\Gamma = \oint_{C^*} \Phi'(z) \, dz = 2\pi i c_{-1},$$

whence $c_{-1} = \Gamma/(2\pi i)$. Thus,

$$[\Phi'(z)]^2 = \left(\overline{\mathbf{V}}_\infty + \frac{\Gamma}{2\pi i z} + \frac{c_{-2}}{z^2} + \cdots \right)^2$$

$$= \overline{\mathbf{V}}_\infty{}^2 + \frac{\overline{\mathbf{V}}_\infty \Gamma}{\pi i z} + \frac{c_{-2}'}{z^2} + \frac{c_{-3}'}{z^3} + \cdots,$$

where $c_{-2}{}', c_{-3}{}', \ldots$ are certain constants, and the residue of $[\Phi'(z)]^2$ at infinity is seen to be $-\overline{V}_\infty \Gamma/(\pi i)$. Consequently,

$$\overline{\mathbf{P}} = \frac{i\rho}{2} \cdot 2\pi i \frac{\overline{\mathbf{V}}_\infty \Gamma}{\pi i} = i\rho \Gamma \overline{\mathbf{V}}_\infty.$$

Taking conjugates, we obtain the formula

$$\mathbf{P} = -i\rho\Gamma\mathbf{V}_\infty; \tag{55}$$

this expresses the well-known *theorem of Joukowski*:

For a plane flow of an ideal incompressible fluid which streamlines a contour, the thrust acting per unit height on the cylinder represented by this contour is equal in magnitude to the product of the circulation, the density, and the magnitude of the velocity at infinity; and its direction is obtained from that of the velocity at infinity by rotating the latter through a right angle in a sense opposite to that of the circulation around the contour. (Thus, this rotation is clockwise or anticlockwise according as whether $\Gamma > 0$ or $\Gamma < 0$.)

If the contour C has a sharp corner, then, by Chaplygin's condition, this point will be the rear stagnation point of the flow and, by formula (73) of Art. 44,

$$\Gamma = 4\pi v_\infty R \sin(\phi_0 - \theta); \tag{56}$$

here, $v_\infty = |\mathbf{V}_\infty|$, $\theta = \arg \mathbf{V}_\infty$, and ϕ_0 is the argument of the image of this corner point (the rear stagnation point of the flow) under the transformation $\zeta = g(z)$ which maps the domain exterior to C onto the exterior of the circle $|\zeta| = R$ in such a way as to satisfy the normalization conditions $g(\infty) = \infty$, $g'(\infty) = 1$. In this case, therefore, Joukowski's formula for the magnitude of the thrust is

$$P = |\mathbf{P}| = 4\pi\rho R v_\infty{}^2 |\sin(\phi_0 - \theta)|. \tag{57}$$

Example. *The problem of complete streamlining for a flat strip.* We suppose the strip cuts the z-plane normally along the segment $-a \leqslant x \leqslant a$ of the x-axis. The function $\zeta_1 = z/a$ maps this segment onto a segment of length 2 units and it follows readily that the function mapping the domain exterior to the original segment onto the domain $|\zeta_2| > 1$ is given by

$$\zeta_2 = \zeta_1 + \sqrt{(\zeta_1{}^2 - 1)} = \frac{1}{a}\{z + \sqrt{(z^2 - a^2)}\}$$

(see Art. 26). In this mapping, however, the derivative at $z = \infty$ is

$$\left(\frac{d\zeta_2}{dz}\right)_{z=\infty} = \frac{1}{a}\left(1 + \frac{z}{\sqrt{(z^2-a^2)}}\right)_{z=\infty} = \frac{2}{a}\,.$$

Accordingly, a function satisfying the requisite normalization conditions is

$$\zeta = g(z) = \frac{a}{2}\zeta_2 = \tfrac{1}{2}\{z + \sqrt{(z^2-a^2)}\};$$

this maps the exterior of the original segment on the exterior of the circle $|\zeta| = R = a/2$. Thus, by (51), the complex potential for the flow is

$$w = \Phi(z) = v_\infty[z\cos\theta - (i\sin\theta)\sqrt{(z^2-a^2)}] + \frac{\Gamma}{2\pi i}\,\mathrm{Ln}[z + \sqrt{(z^2-a^2)}].$$

According to Chaplygin's condition (Art. 44) we may take the right-hand end $z = a$ of the segment as the rear stagnation point; the image of this point under the mapping $\zeta = g(z)$ is $\zeta_0 = a/2$, so that $\phi_0 = \arg\zeta_0 = 0$. Thus, by (56),

$$\Gamma = 4\pi v_\infty R\sin(\phi_0 - \theta) = -2\pi v_\infty a\sin\theta,$$

and the complex potential is

$$\begin{aligned} w = \Phi(z) = v_\infty\{&z\cos\theta - (i\sin\theta)\sqrt{(z^2-a^2)} \\ &+ ia\sin\theta \,.\, \mathrm{Ln}[z + \sqrt{(z^2-a^2)}]\}. \end{aligned}$$

The derivative of this potential is

$$\begin{aligned} \overline{\mathbf{V}} = \Phi'(z) &= v_\infty\left\{\cos\theta - i\sin\theta \,.\, \frac{z-a}{\sqrt{(z^2-a^2)}}\right\} \\ &= v_\infty\left\{\cos\theta - i\sin\theta \,.\, \sqrt{\left(\frac{z-a}{z+a}\right)}\right\}. \end{aligned}$$

On the segment $-a \leqslant x \leqslant a$ the velocity is real:

$$\mathbf{V} = \overline{\Phi'(x)} = v_\infty\left\{\cos\theta \pm \sin\theta \,.\, \sqrt{\left(\frac{a-x}{a+x}\right)}\right\}.$$

From this equation we can easily find the critical points of the flow: with an obvious notation we have

$$\frac{a-x_0}{a+x_0} = \cot^2\theta,$$

whence

$$x_0 = -a\cos 2\theta.$$

This gives the forward stagnation point of the flow; the rear stagnation point is not considered to be a critical point as it occurs at the sharp edge (see Art. 44).

The streamlines of the flow are shown in Fig. 105. By (55) the thrust per unit length acting on the plate is

$$\mathbf{P} = 2\pi a\rho v_\infty^2(\sin\theta)ie^{i\theta};$$

the magnitude of this thrust is

$$P = |\mathbf{P}| = 2\pi a\rho v_\infty^2|\sin\theta|$$

and is thus *proportional to the sine of the angle of attack* θ.

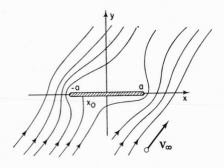

FIG. 105

71. The simplest classes of analytic functions

Definition. A function which is regular at every point of the open plane is called an *integral function*.

Suppose such a function $f(z)$ expanded in a Taylor series with centre at the point $z = 0$:

$$f(z) = c_0 + c_1 z + c_2 z^2 + \ldots + c_n z^n + \ldots . \qquad (58)$$

By Theorem 6 of Art. 62, this series converges for all finite z, so that (58) is also the Laurent expansion of $f(z)$ in any deleted neighbourhood of $z = \infty$. Hence it follows that (1) if an integral function $f(z)$ is regular at infinity it is a constant: $f(z) \equiv c_0$; (2) if $z = \infty$ is the pole of an integral function, then the function is a polynomial (*a rational integral function*). If $z = \infty$ is an essential singularity of an integral function $f(z)$ we call $f(z)$ a *transcendental integral function*. The functions e^z, $\sin z$ and $\cos z$ are of this last type.

Definition. A function $f(z)$ whose only singularities in the finite plane are poles (the function being regular at all other finite points) is called a *meromorphic function*.

It follows immediately from the definition that a meromorphic function $f(z)$ can have only a finite number of singularities (poles) in any bounded closed region of the plane: for, otherwise, there would exist a sequence $\{a_k\}$ of distinct poles of $f(z)$ converging to a (finite) point a in the region; such a point a would necessarily be a non-isolated singularity of $f(z)$, contradicting our hypothesis that any finite singular point of $f(z)$ must be a pole. In the *whole* finite plane a meromorphic function may have infinitely many poles; examples of such functions are $1/\sin z$, $\tan z$, and $\cot z$.

We now prove the following result:

THEOREM 19. *If the function $f(z)$ has no singularities in the closed plane other than poles (we adopt the usual convention that $f(z)$ is to be regarded as regular at $z = \infty$ if it has a removable singularity at this point) then the number of these singular points is finite and $f(z)$ is a rational function.*

For, suppose if possible that $f(z)$ has infinitely many singular points on the sphere; then, it is clear that these points would have at least one point of accumulation (a, say) and any deleted neighbourhood of a would contain infinitely many poles of $f(z)$, so that a would be a non-isolated singularity of $f(z)$ on the sphere. This would contradict our hypothesis. Accordingly, $f(z)$ can have only a finite number of poles in the closed plane. Let

$$a_1, a_2, \ldots, a_p$$

be the finite poles of $f(z)$ and let

$$g_1(z) = \frac{c_{-m_1}^{(1)}}{(z-a_1)^{m_1}} + \frac{c_{-m_1+1}^{(1)}}{(z-a_1)^{m_1-1}} + \ldots + \frac{c_{-1}^{(1)}}{z-a_1},$$

$$g_2(z) = \frac{c_{-m_2}^{(2)}}{(z-a_2)^{m_2}} + \frac{c_{-m_2+1}^{(2)}}{(z-a_2)^{m_2-1}} + \ldots + \frac{c_{-1}^{(2)}}{z-a_2},$$

$$\cdots \cdots \cdots \cdots \cdots \cdots \cdots \cdots,$$

$$g_p(z) = \frac{c_{-m_p}^{(p)}}{(z-a_p)^{m_p}} + \frac{c_{-m_p+1}^{(p)}}{(z-a_p)^{m_p-1}} + \ldots + \frac{c_{-1}^{(p)}}{z-a_p},$$

be the principal parts of the Laurent expansions of $f(z)$ in appropriate deleted neighbourhoods of these poles. Let

$$g(z) = A_1z + A_2z^2 + \ldots + A_mz^m$$

be the principal part of the Laurent expansion of $f(z)$ in some deleted neighbourhood of $z = \infty$. (If $f(z)$ is regular at infinity we suppose $g(z)$ to be identically zero.) We now write

$$\phi(z) = f(z) - g_1(z) - g_2(z) - \ldots - g_p(z) - g(z).$$

This function is regular at all finite points $z \neq a_k$ ($k = 1, 2, \ldots, p$), being the sum of a finite number of regular functions at each such point. At each of the points a_k, $\phi(z)$ has a removable singularity: for, by our construction of the function $\phi(z)$, its Laurent expansion in some deleted neighbourhood of each a_k will have a zero principal part. (The principal part of $f(z)$ at a_k is removed when we subtract $g_k(z)$; the remaining functions $g(z)$ and $g_{k'}(z)$ ($k' \neq k$) are all regular at a_k and thus have zero principal parts at this point.) Similarly, we can show that $\phi(z)$ has a removable singularity at $z = \infty$. Defining $\phi(z)$ by continuity at $z = a_k$ ($k = 1, 2, \ldots, p$) and at $z = \infty$, we obtain a function which is regular at every point of the closed plane. By Remark 2 of Art. 69 it follows that $\phi(z)$ is a constant: suppose $\phi(z) \equiv A_0$. Then,

$$f(z) = A_0 + g(z) + \sum_{k=1}^{p} g_k(z)$$

$$= A_0 + A_1z + A_2z^2 + \ldots + A_mz^m$$

$$+ \frac{c_{-m_1}^{(1)}}{(z-a_1)^{m_1}} + \frac{c_{-m_1+1}^{(1)}}{(z-a_1)^{m_1-1}} + \ldots + \frac{c_{-1}^{(1)}}{(z-a_1)}$$

$$+ \cdots \cdots \cdots \cdots \cdots \cdots$$

$$+ \frac{c_{-m_p}^{(p)}}{(z-a_p)^{m_p}} + \frac{c_{-m_p+1}^{(p)}}{(z-a_p)^{m_p-1}} + \ldots + \frac{c_{-1}^{(p)}}{(z-a_p)}. \tag{59}$$

This completes the proof.

Remark 1. The reader will recognize formula (59) as the familiar expansion of a rational function as the sum of a polynomial and certain partial fractions. The above discussion provides an elegant derivation of this expansion.

Remark 2. By carrying out simple arithmetical operations on the right-hand side of (59) we can represent $f(z)$ as the ratio of two polynomials (rational integral functions). It can also be shown that an *arbitrary meromorphic function can be represented as the ratio of two integral functions* (see, e.g. Knopp, *Theory of Functions*, Dover, 1945).

Exercises

1. Find the domain of absolute convergence of each of the following series:

$$(a) \quad \sum_{n=1}^{+\infty} \frac{1}{n^z}; \qquad (b) \quad \frac{a_0}{2} + \sum_{n=1}^{+\infty} (a_n \cos nz + b_n \sin nz),$$

where a_n, b_n and z are complex (the Fourier series in the complex domain).

2. Find the radius of convergence of each of the following series:

$$(a) \quad \sum_{n=1}^{+\infty} \left(\frac{z}{n}\right)^n; \qquad (b) \quad \sum_{n=1}^{+\infty} n^{\ln n} z^n.$$

3. Find the Taylor expansions, about the centre $z = i$, of all branches of the following functions: (a) $\sqrt[3]{z}$; (b) $\operatorname{Ln} z$.

4. Find the first three terms of the Taylor expansion about the centre $z = 0$ of that branch of the function $f(z) = (1+z)^{1/z}$ for which $f(0) = e$.

5. Prove that the function represented in $|z| < 1$ by the series

$$\sum_{n=1}^{+\infty} z^{2^n}$$

has the circle $|z| = 1$ as its natural boundary.

6. Find how many different analytic functions are represented by each of the following expressions, and state whether each of

these functions is single-valued or many-valued: (a) $\sqrt{e^z}$, (b) $\sqrt{(\cos z)}$, (c) $\cos\sqrt{z}$, (d) $\sqrt{(1-\sin^2 z)}$, (e) $(\sin\sqrt{z})/\sqrt{z}$, (f) $\mathrm{Ln}\, e^z$, (g) $\mathrm{Ln} \sin z$.

7. The coefficient of the nth power of z in the Taylor expansion, about $z = 0$, of the function

$$f(z) = \frac{4-z^2}{4-4zt+z^2} \quad (-1 \leqslant t \leqslant 1)$$

is called a Chebychev polynomial (notation: $T_n(t)$). Prove that

$$T_n(t) = \frac{1}{2^{n-1}} \cos(n \arccos t).$$

8. Find the expansion in a Fourier series of the following functions ($|a| < 1$):

(a) $\dfrac{a \sin t}{1 - 2a \cos t + a^2}$;   (b) $\ln(1 - 2a \cos t + a^2)$.

9. Find which of the following functions is regular, or has regular branches, in a deleted neighbourhood of $z = \infty$:

(a) $(\sqrt{2}) \cos\left(z + \dfrac{\pi}{4}\right)$,   (b) $\sqrt{[(z-1)(z-2)]}$,   (c) $\mathrm{Ln}\dfrac{1}{1-z}$,

(d) $\mathrm{Ln}\dfrac{a-z}{b-z}$.

For each such function or regular branch find the corresponding Laurent expansion.

10. The coefficient of the nth power of z in the Laurent expansion of the function $e^{t(z-z^{-1})/2}$ in a deleted neighbourhood of $z = \infty$ is called the Bessel function of order n (notation: $J_n(t)$, $n = 0, \pm 1, \pm 2, \ldots$). Find the representation of the Bessel function $J_n(t)$ as a power series in t and as an integral.

11. The zeros $z_k = 1 - (1/k\pi)$ ($k = 1, 2, \ldots$) of the function $f(z) = \sin\{1/(1-z)\}$ form a sequence of distinct points converging to the point $z = 1$, but $f(z)$ is not identically zero. Why does this not contradict the uniqueness theorem of Art. 62?

12. Explain the essential difference in behaviour, near the origin, of the following functions:

(a) the function of the real variable x defined by

$$y = \begin{cases} e^{-1/x^2}, & x \neq 0, \\ 0, & x = 0; \end{cases}$$

(b) the function of the complex variable z defined by

$$w = \begin{cases} e^{-1/z^2}, & z \neq 0, \\ 0, & z = 0. \end{cases}$$

13. Give a direct verification of Sokhotski's theorem (Art. 68) for the essential singularity at $z = \infty$ of the function $w = \sin z$ by showing that, given any complex $A \neq \infty$, the points at which $\sin z = A$ can be arranged in a sequence converging to $z = \infty$.

14. Find the nature of each singularity of each of the following functions:

(a) $\dfrac{e^{1/(z-1)}}{e^z - 1}$, (b) $\dfrac{1}{\sin z + \cos z}$, (c) $\dfrac{1 - e^z}{1 + e^z}$, (d) $z^2 e^{-z}$.

15. For what value of a is the function

$$F(z) = \int_{z_0}^{z} e^z \left(\frac{1}{z} + \frac{a}{z^3} \right) dz$$

single-valued?

16. Find the residue at each isolated singularity for each of the following functions:

(a) $\dfrac{1}{\sin z}$ $(z \neq \infty)$, (b) $\dfrac{z^{2n}}{1 + z^n}$, (c) $\dfrac{z^{2n}}{(1 + z)^n}$,

(d) $\cos z - \sin z$, (e) $z^n e^z$, (f) $\dfrac{e^z}{1 + z}$, (g) $e^z \ln \dfrac{z - a}{z - b}$.

17. Determine the flow across, and the circulation around, the circle $|z - e^{i\pi/4}| = 1$ given that the complex potential describing the fluid motion is $\Phi(z) = \arctan(z^2)$.

18. Find the total charge lying in the disc $|z| < n + \frac{1}{2}$ if the potential for the field is $F(z) = 2qi \operatorname{Ln}(1/\sin \pi z)$.

CHAPTER VII

APPLICATIONS OF THE THEORY OF RESIDUES

72. Evaluation of integrals of the form

$$\int_0^{2\pi} R(\sin x, \cos x) \, . \, \mathrm{d}x.$$

HERE, R denotes a rational function of the variables $\sin x$ and $\cos x$; we suppose $R(\sin x, \cos x)$ to be a continuous function of x on the closed interval $[0, 2\pi]$. We illustrate the method by means of the following examples.

Example 1.

$$I = \int_0^{2\pi} \frac{\mathrm{d}x}{1 - 2p \cos x + p^2} \quad (0 < p < 1).$$

We put

$$e^{ix} = z; \tag{1}$$

then, $ix = \ln z$, $\mathrm{d}x = \mathrm{d}z/(iz)$, $\cos x = \frac{1}{2}(e^{ix} + e^{-ix}) = \frac{1}{2}(z + z^{-1})$, and the point z describes the unit circle as x ranges from 0 to 2π. Accordingly,

$$I = \oint_{(|z|=1)} \frac{\mathrm{d}z}{iz[1 - pz - (p/z) + p^2]} = \oint_{(|z|=1)} \frac{i \, \mathrm{d}z}{pz^2 - (p^2 + 1)z + p}.$$

The integrand has two poles; these points (z_1, z_2, say) are the roots of the equation

$$pz^2 - (p^2 + 1)z + p = 0,$$

whence $z_1 = p$, $z_2 = 1/p$. As $0 < p < 1$, the pole z_2 lies outside the unit disc; thus, by Cauchy's residue theorem, (Art. 48),

$$I = i \oint_{(|z|=1)} \frac{\mathrm{d}z}{pz^2 - (p^2 + 1)z + p} = i\{2\pi i \, . \, \mathrm{res} f(z_1)\},$$

where $\operatorname{res} f(z_1)$, the residue of the integrand at the point $z = z_1$, is given by formula (42) of Art. 67:

$$\operatorname{res} f(z_1) = 1 \Bigg/ \left[\frac{\mathrm{d}}{\mathrm{d}z} \{ pz^2 - (p^2+1)z + p \} \right]_{z=p} = \frac{1}{p^2-1}.$$

Thus,

$$I = \int\limits_0^{2\pi} \frac{\mathrm{d}x}{1 - 2p\cos x + p^2} = -2\pi \frac{1}{p^2-1} = \frac{2\pi}{1-p^2}. \tag{2}$$

We note that the value of the integral on the left in (2) is given immediately by Poisson's formula (60) of Art. 56 when we put $\psi = x$, $\phi = 0$, $R = 1$, $r = p$, $u(\zeta) \equiv 1/(1-p^2)$ ($=$const.).

Example 2. By means of the same substitution (1) we can evaluate the integral

$$I = \int\limits_0^{2\pi} \frac{\mathrm{d}x}{(p+q\cos x)^2} = \oint\limits_{(|z|=1)} \frac{\mathrm{d}z}{iz\left\{ p + \dfrac{q}{2}\left(z + \dfrac{1}{z} \right) \right\}^2}$$

$$= -i \oint\limits_{(|z|=1)} \frac{z\,\mathrm{d}z}{\left\{ \dfrac{q}{2}z^2 + pz + \dfrac{q}{2} \right\}^2}.$$

The integrand in the integral on the right has poles of the second order at each of the points

$$z_1 = \frac{1}{q}\left[-p + \sqrt{(p^2-q^2)} \right], \qquad z_2 = \frac{1}{q}\left[-p - \sqrt{(p^2-q^2)} \right].$$

We suppose $p > q > 0$; then, the pole z_2 lies outside the unit circle. The residue c_{-1} at the point z_1 is given by formula (40) of Art. 67 when we take $m = 2$: we have

$$\frac{q}{2}z^2 + pz + \frac{q}{2} = \frac{q}{2}(z - z_1)(z - z_2),$$

whence

$$c_{-1} = \lim_{z \to z_1} \left[\frac{\mathrm{d}}{\mathrm{d}z}\left\{ \frac{z(z - z_1)^2}{(q^2/4)(z - z_1)^2(z - z_2)^2} \right\} \right]$$

$$= \frac{4}{q^2}\left[\frac{\mathrm{d}}{\mathrm{d}z}\frac{z}{(z - z_2)^2} \right]_{z=z_1} = -\frac{4}{q^2}\frac{z_1 + z_2}{(z_1 - z_2)^3} = \frac{p}{(p^2-q^2)^{3/2}}.$$

Thus, by the residue theorem,

$$I = \int\limits_0^{2\pi} \frac{dx}{(p+q\cos x)^2} = -i2\pi c_{-1} = \frac{2\pi p}{(p^2-q^2)^{3/2}} \quad (p > q > 0). \tag{3}$$

Integrals of several other types can be evaluated by similar methods:

Example 3. To evaluate the integral

$$I = \int\limits_0^\pi \cot(x-a) \,.\, dx$$

where $a = \alpha + i\beta$, $\beta \neq 0$ (the integral diverges for $\beta = 0$) it is convenient to put

$$e^{2i(x-a)} = z.$$

Then,

$$dx = \frac{1}{2iz}dz, \qquad \cot(x-a) = i\frac{e^{i(x-a)}+e^{-i(x-a)}}{e^{i(x-a)}-e^{-i(x-a)}} = i\frac{z+1}{z-1};$$

and, as x ranges from 0 to π, the point z describes the circle

$$|z| = \left|e^{2\beta+2i(x-\alpha)}\right| = e^{2\beta}.$$

Thus,

$$I = \oint\limits_{(|z|=e^{2\beta})} i\frac{z+1}{z-1} \cdot \frac{dz}{2iz} = \frac{1}{2} \oint\limits_{(|z|=e^{2\beta})} \frac{z+1}{z-1} \cdot \frac{dz}{z}.$$

For $\beta > 0$ the radius of the path is $e^{2\beta} > 1$; this path will then enclose both poles of the integrand. These poles (at $z_1 = 0$ and $z_2 = 1$) are each of the first order and the corresponding residues are

$$r_1 = \frac{\phi(0)}{\psi'(0)} = -1, \qquad r_2 = \frac{\phi(1)}{\psi'(1)} = 2.$$

We evaluate these residues by means of formula (42) of Art. 67: the first is obtained by taking $\phi(z) = (z+1)/(z-1)$, $\psi(z) = z$; the second by taking $\phi(z) = (z+1)/z$, $\psi(z) = z-1$. For $\beta < 0$ the radius of the path is $e^{2\beta} < 1$ and the path then encloses only the one pole at $z_1 = 0$, the corresponding residue being $r_1 = -1$.

Thus,

$$I = \begin{cases} \tfrac{1}{2} 2\pi i (r_1 + r_2) = \pi i & \text{for } \beta > 0, \\ \tfrac{1}{2} 2\pi i r_1 = -\pi i & \text{for } \beta < 0. \end{cases}$$

These results can be combined in the one formula

$$I = \int_0^\pi \cot(x-a) \, . \, \mathrm{d}x = \pi i \operatorname{sgn} \beta \quad (\operatorname{Im} a = \beta \neq 0), \tag{4}$$

where $\operatorname{sgn} \beta$ is equal to $+1$ for $\beta > 0$ and to -1 for $\beta < 0$.

73. Integrals of the form $\displaystyle\int_{-\infty}^{+\infty} R(x) \, . \, \begin{Bmatrix} \sin \\ \cos \end{Bmatrix} \alpha x \, . \, \mathrm{d}x.$

Here, $R(x)$ is a rational function of x. We begin by evaluating integrals in which the trigonometrical function is absent:

$$I = \int_{-\infty}^{+\infty} R(x) \, . \, \mathrm{d}x. \tag{5}$$

To ensure the existence of the integral (5) we require that $R(x)$ be continuous for all real x and that the degree n of the numerator of $R(x)$ be at least *two* less than the degree m of the denominator. (The integral (5) will be divergent if $m \leqslant n+1$.)

Example 1. To evaluate the integral

$$I = \int_{-\infty}^{+\infty} \frac{\mathrm{d}x}{(x^2+a^2)^3} \quad (a > 0)$$

we take a contour L consisting of the segment $[-R, R]$ of the real axis and the upper semicircle $|z| = R$, $\operatorname{Im} z \geqslant 0$ (Fig. 106), and consider the function

$$f(z) = \frac{1}{(z^2+a^2)^3} \, .$$

20

For $R > a$, L encloses the pole of $f(z)$ at $z_0 = ia$; this pole is of third order, the corresponding residue being

$$c_{-1} = \frac{1}{2!} \lim_{z \to z_0} \left[\frac{d^2}{dz^2} \left\{ \frac{(z-ai)^3}{(z^2+a^2)^3} \right\} \right] = \frac{1}{2} \left[\frac{d^2}{dz^2} \frac{1}{(z+ai)^3} \right]_{z=ai}$$

$$= \frac{1}{2} \cdot \frac{3.4}{(2ai)^5} = \frac{3}{16a^5 i} \,.$$

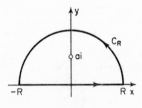

Fig. 106

By Cauchy's residue theorem,

$$\oint_L f(z) \, dz = \int_{-R}^{R} f(x) \, dx + \int_{C_R} f(z) \, dz = 2\pi i c_{-1} = \frac{3\pi}{8a^5} \,, \qquad (6)$$

where C_R is the upper semicircle $|z| = R$, $\operatorname{Im} z \geqslant 0$. From the fundamental inequality for integrals (Art. 46) it follows that, for $R > 2a$,

$$\left| \int_{C_R} f(z) \, dz \right| \leqslant \frac{1}{R^6} \cdot \max_{(|z|=R)} \left(\frac{1}{|1+(a^2/z^2)|^3} \right) \cdot \pi R$$

$$= \frac{\pi}{R^5} \cdot \frac{1}{[1-(a^2/R^2)]^3} < \frac{\pi}{R^5(1-\frac{1}{4})^3} = \frac{64\pi}{27R^5} \,.$$

Thus,

$$\lim_{R \to +\infty} \int_{C_R} f(z) \, dz = 0.$$

Letting $R \to +\infty$ in (6) we obtain the required integral:

$$I = \int\limits_{-\infty}^{+\infty} f(x) \, \mathrm{d}x = \int\limits_{-\infty}^{+\infty} \frac{\mathrm{d}x}{(x^2+a^2)^3} = \frac{3\pi}{8a^5} \, . \qquad (7)$$

The elementary methods of evaluating the integral in (7) involve threefold integration by parts or trigonometrical substitution; either method is rather tedious.

Integrals containing the trigonometrical factor are evaluated by a similar method:

Example 2. To evaluate the integral

$$I = \int\limits_{0}^{+\infty} \frac{\cos x \, . \, \mathrm{d}x}{x^2+a^2} \quad (a > 0)$$

we choose the same contour L as in the preceding example and consider the function

$$f(z) = \frac{e^{iz}}{z^2+a^2} \, .$$

For real $z = x$, the real part of this function is identical with our integrand. On the semicircle C_R we have $|e^{iz}| = e^{-y} \leqslant 1$, since $y = \operatorname{Im} z \geqslant 0$; thus, for $R > 2a$ it follows as before that

$$| \int\limits_{C_R} f(z) \, \mathrm{d}z| \leqslant \frac{1}{R^2(1-\frac{1}{4})} \, . \, \pi R = \frac{4\pi}{3R} \, ,$$

so that

$$\lim_{R\to+\infty} \int\limits_{C_R} f(z) \, \mathrm{d}z = 0.$$

(Had we taken $f(z) = (\cos z)/(z^2+a^2)$ we would not have obtained a similar bound for

$$\int\limits_{C_R} f(z) \, \mathrm{d}z,$$

since the upper bound of $|\cos z|$ on C_R tends to $+\infty$ much faster than R as $R \rightarrow +\infty$.) For $R > a$ the function $f(z)$ has exactly one pole in the interior domain bounded by L; this pole, at $z = ai$, is of first order, the corresponding residue being

$$c_{-1} = \frac{\phi(ai)}{\psi'(ai)} = \frac{e^{-a}}{2ai} = \frac{1}{2ae^a i} \, .$$

(Here, $\phi(z) = e^{iz}$ and $\psi(z) = z^2 + a^2$.) By the residue theorem,

$$\oint_L f(z) \, \mathrm{d}z = \int_{-R}^{R} \frac{e^{ix}}{x^2 + a^2} \mathrm{d}x + \int_{C_R} f(z) \, \mathrm{d}z = 2\pi i c_{-1} = \frac{\pi}{ae^a} \, . \qquad (8)$$

Equating real parts, we have

$$\int_{-R}^{R} \frac{\cos x}{x^2 + a^2} \, \mathrm{d}x + \mathrm{Re} \int_{C_R} f(z) \, \mathrm{d}z = \frac{\pi}{ae^a} \, .$$

Letting $R \rightarrow +\infty$ in this result it follows immediately that $2I = \pi/(ae^a)$, whence

$$I = \int_{0}^{+\infty} \frac{\cos x}{x^2 + a^2} \, \mathrm{d}x = \frac{\pi}{2ae^a} \, . \qquad (9)$$

It may be noted that the indefinite integral

$$\int \frac{\cos x}{x^2 + a^2} \, \mathrm{d}x$$

cannot be expressed in terms of elementary functions.

Example 3. To evaluate the integral

$$I = \int_{0}^{+\infty} \frac{\sin x}{x} \, \mathrm{d}x$$

we consider the auxiliary function

$$f(z) = \frac{e^{iz}}{z};$$

for real $z = x$, the imaginary part of this function is identical with the integrand. The contour shown in Fig. 106 cannot be used here, since $f(z)$ becomes infinite at $z = 0$. To avoid this difficulty we remove from the semicircular domain shown in Fig. 106 the small semicircular region defined by $|z| \leqslant r, y > 0$ $(0 < r < R)$. Later we shall let r tend to $+0$ and R tend to $+\infty$. In the domain which then remains (see Fig. 107) the function $f(z)$ is regular; consequently, by Cauchy's theorem (Art. 47),

$$\int_{-R}^{-r} \frac{e^{ix}}{x}\,dx + \int_{C_r} \frac{e^{iz}}{z}\,dz + \int_{r}^{R} \frac{e^{ix}}{x}\,dx + \int_{C_R} \frac{e^{iz}}{z}\,dz = 0. \qquad (10)$$

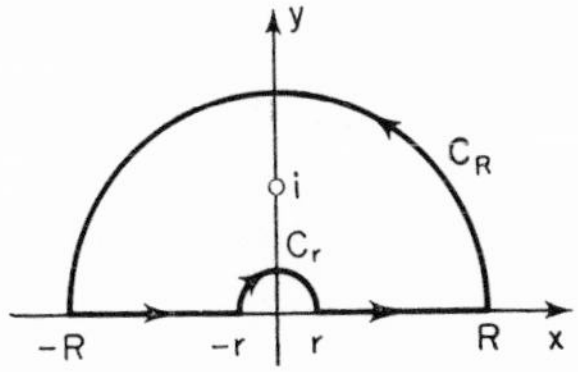

FIG. 107

In finding a bound for the fourth integral the fact that $|e^{iz}| \leqslant 1$ on C_R for all $R > 0$ is not sufficient, since the length of the path C_R and the modulus of the denominator of the integrand are of the same order as $R \to +\infty$. However, the functions e^{iz}/z and e^{iz}/z^2 are regular in a simply-connected domain containing the path C_R, and it follows readily that we can apply the formula for integration by parts, putting $u = 1/z$, $dv = e^{iz}\,dz$: thus,

$$\int_{C_R} \frac{e^{iz}}{z}\,dz = \left[\frac{e^{iz}}{iz}\right]_{-R}^{R} + \int_{C_R} \frac{e^{iz}}{iz^2}\,dz = \frac{2\cos R}{iR} + \frac{1}{i}\int_{C_R} \frac{e^{iz}}{z^2}\,dz.$$

The term $(2\cos R)/(iR)$ tends to zero as $R \to +\infty$; also, the modulus of the integral on the right does not exceed $(1/R^2)\,\pi R = \pi/R$, so that it, too, tends to zero as $R \to +\infty$. Accordingly, the fourth integral in (10) tends to zero as $R \to +\infty$. In order to examine the behaviour of the second integral in (10) as $r \to +0$ we consider the Laurent expansion of e^{iz}/z in $0 < |z| < +\infty$:

$$\frac{e^{iz}}{z} = \frac{1}{z}\left\{1 + \frac{iz}{1!} + \frac{(iz)^2}{2!} + \frac{(iz)^3}{3!} + \ldots\right\} = \frac{1}{z} + P(z)$$

where $P(z)$ is regular at $z = 0$. The function $P(z)$ is bounded in any (finite) neighbourhood of $z = 0$; since the length of the semicircle C_r tends to $+0$ as $r \to +0$, it follows that

$$\lim_{r \to +0} \int_{C_r} P(z)\, \mathrm{d}z = 0.$$

Thus,

$$\lim_{r \to +0} \int_{C_r} \frac{e^{iz}}{z}\, \mathrm{d}z = \lim_{r \to +0} \left\{ \int_{C_r} \frac{1}{z}\, \mathrm{d}z + \int_{C_r} P(z)\, \mathrm{d}z \right\} = \lim_{r \to +0} \int_{C_r} \frac{\mathrm{d}z}{z}.$$

Putting $z = re^{i\phi}$, $\mathrm{d}z = rie^{i\phi}\, \mathrm{d}\phi$ in the last integral we get

$$\int_{C_r} \frac{\mathrm{d}z}{z} = \int_{\pi}^{0} i\, \mathrm{d}\phi = -i\pi.$$

It is easily shown that

$$\int_{-\infty}^{+\infty} \frac{1}{x} \sin x\, \mathrm{d}x$$

exists as a Cauchy–Riemann integral and is equal to $2I$. Accordingly separating real and imaginary parts in (10) and letting $r \to +0$ and $R \to +\infty$, we have

$$\int_{-\infty}^{0} \frac{\sin x}{x}\, \mathrm{d}x + \int_{0}^{+\infty} \frac{\sin x}{x}\, \mathrm{d}x - \pi = 0,$$

and it follows immediately that

$$I = \int_{0}^{+\infty} \frac{\sin x}{x}\, \mathrm{d}x = \frac{\pi}{2}. \qquad (11)$$

Example 4. In exactly the same way we evaluate the integral

$$I = \int_{0}^{+\infty} \frac{\cos ax - \cos bx}{x^2}\, \mathrm{d}x \quad (a \geqslant 0, \quad b \geqslant 0).$$

It is easily shown that I exists as a Cauchy–Riemann integral and that

$$I = \frac{1}{2} \lim_{R \to +\infty} \int_{-R}^{R} \frac{1}{x^2}(\cos ax - \cos bx)\, \mathrm{d}x.$$

(Note that I cannot be represented as the difference of the integrals

$$\int_{0}^{+\infty} \frac{\cos ax}{x^2}\, \mathrm{d}x \quad \text{and} \quad \int_{0}^{+\infty} \frac{\cos bx}{x^2}\, \mathrm{d}x,$$

since both these integrals diverge.) We consider the auxiliary function

$$f(z) = \frac{e^{iaz} - e^{ibz}}{z^2}$$

and take the integral of $f(z)$ around the contour of Fig. 107:

$$\int_{-R}^{-r} f(x)\, \mathrm{d}x + \int_{C_r} f(z)\, \mathrm{d}z + \int_{r}^{R} f(x)\, \mathrm{d}x + \int_{C_R} f(z)\, \mathrm{d}z = 0. \qquad (12)$$

It is easier to find a bound for the integral along C_R than it was for the corresponding integral in the preceding example: as $a \geqslant 0$, $b \geqslant 0$ it follows that, on C_R, $|e^{iaz}| = e^{-ay} \leqslant 1$ and $|e^{ibz}| = e^{-by} \leqslant 1$, so that $|f(z)| \leqslant 2/R^2$ and

$$\left| \int_{C_R} f(z)\, \mathrm{d}z \right| \leqslant \frac{2}{R^2} \cdot \pi R$$
$$\to 0 \qquad \text{as } R \to +\infty.$$

To find a bound for the integral along C_r we consider the Laurent expansion of $f(z)$ in $0 < |z| < +\infty$:

$$f(z) = \frac{1}{z^2}\left\{ i(a-b)z + \frac{(iaz)^2 - (ibz)^2}{2!} + \dots \right\} = \frac{i(a-b)}{z} + P(z),$$

where $P(z)$ is a function which is regular at $z = 0$. Proceeding as in Example 3 we see that

$$\lim_{r \to 0} \int_{C_r} f(z)\, \mathrm{d}z = i(a-b)(-i\pi) = (a-b)\pi.$$

Thus, separating real parts in (12) and letting $r \to +0$ and $R \to +\infty$, we have

$$\int_{-\infty}^{+\infty} \frac{\cos ax - \cos bx}{x^2}\, \mathrm{d}x + (a-b)\pi = 0,$$

and it follows that the integral required is

$$I = \int_{0}^{+\infty} \frac{\cos ax - \cos bx}{x^2}\, \mathrm{d}x = \frac{b-a}{2}\pi. \tag{13}$$

74. Other integrals

The ease with which we can evaluate definite integrals of many other types depends on our choosing suitable auxiliary contours. We shall again illustrate by means of examples.

Example 1. The *Fresnel integrals*

$$\int_{0}^{+\infty} \cos x^2 \,.\, \mathrm{d}x, \qquad \int_{0}^{+\infty} \sin x^2 \,.\, \mathrm{d}x$$

are conveniently evaluated simultaneously. We consider the auxiliary function

$$f(z) = e^{iz^2};$$

for real $z = x$ the real and imaginary parts of $f(z)$ are the integrands in the above integrals. Also, we note that, along the ray arg $z = \pi/4$ (that is, for $z = re^{i\pi/4}$) $f(z)$ equals the integrand e^{-r^2} in the well-known Poisson integral (see Exercise 9 at end of this chapter)

$$\int_{0}^{+\infty} e^{-r^2}\, \mathrm{d}r = \tfrac{1}{2}\sqrt{\pi}. \tag{14}$$

We make use of this fact by choosing the contour shown in Fig. 108: as $f(z)$ is regular inside and on this contour, it follows from Cauchy's theorem that

$$\int_{0}^{R} e^{ix^2}\, \mathrm{d}x + \int_{C_R} e^{iz}\ \mathrm{d}z + \int_{R}^{0} e^{-r^2} \,.\, e^{i\pi/4}\, \mathrm{d}r = 0. \tag{15}$$

Here, C_R denotes the circular arc (with centre $z = 0$) joining the points R and $Re^{i\pi/4}$; also, in taking the integral along the segment of the ray $\arg z = \pi/4$, we have written $z = re^{i\pi/4}$, $\mathrm{d}z = e^{i\pi/4}$. $\mathrm{d}r$. As in the preceding examples we shall let R tend to $+\infty$. To find

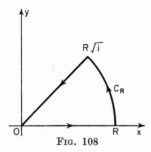

Fɪɢ. 108

a bound for the second integral in (15) we can again use the method of integration by parts (cf. Example 3, Art. 73):

$$\int\limits_{C_R} e^{iz^2}\,\mathrm{d}z = \int\limits_{C_R} \frac{1}{2iz}\left(\frac{\mathrm{d}}{\mathrm{d}z}e^{iz^2}\right)\mathrm{d}z = \left[\frac{e^{iz^2}}{2iz}\right]_R^{Re^{i\pi/4}} + \frac{1}{2i}\int\limits_{C_R} \frac{e^{iz^2}}{z^2}\,\mathrm{d}z.$$

Here, on the right, the modulus of the first term is

$$\left|\frac{e^{-R^2}}{2ie^{i\pi/4}R} - \frac{e^{iR^2}}{2iR}\right| \leqslant \frac{e^{-R^2}}{2R} + \frac{1}{2R}$$
$$\to 0 \quad \text{as } R \to +\infty;$$

also, putting $z = R \cdot e^{i\phi}$ we see that, on the arc $C_R(0 \leqslant \phi \leqslant \pi/4)$, the modulus of the integrand function is

$$\left|\frac{e^{iz^2}}{z^2}\right| = \left|\frac{e^{iR^2(\cos 2\phi + i\sin 2\phi)}}{R^2 e^{i2\phi}}\right| = \frac{e^{-R^2 2\sin\phi}}{R^2} \leqslant \frac{1}{R^2},$$

since $\sin 2\phi \geqslant 0$ so that $e^{-R^2\sin 2\phi} \leqslant 1$. Accordingly, by the fundamental inequality for integrals we have

$$\left|\int\limits_{C_R} \frac{e^{iz^2}}{z^2}\,\mathrm{d}z\right| \leqslant \frac{1}{R^2} \cdot \frac{\pi}{4}R = \frac{\pi}{4R}$$
$$\to 0 \quad \text{as } R \to +\infty.$$

Thus, letting $R \to +\infty$ in (15), we have

$$\int\limits_0^{+\infty} e^{ix^2}\,\mathrm{d}x - e^{i\pi/4}\int\limits_0^{+\infty} e^{-r^2}\,\mathrm{d}r = 0,$$

whence, by (14),

$$\int\limits_{0}^{+\infty} e^{ix^2}\,\mathrm{d}x = \int\limits_{0}^{+\infty} \cos x^2 \cdot \mathrm{d}x + i\int\limits_{0}^{+\infty} \sin x^2 \cdot \mathrm{d}x = e^{i\pi/4}\frac{\sqrt{\pi}}{2}$$

$$= \frac{1+i}{\sqrt{2}} \cdot \frac{\sqrt{\pi}}{2}\,.$$

Comparing real and imaginary parts we obtain both the required integrals:

$$\int\limits_{0}^{+\infty} \cos x^2 \cdot \mathrm{d}x = \int\limits_{0}^{+\infty} \sin x^2 \cdot \mathrm{d}x = \frac{1}{2}\sqrt{\frac{\pi}{2}}\,. \tag{16}$$

Example 2. To evaluate the integral

$$\int\limits_{-\infty}^{+\infty} \frac{e^{ax}}{1+e^x}\,\mathrm{d}x \quad (0 < a < 1)$$

we consider the function

$$f(z) = \frac{e^{az}}{1+e^z}\,.$$

It is easily shown that

$$\int\limits_{-\infty}^{+\infty} f(x)\,\mathrm{d}x$$

exists as a Cauchy–Riemann integral and equals

$$\lim_{R\to+\infty} \int\limits_{-R}^{R} f(x)\,\mathrm{d}x.$$

Making use of the fact that e^z has the imaginary period $2\pi i$ and that the effect of increasing z by $2\pi i$ is to change e^{az} by the constant factor $e^{2\pi ai}$ (we have $e^{a(z+2\pi i)} = e^{az} \cdot e^{2\pi ai}$), we choose the rectangle shown in Fig. 109 as contour of integration. In the interior domain bounded by this rectangle, $f(z)$ has exactly one singularity, the point

$z = \pi i$; at this point, $e^z + 1 = 0$ and $f(z)$ has a first-order pole, the corresponding residue being

$$c_{-1} = e^{a\pi i} \bigg/ \left[\frac{\mathrm{d}}{\mathrm{d}z}(1+e^z)\right]_{z=\pi i}$$

$$= \frac{e^{a\pi i}}{e^{\pi i}} = -e^{a\pi i}.$$

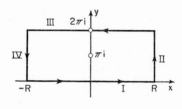

Fɪɢ. 109

By Cauchy's residue theorem,

$$\int_{\mathrm{I}} f(z)\,\mathrm{d}z + \int_{\mathrm{II}} f(z)\,\mathrm{d}z + \int_{\mathrm{III}} f(z)\,\mathrm{d}z + \int_{\mathrm{IV}} f(z)\,\mathrm{d}z = -2\pi i e^{a\pi i}. \quad (17)$$

Here,

$$\int_{\mathrm{I}} f(z)\,\mathrm{d}z = \int_{-R}^{R} \frac{e^{ax}\,\mathrm{d}x}{1+e^x},$$

and

$$\int_{\mathrm{III}} f(z)\,\mathrm{d}z = \int_{R}^{-R} \frac{e^{a(x+2\pi i)}}{1+e^{x+2\pi i}}\,\mathrm{d}x = -e^{2a\pi i}\int_{-R}^{R}\frac{e^{ax}}{1+e^x}\,\mathrm{d}x.$$

On the segment II we have

$$|f(z)| = \left|\frac{e^{a(R+iy)}}{1+e^{R+i\,y}}\right| \leqslant \frac{e^{aR}}{e^R - 1},$$

since (see formula (17), Introduction)

$$|e^{R+iy}+1| \geqslant |e^{R+iy}|-1 = e^R-1 > 0;$$

thus,

$$\left| \int\limits_{II} f(z) \, \mathrm{d}z \right| \leqslant 2\pi \frac{e^{aR}}{e^R-1} = 2\pi \frac{e^{(a-1)R}}{1-e^{-R}}$$

$$\to 0 \quad \text{as } R \to +\infty,$$

since, by hypothesis, $a < 1$. Similarly, on segment IV,

$$|f(z)| = \left| \frac{e^{a(-R+iy)}}{1+e^{-R+iy}} \right| \leqslant \frac{e^{-aR}}{1-e^{-R}},$$

since $|1+e^{-R+iy}| \geqslant 1-|e^{-R+iy}| = 1-e^{-R} > 0$; thus,

$$\left| \int\limits_{IV} f(z) \, \mathrm{d}z \right| \leqslant 2\pi \frac{e^{-aR}}{1-e^{-R}}$$

$$\to 0 \quad \text{as } R \to +\infty,$$

since, by hypothesis, $a > 0$. As $0 < a < 1$, it follows, letting $R \to +\infty$ in (17), that

$$\int\limits_{-\infty}^{+\infty} \frac{e^{ax}}{1+e^x} \, \mathrm{d}x - e^{2a\pi i} \int\limits_{-\infty}^{+\infty} \frac{e^{ax}}{1+e^x} \, \mathrm{d}x = -2\pi i e^{a\pi i},$$

whence

$$\int\limits_{-\infty}^{+\infty} \frac{e^{ax}}{1+e^x} \, \mathrm{d}x = -2\pi i \frac{e^{a\pi i}}{1-e^{2a\pi i}} = \pi \frac{2i}{e^{a\pi i}-e^{-a\pi i}}$$

$$= \frac{\pi}{\sin a\pi} \quad (0 < a < 1). \tag{18}$$

It will be clear that this integral diverges for $a \leqslant 0$ and for $a \geqslant 1$.

Example 3. The integral

$$\int\limits_{-\infty}^{+\infty} \frac{e^{ax}-e^{bx}}{1-e^x} \, \mathrm{d}x \quad (0 < a < 1, \quad 0 < b < 1)$$

cannot be expressed as the difference of

$$\int\limits_{-\infty}^{+\infty} \frac{e^{ax}}{1-e^x}\, \mathrm{d}x \quad \text{and} \quad \int\limits_{-\infty}^{+\infty} \frac{e^{bx}}{1-e^x}\, \mathrm{d}x$$

since each of these integrals diverges, the integrands becoming infinite at $x = 0$. We note that, for $z = x + i\pi$,

$$1 - e^z = 1 - e^{x+i\pi} = 1 + e^x;$$

the expression $1 + e^x$ does not vanish for any real x, and it will be clear that we can use the result of Example 2, above, to evaluate the integrals of $e^{az}/(1-e^z)$ and $e^{bz}/(1-e^z)$ along the line $y = i\pi$, $-\infty < x < +\infty$. Accordingly, we take

$$f(z) = \frac{e^{az} - e^{bz}}{1 - e^z}$$

and choose as path of integration the contour shown in Fig. 110. The point $z = 0$ is excluded since $f(z)$ is not defined at this point; this is achieved by indenting the contour so that it passes along the semicircle c_r with centre at the origin and radius

$$r \quad (0 < r < 1 < R).$$

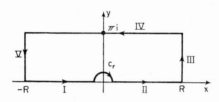

Fig. 110

The function $f(z)$ is regular inside and on this contour; hence, by Cauchy's theorem, we have, with an obvious notation,

$$\int\limits_{\mathrm{I}} + \int\limits_{c_r} + \int\limits_{\mathrm{II}} + \int\limits_{\mathrm{III}} + \int\limits_{\mathrm{IV}} + \int\limits_{\mathrm{V}} = 0. \tag{19}$$

In some deleted neighbourhood of $z = 0$ the function $f(z)$ is represented by the expansion

$$f(z) = \frac{\left\{1 + az + \frac{(az)^2}{2!} + \ldots\right\} - \left\{1 + bz + \frac{(bz)^2}{2!} + \ldots\right\}}{1 - \left\{1 + z + \frac{z^2}{2!} + \ldots\right\}}$$

$$= \frac{\left\{(a-b) + \frac{a^2 - b^2}{2!} z + \ldots\right\}}{-\left\{1 + \frac{z}{2!} + \ldots\right\}} = (b-a) + c_1 z + c_2 z^2 + \ldots \text{(say)},$$

whence $f(z)$ has this point as a removable singularity. Thus, $f(z)$ is bounded in some deleted neighbourhood of $z = 0$, and it follows that the integral

$$\int_{c_r} f(z)\, \mathrm{d}z$$

in (19) tends to 0 as $r \to +0$. By hypothesis, $0 < a < 1, 0 < b < 1$; it is then easily shown, as in the preceding example, that

$$\int_{\text{III}} f(z)\, \mathrm{d}z \quad \text{and} \quad \int_{\text{IV}} f(z)\, \mathrm{d}z$$

both tend to 0 as $R \to +\infty$. It is easily shown that

$$\int_{-\infty}^{+\infty} f(x)\, \mathrm{d}x$$

exists as a Cauchy–Riemann integral and is equal to the limit of

$$\left\{\int_r^R f(x)\, \mathrm{d}x + \int_{-R}^{-r} f(x)\, \mathrm{d}x\right\}$$

as $(r, R) \to (+0, +\infty)$. Accordingly, letting $r \to +0$ and $R \to +\infty$ in (19), we have

$$\int_{-\infty}^{0} \frac{e^{ax} - e^{bx}}{1 - e^x}\, \mathrm{d}x + \int_{0}^{+\infty} \frac{e^{ax} - e^{bx}}{1 - e^x}\, \mathrm{d}x + \int_{+\infty}^{-\infty} \frac{e^{a(x+\pi i)} - e^{b(x+\pi i)}}{1 - e^{x+\pi i}}\, \mathrm{d}x = 0,$$

whence, by Example 2,

$$\int_{-\infty}^{+\infty} \frac{e^{ax}-e^{bx}}{1-e^x}\,dx = \frac{\pi e^{a\pi i}}{\sin a\pi} - \frac{\pi e^{b\pi i}}{\sin b\pi} = \pi(\cot a\pi + i) - \pi(\cot b\pi + i)$$

$$= \pi(\cot a\pi - \cot b\pi) \quad (0 < a < 1, \ 0 < b < 1). \tag{20}$$

Example 4. The integral

$$\int_{0}^{+\infty} e^{-ax^2}\cos bx \,.\, dx \quad (a > 0)$$

occurs in the theory of heat conduction; it is a generalization of Poisson's integral (14). It is again easy to show that this integral exists as a Cauchy–Riemann integral and is equal to

$$\tfrac{1}{2}\lim_{R\to +\infty} \int_{-R}^{R} e^{-ax^2}\cos bx \,dx.$$

To evaluate it we consider the function

$$f(z) = e^{-az^2}.$$

On the real axis ($z = x$) this function equals e^{-ax^2}, so that its integral along the positive real axis is given by formula (14). On the straight line $y = h$ ($h = \text{const.}$), $f(z)$ is given by

$$e^{-a(x+ih)^2} = e^{-a(x^2-h^2)} \,.\, e^{-2ahxi} = e^{ah^2} \,.\, e^{-ax^2}(\cos 2ahx - i\sin 2ahx),$$

so that its real part on this line is e^{ah^2} times the integrand $e^{-ax^2}\cos bx$ in the given integral, provided $h = b/2a$. We shall suppose $b > 0$

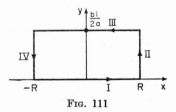

Fig. 111

and choose as path of integration the rectangular contour shown in Fig. 111. By Cauchy's theorem we have, with an obvious notation,

$$\int_{\mathrm{I}} + \int_{\mathrm{II}} + \int_{\mathrm{III}} + \int_{\mathrm{IV}} = 0.$$

Noting that e^{-ax^2} is an even function of x, and putting $t = x\sqrt{a}$, we have

$$\int_{\mathrm{I}} = \int_{-R}^{R} e^{-ax^2}\, \mathrm{d}x = \frac{2}{\sqrt{a}} \int_{0}^{R/\sqrt{a}} e^{-t^2}\cdot \mathrm{d}t;$$

letting $R \to +\infty$, and using (14), we see that

$$\lim_{R \to +\infty} \int_{\mathrm{I}} = \frac{2}{\sqrt{a}} \cdot \frac{\sqrt{\pi}}{2} = \sqrt{\frac{\pi}{a}}\,.$$

Also, we have

$$\int_{\mathrm{III}} = \int_{R}^{-R} e^{-a\{x+ib/(2a)\}^2}\cdot \mathrm{d}x = -e^{b^2/(4a)} \int_{-R}^{R} e^{-ax^2}\cdot e^{-ibx}\cdot \mathrm{d}x.$$

Finally, on the segments II and IV, where $x = \pm R$ $(0 \leqslant y \leqslant \tfrac{1}{2}b/a)$,

$$\left|e^{-az^2}\right| = \left|e^{-a(R^2-y^2 \pm 2iRy)}\right| = e^{-a(R^2-y^2)} \leqslant e^{b^2/(4a)} \cdot e^{-aR^2};$$

as $a > 0$, it follows readily that

$$\int_{\mathrm{II}} \quad \text{and} \quad \int_{\mathrm{IV}}$$

both tend to zero as $R \to +\infty$. Thus, letting $R \to +\infty$, we have

$$\sqrt{(\pi/a)} - e^{b^2/(4a)} \int_{-\infty}^{+\infty} e^{-ax^2}\cdot e^{-ibx}\, \mathrm{d}x = 0.$$

Equating real parts, and using the fact that $e^{-ax^2}\cos bx$ is an even function, we get

$$[\sqrt{(\pi/a)}]e^{-b^2/(4a)} = \int_{-\infty}^{+\infty} e^{-ax^2}\cos bx \cdot \mathrm{d}x = 2\int_{0}^{+\infty} e^{-ax^2}\cos bx \cdot \mathrm{d}x\,.$$

(Comparison of imaginary parts gives

$$\int_{-\infty}^{+\infty} e^{-ax^2}\sin bx \cdot \mathrm{d}x = 0;$$

this result is trivial, as the integrand is *odd*.) Thus, we have shown that, for $a > 0$, $b > 0$,

$$\int\limits_{0}^{+\infty} e^{-ax^2} \cos bx \,.\, \mathrm{d}x = \tfrac{1}{2}[\sqrt{(\pi/a)}]e^{-b^2/(4a)}. \tag{21}$$

It will be clear from (14) and the fact that $\cos(-bx) = \cos bx$ that (21) holds for $a > 0$ and *all* real values of b.

75. Integrals involving multi-valued functions

Example 1. We consider the integral

$$I = \int\limits_{0}^{1} \frac{\sqrt[4]{[x(1-x)^3]}}{(1+x)^3} \,\mathrm{d}x.$$

The integrand function in the complex domain,

$$f(z) = \sqrt[4]{[z(1-z)^3]}/(1+z)^3,$$

has the following properties: (1) in the domain D formed from the finite plane by removing the segment $[0, 1]$, $f(z)$ has four regular branches; (2) each branch assumes different values at matching points on the opposite edges of the cut; (3) each branch has a zero of second order at infinity. Property (1) follows from the fact that, if z makes one positive circuit of a contour enclosing both of the points 0 and 1, the corresponding increments in $\arg z$ and $\arg(1-z)$ are each 2π, so that the increment in $\arg[z(1-z)^3]$ is $2\pi + 3.2\pi = 8\pi$ and $\sqrt[4]{[z(1-z)^3]}$ returns to its original value. In what follows we shall suppose a particular (regular) branch of $f(z)$ has been chosen: for definiteness, suppose this branch to be the one which assumes positive values along the upper edge (I) of the cut $[0, 1]$. At points along I we take $\arg z = \arg(1-z) = 0$. We suppose the point z to make a circuit around the edges of the cut as indicated in Fig. 112: when z passes around the point 1, $\arg z$ remains equal to 0 but $\arg(1-z)$ becomes equal to -2π; thus the value of the root on the lower edge (II) differs from its value at a matching point on the edge (I) by a factor $e^{-i6\pi/4} = e^{-i3\pi/2} = i$. This establishes property (2). Finally, property (3) holds because, for large $|z|$, the numerator of $f(z)$ is of the same order as z whereas the order of the denominator is that of z^3. (For large $|z|$, the numerator is given by

$$\sqrt[4]{(-z^4 + 3z^3 - 3z^2 + z)} = z\left[-1 + \left(\frac{3}{z} - \frac{3}{z^2} + \frac{1}{z^3}\right)\right]^{1/4}$$

$$= \alpha z\left(1 + \frac{b_1}{z} + \frac{b_2}{z^2} + \ldots\right), \qquad \text{say,}$$

where α is a constant of unit modulus; thus, in some neighbourhood of infinity,

$$f(z) = \frac{\alpha z[1 + (b_1/z) + (b_2/z^2) + \ldots]}{z^3[1 + (3/z) + (3/z^2) + (1/z^3)]} = \frac{\alpha}{z^2}\left(1 + \frac{c_1}{z} + \frac{c_2}{z^2} + \ldots\right), \text{ say.})$$

We consider the regular branch of $f(z)$, selected above, in the bounded domain D whose frontier consists of the edges I and II and the circle C_R defined by $|z| = R$ (see Fig. 112); this domain is

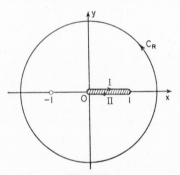

FIG. 112

multiply connected. It will be clear that the residue theorem continues to hold even when one component of the boundary consists of the (adjacent) edges of a cut; thus, with an obvious notation,

$$\int_I + \int_{II} + \oint_{C_R} = 2\pi i c_{-1}$$

where c_{-1} is the residue of the chosen branch of $f(z)$ at $z = -1$. By property (3),

$$\oint_{C_R}$$

vanishes for all sufficiently large R since the residue of this branch at infinity is zero (see Art. 69). By property (2), the integrals

$$\int_I \text{ and } \int_{II}$$

along the edges of the cut [0, 1] do not cancel out:

$$\int\limits_{I} + \int\limits_{II} = \int\limits_{0}^{1} \frac{\sqrt[4]{[x(1-x)^3]}}{(1+x)^3}\,\mathrm{d}x + i \int\limits_{1}^{0} \frac{\sqrt[4]{[x(1-x)^3]}}{(1+x)^3}\,\mathrm{d}x = (1-i)I,$$

whence

$$I = \frac{2\pi i}{1-i}\, c_{-1}. \qquad (22)$$

It remains to find the residue c_{-1}: the chosen branch of $f(z)$ has a pole of third order at $z = -1$, so that, by formula (40) of Art. 67,

$$c_{-1} = \tfrac{1}{2} \lim_{z \to -1} \left[\frac{\mathrm{d}^2}{\mathrm{d}z^2}\{(1+z)^3 f(z)\} \right]$$

$$= \tfrac{1}{2}\left[\frac{\mathrm{d}^2}{\mathrm{d}z^2}\, \sqrt[4]{\{z(1-z)^3\}} \right]_{z=-1}.$$

In performing this calculation we must be careful to restrict ourselves to the chosen branch of $f(z)$; for this branch the arguments of z and $1-z$ at $z = -1$ are to be taken equal to π and 0, respectively, so that, following the differentiation we put $z = e^{i\pi}$, $1-z = 2$. Using Leibnitz's formula, we have

$$c_{-1} = \tfrac{1}{2}[\tfrac{1}{4}(-\tfrac{3}{4})z^{-7/4}(1-z)^{3/4} - 2\cdot\tfrac{1}{4}z^{-3/4}\cdot\tfrac{3}{4}(1-z)^{-1/4}$$

$$+ z^{1/4}\cdot\tfrac{3}{4}(-\tfrac{1}{4})(1-z)^{-5/4}]_{z=-1}$$

$$= \tfrac{1}{2}\{\tfrac{3}{16}e^{-7\pi i/4}\cdot 2^{3/4} - \tfrac{3}{8}e^{-3\pi i/4}\cdot 2^{-1/4} - \tfrac{3}{16}e^{i\pi/4}\cdot 2^{-5/4}\}$$

$$= -\frac{3}{64\sqrt[4]{2}}e^{i\pi/4} = -\frac{3\sqrt[4]{2}}{128}(1+i).$$

From (22) it follows that

$$I = \int\limits_{0}^{1} \frac{\sqrt[4]{[x(1-x)^3]}}{(1+x)^3}\,\mathrm{d}x = -\frac{2\pi i}{1-i}\cdot\frac{3\sqrt[4]{2}}{128}(1+i) = \frac{3\pi\sqrt[4]{2}}{64}. \qquad 3)$$

Example 2. To evaluate the integral

$$I = \int\limits_{0}^{+\infty} \frac{\ln x}{(x^2+1)^2}\,\mathrm{d}x$$

we choose the contour shown in Fig. 113 ($0 < r < 1 < R$); the contour is indented around the origin since the integrand becomes infinite at $z = 0$. In the interior domain bounded by this contour the function

$$f(z) = \frac{\ln z}{(z^2+1)^2}$$

is single-valued; here, ln denotes the principal branch of the logarithm (that is, we suppose $0 \leqslant \arg z \leqslant \pi$). The function has a pole of the second order at $z = i$, the corresponding residue being

$$c_{-1} = \lim_{z \to i}\left[\frac{\mathrm{d}}{\mathrm{d}z}\{(z-i)^2 f(z)\}\right] = \left[\frac{\mathrm{d}}{\mathrm{d}z}\frac{\ln z}{(z+i)^2}\right]_{z\,=\,i} = \frac{\pi+2i}{8}\,.$$

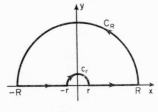

Fig. 113

By Cauchy's residue theorem, we have, with an obvious notation,

$$\int\limits_{-R}^{-r} + \int\limits_{c_r} + \int\limits_{r}^{R} + \int\limits_{C_R} = 2\pi i c_{-1} = \frac{\pi^2}{4}i - \frac{\pi}{2}\,.$$

To find a bound for

$$\int\limits_{C_R}$$

we note that, for $z = Re^{i\phi}$ $(R > e^\pi, 0 \leqslant \phi \leqslant \pi)$,

$$|\ln z| = \sqrt{\{(\ln R)^2 + \phi^2\}} \leqslant \sqrt{\{(\ln R)^2 + \pi^2\}} < (\sqrt{2}) \ln R$$

and

$$\frac{1}{|z^2+1|^2} \leqslant \frac{1}{R^4[1-(1/R^2)]^2} < \frac{1}{R^4[1-(1/2^2)]^2} = \frac{16}{9R^4},$$

since

$$\pi < \ln R \quad \text{and} \quad 1 - \frac{1}{R^2} > 1 - \frac{1}{(e^\pi)^2} > 1 - \frac{1}{2^2}.$$

Thus, by the fundamental inequality for integrals,

$$\left| \int_{C_R} \right| \leqslant \frac{16(\sqrt{2}) \ln R}{9R^4} \pi R, \qquad (R > e^\pi)$$

and it follows immediately that

$$\int_{C_R} \to 0 \quad \text{as} \quad R \to +\infty.$$

To find a bound for

$$\int_{c_r}$$

we use the fact that, for $z = re^{i\phi}$ $(0 < r < e^{-\pi}, 0 \leqslant \phi \leqslant \pi)$,

$$|\ln z| = \sqrt{\{(\ln r)^2 + \phi^2\}} \leqslant (\sqrt{2}) \ln(1/r)$$

and

$$\frac{1}{|z^2+1|^2} \leqslant \frac{1}{(1-r^2)^2} < \frac{1}{[1-\{1/(e^\pi)^2\}]^2} < \frac{1}{(1-1/2^2)^2} = \frac{16}{9}.$$

Accordingly,

$$\left| \int_{c_r} \right| \leqslant \frac{16\sqrt{2}}{9} \pi r \ln(1/r),$$

and it follows that

$$\int_{c_r} \to 0$$

as $r \to +0$. Thus, in the limit, as $r \to +0$ and $R \to +\infty$, we have:

$$\int\limits_{-\infty}^{0} \frac{\ln z}{(z^2+1)^2}\,\mathrm{d}z + \int\limits_{0}^{+\infty} \frac{\ln x}{(x^2+1)^2}\,\mathrm{d}x = \frac{\pi^2}{4}i - \frac{\pi}{2}.$$

For $z < 0$, $\ln z = \ln(-z) + i\pi$; thus, writing $z = -x$ and $\mathrm{d}z = -\mathrm{d}x$, we have

$$\int\limits_{-\infty}^{0} \frac{\ln z}{(z^2+1)^2}\,\mathrm{d}z = \int\limits_{-\infty}^{0} \frac{\ln(-z)}{(z^2+1)^2}\,\mathrm{d}z + i\pi \int\limits_{-\infty}^{0} \frac{\mathrm{d}z}{(z^2+1)^2}$$

$$= \int\limits_{0}^{+\infty} \frac{\ln x}{(x^2+1)^2}\,\mathrm{d}x + i\pi \int\limits_{0}^{+\infty} \frac{\mathrm{d}x}{(x^2+1)^2},$$

so that

$$2\int\limits_{0}^{+\infty} \frac{\ln x}{(x^2+1)^2}\,\mathrm{d}x + i\pi \int\limits_{0}^{+\infty} \frac{\mathrm{d}x}{(x^2+1)^2} = \frac{\pi^2}{4}i - \frac{\pi}{2}. \qquad (24)$$

Equating real parts in this relation we find

$$I = \int\limits_{0}^{+\infty} \frac{\ln x}{(x^2+1)^2}\,\mathrm{d}x = -\frac{\pi}{4}. \qquad (25)$$

Equating imaginary parts we obtain the elementary result

$$\int\limits_{0}^{+\infty} \frac{\mathrm{d}x}{(x^2+1)^2} = \frac{\pi}{4}.$$

(It is easily shown that all the Cauchy–Riemann integrals appearing above exist finitely.)

Example 3. To evaluate the integral

$$\int\limits_{0}^{+\infty} \frac{\ln x}{(x+a)^2+b^2}\,\mathrm{d}x \qquad (a,\ b \text{ real};\ b > 0)$$

we choose the contour shown in Fig. 114 $(0 < r < \sqrt{(a^2+b^2)} < R)$ and consider the auxiliary function

$$f(z) = \frac{(\ln z)^2}{(z+a)^2+b^2}.$$

Here, ln denotes a branch of the logarithm such that, for $z \neq 0$, $\ln z = \ln|z| + i\theta$ where $z = |z|e^{i\theta}$, $0 < \theta < 2\pi$; then, on the upper and lower edges (II and I) of the cut $[r, R]$, where $z = x$, the respective values assumed by $(\ln z)^2$ under continuous extension are $(\ln x)^2$ and $(\ln x + 2\pi i)^2 = (\ln x)^2 + 4\pi i \ln x - 4\pi^2$. It will be clear

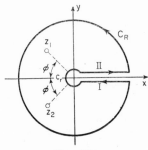

Fig. 114

that the integrals along I and II of the term involving $(\ln x)^2$ will cancel, so that we shall be able to evaluate the required integral. In the domain enclosed by our contour, $f(z)$ has exactly two singularities: these are first order poles and are situated at the points $z_1 = -a+ib$, $z_2 = -a-ib$, the corresponding residues being

$$c_{-1}' = (\ln z_1)^2 \Big/ \left[\frac{d}{dz}\{(z+a)^2+b^2\}\right]_{z=z_1} = \{\ln(-a+ib)\}^2/(2bi)$$

$$= \{\ln \rho + i(\pi-\phi)\}^2/(2bi),$$

$$c_{-1}'' = (\ln z_2)^2 \Big/ \left[\frac{d}{dz}\{(z+a)^2+b^2\}\right]_{z=z_2} = \{\ln(-a-ib)\}^2/(-2bi)$$

$$= \{\ln \rho + i(\pi+\phi)\}^2/(-2bi),$$

where $\rho = \sqrt{(a^2+b^2)}$ and $\phi = \arctan(b/a)$ $(0 < \phi < \pi)$. Thus, with the usual notation, it follows from Cauchy's residue theorem that

$$\int_I + \int_{c_r} + \int_{II} + \int_{C_R} = 2\pi i(c_{-1}' + c_{-1}'') = \frac{\pi}{b} 4\phi(\pi - i \ln \rho).$$

In the same way as in the preceding example we can show that

$$\lim_{r \to +0} \int_{c_r} = \lim_{R \to +\infty} \int_{C_R} = 0;$$

accordingly, if we let $r \to +0$ and $R \to +\infty$, it follows from the above that

$$\int_{+\infty}^{0} \frac{(\ln x + 2\pi i)^2}{(x+a)^2 + b^2} \, dx + \int_{0}^{+\infty} \frac{(\ln x)^2}{(x+a)^2 + b^2} \, dx$$

$$= -4\pi i \int_{0}^{+\infty} \frac{\ln x}{(x+a)^2 + b^2} \, dx + 4\pi^2 \int_{0}^{+\infty} \frac{dx}{(x+a)^2 + b^2}$$

$$= -\frac{4\pi\phi}{b}(-\pi + i \ln \rho) \,,$$

all four Cauchy–Riemann integrals existing finitely. Comparison of the imaginary parts gives the required integral:

$$\int_{0}^{+\infty} \frac{\ln x}{(x+a)^2 + b^2} \, dx = \frac{\phi \ln \rho}{b} = \frac{\ln(a^2 + b^2)}{2b} \cdot \text{arc} \tan \frac{b}{a}$$

$$(a, b \text{ real}; \ b > 0; \ 0 < \text{arc} \tan(b/a) < \pi). \quad (26)$$

(It will be clear that $\text{arc} \tan(b/a) = \pi/2$ if $a = 0$.)

Example 4. To evaluate the integral

$$I = \int_{0}^{+\infty} \frac{x^{a-1}}{1+x} \, dx \qquad (0 < a < 1)$$

we again take the contour shown in Fig. 114 $(0 < r < 1 < R)$. The auxiliary function considered is

$$f(z) = \frac{z^{a-1}}{1+z} = \frac{e^{(a-1)\ln z}}{1+z};$$

here, again, $\ln z = \ln|z| + i\theta$ ($z = |z|e^{i\theta}$, $0 < \theta < 2\pi$) and $f(z)$ is defined on the edges I and II of the cut $[r, R]$ by continuity from within the enclosed domain D, so that $f(z) = e^{(a-1)\ln x}/(1+x)$ on II and $f(z) = e^{(a-1)(\ln x + i2\pi)}/(1+x)$ on I. The function $f(z)$ is regular at all points of D other than the point $z = -1$ where $f(z)$ has a pole of first order, the corresponding residue being

$$\operatorname{res} f(-1) = \frac{e^{(a-1)\ln(-1)}}{[(d/dz)(1+z)]_{z=-1}} = e^{i\pi(a-1)} = -e^{ia\pi}.$$

Accordingly, by Cauchy's residue theorem,

$$\int_{\text{I}} + \int_{c_r} + \int_{\text{II}} + \int_{C_R} = -2\pi i e^{ia\pi}.$$

To find a bound for

$$\int_{C_R}$$

we note that, for $|z| = R > 1$,

$$|f(z)| = R^{a-1}/|1+z| \leqslant R^{a-1}/(R-1);$$

thus, for $R > 1$, since $a < 1$,

$$\left| \int_{C_R} \right| \leqslant 2\pi R^a/(R-1) \to 0 \quad \text{as} \quad R \to +\infty.$$

Similarly, if $|z| = r < 1$,

$$|f(z)| = r^{a-1}/|1+z| \leqslant r^{a-1}/(1-r);$$

thus, for $0 < r < 1$,

$$\left| \int_{c_r} \right| \leqslant 2\pi r^a/(1-r).$$

As $a > 0$, it follows that

$$\int_{c_r} \to 0$$

as $r \to +0$. Thus, in the limit, as $r \to +0$ and $R \to +\infty$, we have

$$\int\limits_{\substack{+\infty \\ (\mathrm{I})}}^{0} f(z)\,\mathrm{d}z + \int\limits_{\substack{0 \\ (\mathrm{II})}}^{+\infty} f(z)\,\mathrm{d}z = -2\pi i e^{ia\pi},$$

both Cauchy–Riemann integrals existing finitely. On the upper edge II, $z = x$ and $f(z) = x^{a-1}/(1+x)$; on the lower edge I, $z = x e^{i2\pi}$ and

$$f(z) = \frac{x^{a-1}e^{i2\pi(a-1)}}{1 + x e^{i2\pi}} = e^{ia2\pi}\frac{x^{a-1}}{1+x}.$$

Accordingly, we have

$$-e^{i2a\pi}\int\limits_{0}^{+\infty}\frac{x^{a-1}}{1+x}\,\mathrm{d}x + \int\limits_{0}^{+\infty}\frac{x^{a-1}}{1+x}\,\mathrm{d}x = -2\pi i e^{ia\pi},$$

whence

$$I = \int\limits_{0}^{+\infty}\frac{x^{a-1}}{1+x}\,\mathrm{d}x = \frac{2\pi i e^{ia\pi}}{e^{i2a\pi}-1}$$

$$= \pi\frac{2i}{e^{ia\pi}-e^{-ia\pi}} = \frac{\pi}{\sin a\pi}\quad (0 < a < 1). \tag{27}$$

This integral can be obtained from that of Example 2 in Art. 74 by putting $t = e^x$ in the latter.

76. The representation of functions by integrals

We consider the integral

$$f(t) = \frac{1}{2\pi i}\int\limits_{a-i\infty}^{a+i\infty}\frac{e^{zt}}{z}\,\mathrm{d}z,$$

the path of integration being the straight line $\operatorname{Re} z = a(a > 0)$ parallel to the imaginary axis. To begin, we suppose $t < 0$. For any given value of t the function e^{zt}/z is regular inside and on the contour formed from the arc C_R of the circle $|z| = R$ $(R > a)$ and the segment of the line Re $z = a$ which joins the points $a - ih$ and $a + ih$ (see Fig. 115); by Cauchy's theorem (Art. 47),

$$\int_{a-ih}^{a+ih} \frac{e^{zt}}{z}\, dz + \int_{C_R} \frac{e^{zt}}{z}\, dz = 0. \tag{28}$$

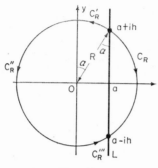

Fig. 115

Here, $h = \sqrt{(R^2 - a^2)}$ and the contour is described in the negative (clockwise) sense. To find a bound for the second integral in (28) we can use the formula for integration by parts:

$$\int_{C_R} \frac{e^{zt}}{z}\, dz = \frac{1}{t} \int_{C_R} \frac{1}{z}\left(\frac{d}{dz} e^{zt}\right) dz = -\frac{1}{t}\left[\frac{e^{zt}}{z}\right]_{a-ih}^{a+ih} + \frac{1}{t} \int_{C_R} \frac{e^{zt}}{z^2}\, dz.$$

As a and t are fixed, we have

$$\left|\frac{1}{t}\left[\frac{e^{zt}}{z}\right]_{a-ih}^{a+ih}\right| = \left|\frac{1}{t}\left(\frac{e^{(a+ih)t}}{a+ih} - \frac{e^{(a-ih)t}}{a-ih}\right)\right|$$

$$\leqslant \frac{2e^{at}}{|t|\,.\,R} \to 0 \text{ as } R \to +\infty.$$

Also, on C_R, $|e^{zt}/z^2| = e^{xt}/R^2 \leqslant 1/R^2$ (since $x > 0$, $t < 0$, so that $e^{xt} < 1$); thus,

$$\left|\int_{C_R} \frac{e^{zt}}{z^2}\, dz\right| \leqslant \frac{1}{R^2}\pi R = \frac{\pi}{R} \to 0 \text{ as } R \to +\infty.$$

Accordingly, letting $R \to +\infty$ in (28), it follows that

$$2\pi i f(t) = \int_{a-i\infty}^{a+i\infty} \frac{e^{zt}}{z}\, \mathrm{d}z = 0, \qquad (t < 0),$$

so that $f(t) = 0$ whenever $t < 0$. Now suppose $t > 0$. The function e^{zt}/z has only one singularity in the finite plane, a first-order pole at $z = 0$; the residue at this point is

$$c_{-1} = 1/[(\mathrm{d}/\mathrm{d}z)z]_{z=0} = 1.$$

Taking the integral of e^{zt}/z around the contour formed from the circular arcs $C_R{}'$, $C_R{}''$, $C_R{}'''$ and the line-segment joining $a-ih$ to $a+ih$ (see Fig. 115), it follows from Cauchy's residue theorem, with an obvious notation, that

$$\int_{a-ih}^{a+ih} + \int_{C_R{}'} + \int_{C_R{}''} + \int_{C_R{}'''} = 2\pi i c_{-1} = 2\pi i. \qquad (29)$$

The length of each of the arcs $C_R{}'$, $C_R{}'''$ is $\alpha R = R$. arc $\sin(a/R)$, which tends to a as $R \to +\infty$; also, on each of these arcs the modulus of the integrand is $|e^{zt}/z| = e^{xt}/R \leqslant e^{at}/R$, which tends to zero as $R \to +\infty$, since $x \leqslant a$ and t, a are supposed fixed. It follows that

$$\int_{C_R{}'} \quad \text{and} \quad \int_{C_R{}'''}$$

both tend to zero as $R \to +\infty$. To find a bound for

$$\int_{C_R{}''}$$

we can again use the formula for integration by parts:

$$\int_{C_R{}''} = \frac{1}{t} \int_{C_R{}''} \frac{1}{z}\Big(\frac{\mathrm{d}}{\mathrm{d}z}e^{zt}\Big)\, \mathrm{d}z = \frac{1}{t}\Big[\frac{e^{zt}}{z}\Big]_{iR}^{-iR} + \frac{1}{t} \int_{C_R{}''} \frac{e^{zt}}{z^2}\, \mathrm{d}z.$$

We have

$$\Big|\frac{e^{-iRt}}{-iR} - \frac{e^{iRt}}{iR}\Big| \leqslant \frac{2}{R}, \qquad \Big|\frac{e^{zt}}{z^2}\Big| = \frac{e^{xt}}{R^2} \leqslant \frac{1}{R^2},$$

since $x \leqslant 0$ on C_R'' and $t > 0$, and it follows that

$$\int_{C_R''} \to 0$$

as $R \to +\infty$. Thus, letting $R \to +\infty$ in (29), we see that

$$2\pi i f(t) = \int_{a-i\infty}^{a+i\infty} \frac{e^{zt}}{z}\,\mathrm{d}z = 2\pi i \qquad (t > 0),$$

so that $f(t) = 1$ whenever $t > 0$.

Combining the above results we have

$$f(t) = \frac{1}{2\pi i} \int_{a-i\infty}^{a+i\infty} \frac{e^{zt}}{z}\,\mathrm{d}z = \begin{cases} 0 \text{ for } t < 0, \\ 1 \text{ for } t > 0. \end{cases} \qquad (30)$$

Thus the integral in (30) represents the function whose graph is shown in Fig. 116. (Taking $t = 0$ we obtain the divergent integral

$$\frac{1}{2\pi i} \int_{a-i\infty}^{a+i\infty} \frac{\mathrm{d}z}{z};$$

however, the *Cauchy principal value* for this integral exists finitely, being given by

$$\lim_{N \to +\infty} \frac{1}{2\pi i} \int_{a-iN}^{a+iN} \frac{\mathrm{d}z}{z} = \frac{1}{2\pi i} \lim_{N \to +\infty} \ln\frac{a+iN}{a-iN} = \frac{1}{2\pi i} \ln(-1) = \tfrac{1}{2};$$

it will be seen that its value is the arithmetic mean of the limits, on the left and right at $t = 0$, of the function $f(t)$.)

It will be clear that if, in (30), we replace t by $t - \tau$ we obtain the integral

$$\frac{1}{2\pi i} \int_{a-i\infty}^{a+i\infty} \frac{e^{z(t-\tau)}}{z}\,\mathrm{d}z = \begin{cases} 0 \text{ for } t < \tau, \\ 1 \text{ for } t > \tau. \end{cases} \qquad (31)$$

Thus, if we replace τ in (31), first by τ_1 and then by τ_2 ($\tau_1 < \tau_2$) and then subtract the two integrals so obtained, we obtain the following integral representation of the function whose graph is shown in Fig. 117:

$$\frac{1}{2\pi i} \int_{a-i\infty}^{a+i\infty} e^{zt} \frac{e^{-z\tau_1} - e^{-z\tau_2}}{z}\, dz = \begin{cases} 0 \text{ for } t < \tau_1, \\ 1 \text{ for } \tau_1 < t < \tau_2, \\ 0 \text{ for } t > \tau_2. \end{cases} \tag{32}$$

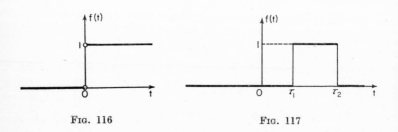

FIG. 116   FIG. 117

In the same way we find the following integral representation of an arbitrary step function such as that shown in Fig. 118:

$$\frac{1}{2\pi i} \sum_{k=0}^{n-1} f(\tau_k) \int_{a-i\infty}^{a+i\infty} e^{zt} \frac{e^{-z\tau_k} - e^{-z\tau_{k+1}}}{z}\, dz$$

$$= \frac{1}{2\pi i} \int_{a-i\infty}^{a+i\infty} e^{zt}\{ \sum_{k=0}^{n-1} f(\tau_k)\, e^{-z\tau_k} \cdot \Delta\tau_k\}dz, \tag{33}$$

where

$$\Delta\tau_k = \frac{1 - e^{-z(\tau_{k+1} - \tau_k)}}{z}$$

$$= (\tau_{k+1} - \tau_k) - \frac{(\tau_{k+1} - \tau_k)^2}{2!}z + \frac{(\tau_{k+1} - \tau_k)^3}{3!}z^2 - \ldots.$$

We now suppose that the number of points τ_k subdividing the interval $[\tau_0, \tau]$ is increased without limit so that the greatest of the differences $(\tau_{k+1} - \tau_k)$ tends to $+0$; then, to the first order of the small quantities concerned, we have $\Delta \tau_k \fallingdotseq (\tau_{k+1} - \tau_k)$, and it will be seen that the sum under the integral sign on the right in (33) will tend, under appropriate conditions, to the integral

$$\int\limits_{\tau_0}^{\tau} f(\tau) \, . \, e^{-z\tau} \, \mathrm{d}\tau;$$

in this way it can be shown that an integral representation of $f(t)$ on the interval $[\tau_0, \tau]$ (see Fig. 118) is

$$f(t) = \frac{1}{2\pi i} \int\limits_{a-i\infty}^{a+i\infty} e^{zt} \left\{ \int\limits_{\tau_0}^{\tau} f(\tau) \, . \, e^{-z\tau} \, \mathrm{d}\tau \right\} \mathrm{d}z.$$

Some care is required in giving a strict proof of this result since $|z|$ is unbounded on the path of integration in the outer integral.

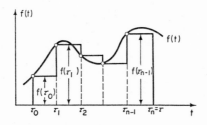

FIG. 118

Omitting a strict proof, we shall content ourselves with stating that this last result holds in the form

$$f(t) = \frac{1}{2\pi i} \int\limits_{a-i\infty}^{a+i\infty} e^{zt} \left\{ \int\limits_{-\infty}^{+\infty} f(\tau) \, . \, e^{-z\tau} \, \mathrm{d}\tau \right\} \mathrm{d}z \tag{34}$$

whenever $f(t)$ is a function which is defined on the whole of the real axis and satisfies the following conditions:

(a) in any finite interval $(-T, T)$ of the real axis $f(t)$ is piecewise smooth (that is, its graph is represented by a piecewise smooth curve; see Art. 8);

(b) the integral

$$\int\limits_{-\infty}^{+\infty} e^{-at} f(t)\, dt$$

converges *absolutely*.

Formula (34) can be written as a pair of formulae:

$$f(t) = \frac{1}{2\pi i} \int\limits_{a-i\infty}^{a+i\infty} e^{zt} g(z)\, dz,$$

where

$$g(z) = \int\limits_{-\infty}^{+\infty} e^{-z\tau} f(\tau)\, d\tau. \tag{35}$$

The function $g(z)$ corresponding with the function $f(t)$ according to the second of the formulae (35) is called the *Laplace transform of* $f(t)$. The first of the formulae (35) is the "inverse" of the second: that is, it expresses the function $f(t)$ in terms of its "transform" $g(z)$. It can also be said that the second formula of (35) is the inverse of the first; for this reason both the formulae in (35) are sometimes called *Laplace transforms*. Laplace transforms are used in solving many problems in mathematical physics. (See, e.g., H. S. Carslaw and J. C. Jaeger, *Operational Methods in Applied Mathematics*, Oxford, 1940; or M. A. Lavrent'ev and B. V. Shabat, *Methods of the Theory of Functions of a Complex Variable*, (Metody teorii funktsii kompleksnogo peremennogo) Fizmatgiz, 1958, Ch. VI.)

77. The logarithmic residue. The principle of the argument

The *logarithmic residue* at $z = a$ of a function $f(z)$ which is regular and non-vanishing in some deleted neighbourhood of this point is the residue of the logarithmic derivative $f'(z)/f(z)$ at $z = a$. We note that the logarithmic derivative $f'(z)/f(z)$ may have singularities, not only at singular points of $f(z)$, but also at the zeros of $f(z)$. For, let the point a be a zero of $f(z)$ of order n; then (see Art. 62) its Taylor expansion in some neighbourhood of a has the form

$$f(z) = c_n(z-a)^n + c_{n+1}(z-a)^{n+1} + \ldots \qquad (c_n \neq 0)$$

so that, in this neighbourhood

$$f'(z) = nc_n(z-a)^{n-1} + (n+1)c_{n+1}(z-a)^n + \ldots$$

and the logarithmic derivative in the corresponding deleted neighbourhood is

$$\frac{f'(z)}{f(z)} = \frac{nc_n(z-a)^{n-1} + (n+1)c_{n+1}(z-a)^n + \ldots}{c_n(z-a)^n + c_{n+1}(z-a)^{n+1} + \ldots}$$

$$= \frac{1}{z-a} \cdot \frac{nc_n + (n+1)c_{n+1}(z-a) + \ldots}{c_n + c_{n+1}(z-a) + \ldots}.$$

As the quotient of two regular functions is regular at a point at which the divisor does not vanish, this quotient can be represented in some neighbourhood of the point concerned as a power series whose constant term is the ratio of the constant terms in the corresponding Taylor expansions of the numerator and divisor; accordingly, in some deleted neighbourhood of $z = a$ we have

$$\frac{f'(z)}{f(z)} = \frac{1}{z-a}\{n + c_0'(z-a) + c_1'(z-a)^2 + \ldots\}$$

$$= \frac{n}{z-a} + c_0' + c_1'(z-a) + \ldots . \tag{36}$$

We have thus obtained the Laurent expansion of the logarithmic derivative $f'(z)/f(z)$ in a deleted neighbourhood of a; it will be clear that $f'(z)/f(z)$ has a first-order pole at $z = a$, the residue at this pole being n. Thus, the *logarithmic residue of a regular function at a zero is equal to the order of that zero.*

Now suppose $f(z)$ has a pole of order p at $z = b$: in some deleted neighbourhood of b we then have

$$f(z) = \frac{c_{-p}}{(z-b)^p} + \frac{c_{-p+1}}{(z-b)^{p-1}} + \ldots \qquad (c_{-p} \neq 0)$$

$$f'(z) = \frac{-pc_{-p}}{(z-b)^{p+1}} + \frac{-(p-1)c_{-p+1}}{(z-b)^p} + \ldots,$$

and

$$\frac{f'(z)}{f(z)} = \frac{1}{z-b} \cdot \frac{-\{pc_{-p} + (p-1)c_{-p+1}(z-b) + \ldots\}}{c_{-p} + c_{-p+1}(z-b) + \ldots}$$

$$= \frac{1}{z-b}\{-p + c_0'(z-b) + c_1'(z-b)^2 + \ldots\}.$$

22

Accordingly, the Laurent expansion of the logarithmic derivative in some deleted neighbourhood of b is given by

$$\frac{f'(z)}{f(z)} = \frac{-p}{z-b} + c_0' + c_1'(z-b) + \ldots . \tag{37}$$

It follows from (37) that $f'(z)/f(z)$ has a first-order pole at $z = b$, the corresponding residue being $-p$. Thus *the logarithmic residue of $f(z)$ at a pole of $f(z)$ is equal to the order of this pole with the sign reversed.*

We use the above results in establishing what is known as the *principle of the argument.* Let D be the interior domain bounded by a contour C and let $f(z)$ be a function which is regular and non-zero at all points of C and has no singularities in D other than poles. We denote the set of these poles by S_1; then, S_1 is either empty or finite: for, if the set S_1 were infinite it would follow (since $\bar{D}$ is bounded) that S_1 has at least one limit point (z_0, say) in $\bar{D}$; such a point z_0 would be a non-isolated singularity of $f(z)$, being a limit-point of poles of $f(z)$, and this would contradict our hypothesis that $f(z)$ has no singularities on $\bar{D}$ other than poles. Similarly, the set S_2 of points in D at which $f(z)$ vanishes is either empty or finite: for, otherwise, it would follow from the identity theorem that $f(z) \equiv 0$ on the domain D_1 formed from D by removing the finite set of points S_1 at which $f(z)$ has poles, and this would imply that $f(z) \equiv 0$ on C, contradicting our hypothesis that $f(z)$ is non-zero at all points of C. Thus we suppose $f(z)$ to have poles at the (finite) set of points $b_1, b_2, \ldots, b_m$ in D, the respective orders being $p_1, p_2, \ldots, p_m$; and that the zeros of $f(z)$ in D consist of the (finite) set of points $a_1, a_2, \ldots, a_l$, the respective orders of these zeros being $n_1, n_2, \ldots, n_l$.

Under the above conditions on $f(z)$ the logarithmic derivative $f'(z)/f(z)$ is regular on C, and has in D at most a finite number of singularities. By Cauchy's residue theorem and the results obtained at the beginning of this article, we have

$$\oint_C \frac{f'(z)}{f(z)} \, dz = 2\pi i(n_1 + n_2 + \ldots + n_l - p_1 - p_2 - \ldots - p_m)$$

$$= 2\pi i(N - P), \tag{38}$$

where N and P denote respectively the number of zeros and poles of $f(z)$ within C, each zero or pole being accorded its appropriate multiplicity.

We now consider the integral on the left in (38). We use the result that, if $F(z)$ is regular in a simply-connected domain D_1 of the finite plane, then

$$F(z_2) - F(z_1) = \int_{\substack{z_1 \\ (k)}}^{z_2} F'(z)\, \mathrm{d}z,$$

where z_1, z_2 are any two points in D_1 and k is any piecewise smooth path in D_1 connecting z_1 to z_2. Let ζ be any point on C; then $f(z)$ is regular at ζ and $f(\zeta) \neq 0$, whence there exists a $\rho = \rho(\zeta) > 0$ such that $f(z)$ is regular and

$$|f(z) - f(\zeta)| < \tfrac{1}{2}|f(\zeta)|$$

whenever $|z - \zeta| < \rho$. Then,

$$|f(z)| \geqslant |f(\zeta)| - |f(z) - f(\zeta)| > \tfrac{1}{2}|f(\zeta)| > 0$$

whenever $|z - \zeta| < \rho$, and it follows that there exists a regular branch of $\operatorname{Ln} f(z)$ in $|z - \zeta| < \rho$. We denote this branch by $\ln f(z)$; then,

$$\frac{\mathrm{d}}{\mathrm{d}z} \ln f(z) = \frac{f'(z)}{f(z)}$$

in $|z - \zeta| < \rho$ and

$$\int_{\substack{z_1 \\ (k)}}^{z_2} \frac{f'(z)}{f(z)}\, \mathrm{d}z = \ln f(z_1) - \ln f(z_2)$$

where z_1, z_2 are any two points in $|z - \zeta| < \rho$ and the path k connecting these points lies in this same ρ-neighbourhood of ζ. Every point ζ on C is the centre of such a ρ-neighbourhood; as C is bounded and closed, it follows from the Heine–Borel theorem that C can be covered by a finite number of overlapping neighbourhoods of this type. It follows that

$$\oint_C \frac{f'(z)}{f(z)}\, \mathrm{d}z = \Delta_C \ln f(z),$$

where $\ln f(z)$ denotes a value of the logarithm which *varies continuously* as z makes one complete circuit of C (beginning and ending at the point z_0, say) and $\Delta_C \ln f(z)$ denotes the corresponding variation in $\ln f(z)$. (In obtaining this result we could proceed as in the derivation of (33) in Art. 37.) We have

$$\ln f(z) = \ln|f(z)| + i \arg f(z),$$

where $\arg f(z)$ denotes a value of the argument which varies continuously as z makes one complete circuit of C; hence, with an obvious notation,

$$\Delta_C \ln f(z) = \Delta_C \ln|f(z)| + i\Delta_C \arg f(z),$$

where

$$\Delta_C \ln|f(z)| = \ln|f(z_0)| - \ln|f(z_0)| = 0.$$

It will be clear that the variation in $\arg f(z)$ will not be zero if, when z makes one complete circuit of C, the image point $w = f(z)$

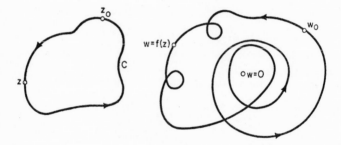

FIG. 119

makes one or more circuits about the origin $w = 0$. (For the case shown in Fig. 119 the final value of $\arg f(z)$ differs from the initial value by 6π.) Accordingly, we have

$$\oint_C \frac{f'(z)}{f(z)}\, dz = i\Delta_C \arg f(z),$$

and formula (38) becomes

$$\frac{1}{2\pi i} \oint_C \frac{f'(z)}{f(z)}\, dz = \frac{1}{2\pi}\Delta_C \arg f(z) = N - P. \tag{39}$$

This result expresses what is called the *principle of the argument*: *if $f(z)$ is regular and non-zero at all points of a contour C and has*

*no singularities other than poles in the interior domain D bounded
by C (from which it follows that $f(z)$ can have at most a finite number
of zeros or poles in D), then the total variation in* arg $f(z)$ *as z makes one
complete (positive) circuit of C is 2π times the difference between the
number of zeros and the number of poles of $f(z)$ in D.* (Here, arg $f(z)$
denotes a value of the argument which varies continuously as z
traces the curve C, and each zero and each pole is reckoned according to its multiplicity.)

To illustrate the application of the principle of the argument
we prove the following theorem due to Rouché:

*Let D be the interior domain bounded by a contour C ; then, if
$f(z)$ and $g(z)$ are regular on $\overline{D}$ and $|f(z)| > |g(z)|$ at each point z
on C, the functions $f(z)$ and $f(z)+g(z)$ have the same number of
zeros in D, each zero being counted according to its multiplicity.*

We define on C a function $F(z) = 1+[g(z)/f(z)]$. By the above
conditions on $f(z)$ and $g(z)$ it follows that, on C,

$$|f(z)| > |g(z)| \geqslant 0$$

and

$$|f(z)+g(z)| \geqslant |f(z)| - |g(z)| > 0,$$

so that

$$\left|\frac{g(z)}{f(z)}\right| < 1.$$

Accordingly, when z traces the curve C, the image point $\omega = F(z)$
remains in the disc $|\omega-1| < 1$. We choose values of arg $f(z)$
and arg $F(z)$ which vary continuously when z makes one complete
circuit of C; then, since $f(z)+g(z) = f(z) \cdot F(z)$ on C, it follows
that the value of arg$\{f(z)+g(z)\}$ defined on C by

$$\arg\{f(z)+g(z)\} = \arg f(z)+\arg F(z)$$

will also vary continuously when z makes one complete circuit of
C. As the disc $|\omega-1| < 1$ does not contain the point $\omega = 0$, it
follows that arg $F(z)$ returns to its original value when z makes one
complete circuit of C; accordingly, with this value of

$$\arg\{f(z)+g(z)\},$$
$$\Delta_C \arg\{f(z)+g(z)\} = \Delta_C \arg f(z).$$

The functions $f(z)$ and $f(z)+g(z)$ satisfy the conditions of the
above principle; as neither has a pole at any point of $\overline{D}$ it follows

(taking multiplicity into account) that $f(z)$ has the same number of zeros in D as the function $f(z)+g(z)$.

Rouche's theorem is often useful in finding the number of zeros of a function in a given domain:

Example 1. To find the number of roots of the equation

$$z^8-4z^5+z^2-1 = 0$$

in the disc $|z| < 1$ we take $f(z) = z^8-4z^5$, $g(z) = z^2-1$. On the circle $|z| = 1$ we have $|f(z)| = |z^3-4| \geqslant 4-|z^3| = 3$ and $|g(z)| \leqslant |z^2|+1 = 2$; thus, the conditions of Rouche's theorem are satisfied and it follows that the required number of roots is equal to the number of roots of the equation $z^8-4z^5 = z^5(z^3-4) = 0$ in the disc $|z| < 1$. Accordingly, the given equation has 5 roots in $|z| < 1$ since $z^3-4 \neq 0$ whenever $|z| < 1$.

Example 2. To find the number of roots of the equation

$$e^{z-\lambda} = z, \qquad (\lambda > 1)$$

in the same disc $|z| < 1$, we take $f(z) = z$ and $g(z) = -e^{z-\lambda}$. On the circle $|z| = 1$ we have $|f(z)| = 1$ and $|g(z)| = e^{x-\lambda} \leqslant e^{1-\lambda} < 1$, since $\lambda > 1$; thus, the number of zeros of $f(z)$ in $|z| < 1$ is equal to the number of zeros of $z-e^{z-\lambda}$ in $|z| < 1$. It follows immediately that the given equation has exactly one root in $|z| < 1$. We note that the continuous real function $\phi(x) = e^{x-\lambda}-x$ is positive for $x = 0$ and negative for $x = 1$ and hence vanishes at some point in the interval $(0, 1)$; it follows that the one zero of $e^{z-\lambda}-z$ in $|z| < 1$ is *positive*.

Example 3. We now prove what is known as the fundamental theorem of algebra: *every polynomial*

$$P(z) = a_0z^n+a_1z^{n-1}+ \ldots +a_n \qquad (a_0 \neq 0, \ n \geqslant 1)$$

of degree $n(\geqslant 1)$ has exactly n zeros (each zero being counted according to its multiplicity).

We take $f(z) = a_0z^n$ and $g(z) = a_1z^{n-1}+ \ldots +a_n$; then, on the circle $|z| = R$ we have $|f(z)| = |a_0|R^n$ and $|g(z)| \leqslant |a_1|R^{n-1}+ \ldots +|a_n|$. It follows immediately that

$$\lim_{z \to \infty} \left| \frac{g(z)}{f(z)} \right| = 0,$$

so that there exists a finite positive R_0 such that $|g(z)| < \frac{1}{2}|f(z)|$ whenever $|z| \geqslant R_0$. Then, for $|z| \geqslant R_0$, we have $|f(z)| > |g(z)|$ and $|P(z)| \geqslant |f(z)| - |g(z)| > \frac{1}{2}|f(z)| > 0$. Thus, $P(z)$ has no zeros in the region $|z| \geqslant R_0$, and (by Rouché's theorem) the number of zeros of $P(z)$ in $|z| < R_0$ is equal to the number of zeros (n) of $a_0 z^n$ in $|z| < R_0$. This gives the required result.

The principle of the argument has other important applications in the theory of servo-mechanisms and automatic controls. (See, e.g., *Fundamentals of Automatic Regulation*, (Osnovy automatiches-koya regulirovaniya) ed. V. V. Solodovnikov, Mashgiz, 1954; H. S. Tsien, *Engineering Cybernetics*, McGraw-Hill, 1954; and M. A. Lavrent'ev and B. V. Shabat, *Methods of the Theory of Functions of a Complex Variable* (Metody teorii funktsii kompleksnogo peremennogo), Fizmatgiz, 1958.)

78. Expansion of $\cot z$ in simple fractions. Mittag-Leffler's theorem

The function

$$\cot z = \frac{\cos z}{\sin z} = i\,\frac{e^{iz} + e^{-iz}}{e^{iz} - e^{-iz}}$$

is meromorphic (see Art. 71); it has poles of the first order at the points $z_k = k\pi$ $(k = 0, \pm 1, \pm 2, \ldots)$, the corresponding residue at z_k being $r_k = [(\cos z)/\{(\mathrm{d}/\mathrm{d}z) \sin z\}]_{z=k\pi} = 1$. We show that this function is bounded on the region R formed from the finite z-plane by removing the open discs

$$|z - z_k| < r \qquad (0 < r < \pi/2; \; k = 0, \pm 1, \pm 2, \ldots)$$

(see Fig. 120). As $\cot z$ is periodic, with period π, it suffices to show that $\cot z$ is bounded on the closed region R_1 formed from the strip $0 \leqslant \operatorname{Re} z \leqslant \pi$ by removing the semicircular regions $|z| < r$, $\operatorname{Re} z \geqslant 0$ and $|z - \pi| < r$, $\operatorname{Re} z \leqslant \pi$. For any point $z \neq k\pi$ we have

$$|\cot z| \leqslant \frac{|e^{iz}| + |e^{-iz}|}{|(|e^{iz}| - |e^{-iz}|)|} = \frac{e^{-y} + e^{y}}{|e^{-y} - e^{y}|};$$

hence, for $y > 1$,

$$|\cot z| \leqslant \frac{e^{y} + e^{-y}}{e^{y} - e^{-y}} = \frac{1 + e^{-2y}}{1 - e^{-2y}} \leqslant \frac{1 + e^{-2}}{1 - e^{-2}};$$

similarly, for $y < -1$,

$$|\cot z| \leqslant \frac{e^{-y} + e^{y}}{e^{-y} - e^{y}} = \frac{1 + e^{2y}}{1 - e^{2y}} \leqslant \frac{1 + e^{-2}}{1 - e^{-2}};$$

it will thus be clear that $|\cot z|$ is bounded on that subset of R_1 for which $|y| > 1$. The boundedness of $|\cot z|$ on that subset of R_1 for which $-1 \leqslant y \leqslant 1$ follows from the properties of a function which is continuous on a bounded closed region (see Art. 13).

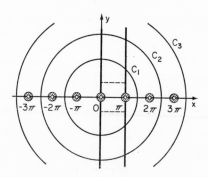

FIG. 120

Accordingly, $|\cot z|$ is bounded on R_1 and it follows that there is a finite constant M such that

$$|\cot z| \leqslant M \tag{40}$$

for all points z of the above region R.

As $\cot z$ has a first-order pole at $z = 0$, the corresponding residue being 1, the Laurent expansion of $\cot z$ in a deleted neighbourhood of $z = 0$ has $1/z$ as its principal part. Accordingly, the function $f(z) = \cot z - (1/z)$ has a removable singularity at $z = 0$. The function $f(z)$ is odd, and it is clear that $f(z)$ will vary continuously and change sign as z moves along the real axis and passes through the origin; thus,

$$\lim_{z \to 0} f(z) = 0.$$

We put $f(0) = 0$, so that $f(z)$ is regular at $z = 0$.

Let C_n denote the circle $|\zeta| = (n + \frac{1}{2})\pi \ (n = 1, 2, \ldots)$ and let z be any point in $|\zeta| < (n + \frac{1}{2})\pi$ which does not coincide with any of the points $0, \pm\pi, \pm 2\pi, \ldots$ The function $f(\zeta)/(\zeta - z)$ then has first-order poles in $|\zeta| < (n+\tfrac{1}{2})\pi$ at the points $\zeta = z$ and $\zeta = z_k = k\pi$ ($k = \pm 1, \pm 2, \dots$) the corresponding residues being

$$r' = \left[\frac{f(\zeta)}{(\mathrm{d}/\mathrm{d}\zeta)(\zeta - z)}\right]_{\zeta = z} = f(z),$$

$$r_k' = \left[\frac{\zeta \cos \zeta - \sin \zeta}{\zeta(\zeta - z) \cdot (\mathrm{d}/\mathrm{d}\zeta) \sin \zeta}\right]_{(\zeta = k\pi)} = \frac{1}{k\pi - z}.$$

Thus, by Cauchy's residue theorem, for

$$|z| < (n+\tfrac{1}{2})\pi, \qquad z \neq \pm \pi, \pm 2\pi, \dots, \pm n\pi,$$

$$\frac{1}{2\pi i} \oint_{C_n} \frac{f(\zeta)\,\mathrm{d}\zeta}{\zeta - z} = f(z) + \sum_{k=-n}^{n}{}' \frac{1}{k\pi - z}, \qquad (41)$$

the prime ($'$) indicating that the term corresponding to $k = 0$ is omitted from the summation; this term is omitted because $\zeta = 0$ is not a pole of $f(\zeta)$. The function $f(\zeta)/\zeta$ has a removable singularity at $\zeta = 0$ and it is easily shown in the same way that

$$\frac{1}{2\pi i} \oint_{C_n} \frac{f(\zeta)}{\zeta}\,\mathrm{d}\zeta = \sum_{k=-n}^{n}{}' \frac{1}{k\pi} = 0. \qquad (42)$$

We note that this result can be obtained formally by putting $z = 0$ in (41).

Using (42) we can write (41) in the form

$$f(z) = -\sum_{k=-n}^{n}{}' \frac{1}{k\pi - z} + \sum_{k=-n}^{n}{}' \frac{1}{k\pi} + \frac{1}{2\pi i} \oint_{C_n} \frac{f(\zeta)\,\mathrm{d}\zeta}{\zeta - z} - \frac{1}{2\pi i} \oint_{C_n} \frac{f(\zeta)}{\zeta}\,\mathrm{d}\zeta$$

$$= \sum_{k=-n}^{n}{}' \left(\frac{1}{z - k\pi} + \frac{1}{k\pi}\right) + \frac{z}{2\pi i} \oint_{C_n} \frac{f(\zeta)\cdot\mathrm{d}\zeta}{\zeta(\zeta - z)}. \qquad (41')$$

We now let $n \to +\infty$, the point z remaining fixed. For points ζ on C_n we have $|\zeta| = \rho_n = (n+\tfrac{1}{2})\pi$, whence

$$1/|\zeta - z| \leqslant 1/(|\zeta| - |z|) = 1/(\rho_n - |z|);$$

also, $0 < r < \pi/2$, so that C_n always lies in the region R in which $|\cot \zeta| \leqslant M$, and it follows that, for all ζ on C_n,

$$|f(\zeta)| \leqslant |\cot \zeta| + 1/|\zeta| \leqslant M + (1/r) = K$$

(say). Thus,

$$\left| \oint_{C_n} \frac{f(\zeta) \cdot d\zeta}{\zeta(\zeta - z)} \right| \leqslant \frac{K \cdot 2\pi\rho_n}{\rho_n(\rho_n - |z|)},$$

so that

$$\oint_{C_n} \to 0$$

as $n \to +\infty$. Accordingly, letting $n \to +\infty$, (41′) becomes

$$f(z) = \sum_{k=-\infty}^{+\infty}{}' \left(\frac{1}{z - k\pi} + \frac{1}{k\pi} \right), \qquad (z \neq 0, \pm\pi, \pm 2\pi, \ldots),$$

whence

$$\cot z = \frac{1}{z} + \sum_{k=-\infty}^{+\infty}{}' \left(\frac{1}{z - k\pi} + \frac{1}{k\pi} \right), \qquad (z \neq 0, \pm\pi, \pm 2\pi, \ldots). \qquad (43)$$

For $|z| < A$ and $|k| \geqslant A$ we have

$$\left| \frac{1}{z - k\pi} + \frac{1}{k\pi} \right| = \left| \frac{z}{k\pi(z - k\pi)} \right| = \frac{|z|}{|\pi - (z/k)| \cdot \pi} \cdot \frac{1}{k^2}$$

$$\leqslant \frac{A}{[\pi - (A/|k|)]\pi} \cdot \frac{1}{k^2} \leqslant \frac{A}{2\pi} \cdot \frac{1}{k^2}.$$

As the series

$$\sum_{k=-\infty}^{+\infty}{}' \frac{1}{k^2}$$

is convergent, it follows that the series (43), with the omission of a finite number of terms, is *uniformly and absolutely convergent on any finite disc* $|z| < A$.

From this it follows, in particular, that for any finite $z \neq k\pi$ ($k = 0, \pm 1, \pm 2, \pm 3, \ldots$), the order of the terms in the series (43) can be rearranged in any desired fashion; thus, pairing terms corresponding to values of k which are numerically equal and of opposite sign, we can write (43) in the form

$$\cot z = \frac{1}{z} + \sum_{k=1}^{+\infty} \frac{2z}{z^2 - k^2\pi^2} \qquad (z \neq 0, \ \pm\pi, \ \pm 2\pi, \ldots). \qquad (44)$$

Replacing z by πz in (43) and (44) we see that

$$\pi \cot \pi z = \frac{1}{z} + \sum_{k=-\infty}^{+\infty}{}' \left(\frac{1}{z-k} + \frac{1}{k} \right)$$

$$= \frac{1}{z} + \sum_{k=1}^{+\infty} \frac{2z}{z^2 - k^2} \qquad (z \neq 0, \ \pm 1, \ \pm 2, \ldots) . \qquad (45)$$

As each pole $z = k\pi$ of the meromorphic function $\cot z$ is of the first order, with residue equal to 1, the expression $1/(z-k\pi)$ is the principal part of the Laurent expansion of $\cot z$ in some deleted neighbourhood of the pole $z = k\pi$ $(k = 0, \ \pm 1, \ \pm 2, \ldots)$. Thus, (43) gives the expansion of $\cot z$ in a series of terms, each of which contains the principal part of the Laurent expansion about the corresponding pole; in this sense the expansion resembles that of a rational function as a sum of partial fractions (see Art. 71). The series

$$\frac{1}{z} + \sum_{k=-\infty}^{+\infty}{}' \frac{1}{z-k\pi},$$

in which each term is the actual principal part at a pole of $\cot z$, is divergent for all finite z; the general term in (43) is obtained from that in the last series by adding a term $1/k\pi$, and the resulting series is then convergent for $z \neq 0, \ \pm\pi, \ \pm 2\pi, \ldots$ We note that

$$\frac{1}{z-k\pi} = -\frac{1}{k\pi} - \frac{z}{k^2\pi^2} - \frac{z^2}{k^3\pi^3} - \cdots,$$

$(|z| < |k|\pi; \ k = \pm 1, \ \pm 2, \ldots)$; it will be seen that the additive term $1/k\pi$ is -1 times the first term in this Taylor expansion, about $z = 0$, of the principal part of $\cot z$ at $z = k\pi$. Mittag-Leffler succeeded in proving that a similar result holds for any meromorphic function. Before stating this result we recall that a function $f(z)$ which is meromorphic in the finite plane can have at most a finite number of poles in any bounded closed region R of the plane; in particular, we may take R defined by

$$n \leqslant |z| \leqslant n+1,$$

and it follows, taking $n = 0, 1, 2, \ldots$, that, even if $f(z)$ has infinitely many poles, these poles a_k can be arranged in a sequence $\{a_k\}$ such that $|a_k| \leqslant |a_{k+1}|$ $(k = 1, 2, \ldots)$.

Mittag-Leffler's theorem. Let $f(z)$ be a meromorphic function with poles at the points $z = a_k$ $(k = 1, 2, \ldots)$ where

$$0 < |a_1| \leqslant |a_2| \leqslant \ldots \leqslant |a_k| \leqslant \ldots .$$

Let the principal part of the Laurent expansion of $f(z)$ in some deleted neighbourhood of $z = 0$ be $h_0(z)$ (we have $h_0(z) \equiv 0$ if $f(z)$ is regular at $z = 0$); let the principal part of $f(z)$ at $z = a_k$ be

$$g_k\left(\frac{1}{z-a_k}\right) = G_k(z),$$

and let

$$h_k{}^p(z) = G_k(0) + G_k{}^{(1)}(0) . z + \ldots + \frac{G_k{}^{(p)}(0)}{p!} z^p$$

be the sum of the first $p+1$ terms of the Taylor expansion of $G_k(z)$ in powers of z. Then, there exists a sequence $\{p_k\}$ of non-negative integers and an integral function $f_0(z)$ such that

$$f(z) = f_0(z) + h_0(z) + \sum_{k=1}^{+\infty} \left\{ g_k\left(\frac{1}{z-a_k}\right) - h_k{}^{p_k}(z) \right\} \qquad (46)$$

for all points z at which $f(z)$ is regular, the series on the right being absolutely and uniformly convergent on the region formed from any finite closed disc $|z| \leqslant A$ by removing the points at which $f(z)$ has poles.

The expansion (46) is called *Mittag-Leffler's expansion of $f(z)$.* It resembles the expansion of a rational function as the sum of a polynomial and certain partial fractions and is important in the theory of meromorphic functions. (See Knopp, *Theory of Functions*, Vol. II, Dover, 1947; Carathéodory, *Theory of Functions*, Vol. I, Chelsea, 1954.)

79. Expansion of $\sin z$ as an infinite product. Weierstrass's theorem

Let ζ be any point of the finite plane such that

$$\zeta \neq 0, \pm \pi, \pm 2\pi, \ldots .$$

Choose a finite positive number A such that $|\zeta| < A$. Defining a function $f(z)$ as above by $f(z) = \cot z - (1/z)$ for

$$z \neq 0, \pm \pi, \pm 2\pi, \ldots$$

and taking $f(0) = 0$, we have

$$f(z) = \sum_{k=1}^{+\infty} \frac{2z}{z^2 - k^2\pi^2} ,$$

the series on the right being absolutely and uniformly convergent on the region R formed from the closed disc $|z| \leqslant A$ by deleting all points of the form $z = \pm \pi, \pm 2\pi, \ldots$ Then, given any $\epsilon > 0$, there exists a positive integer $N_0 = N_0(\epsilon)$ such that the function $\alpha_N(z)$ defined by

$$f(z) = \sum_{k=1}^{N} \frac{2z}{z^2 - k^2\pi^2} + \alpha_N(z) \tag{47}$$

satisfies the inequality

$$|\alpha_N(z)| < \epsilon \tag{48}$$

uniformly on R whenever $N \geqslant N_0$. It will be clear from the results established in the preceding article that $f(z)$ and every $\alpha_N(z)$ are regular at each point of R. It will also be clear that we can join $z = 0$ to $z = \zeta$ ($\neq 0, \pm \pi, \pm 2\pi, \ldots$) by a piecewise-smooth Jordan path L which lies entirely in the *interior* of the region R and which has length $l < 2A$. This path L lies in a *simply-connected* domain D consisting of (interior) points of R. In this domain D we define a function $g(z)$ by $g(z) = (\sin z)/z$ for $z \neq 0$, $g(0) = 1$. As $g(z)$ and the functions $z^2 - k^2\pi^2$ are non-zero in R it follows, since D is simply-connected, that D supports regular branches of the logarithms of these functions; denoting these branches by $\ln g(z)$, etc., we have

$$f(z) = \frac{\mathrm{d}}{\mathrm{d}z} \ln g(z),$$

$$\frac{2z}{z^2 - k^2\pi^2} = \frac{\mathrm{d}}{\mathrm{d}z} \ln(z^2 - k^2\pi^2) \qquad (k = \pm 1, \pm 2, \ldots),$$

for all points z in D. Accordingly, integrating $f(z)$ along L, we have

$$\ln g(\zeta) - \ln g(0) = \sum_{k=1}^{N} \{\ln(\zeta^2 - k^2\pi^2) - \ln(-k^2\pi^2)\} + \int_{0}^{\zeta} \alpha_N(z)\,\mathrm{d}z;$$
$$(L)$$

that is, taking exponentials,

$$\frac{\sin \zeta}{\zeta} \cdot 1 = \left\{ \prod_{k=1}^{N} \frac{\zeta^2 - k^2\pi^2}{-k^2\pi^2} \right\} \cdot e^{\beta_N(\zeta)}, \tag{49}$$

where

$$\beta_N(\zeta) = \int_{0}^{\zeta} \alpha_N(z)\,\mathrm{d}z.$$
$$(L)$$

We have

$$|\beta_N(\zeta)| = \left| \int_{0}^{\zeta} \alpha_N(z)\,\mathrm{d}z \right| < \epsilon \cdot 2A \tag{50}$$
$$(L)$$

whenever $N \geqslant N_0$; thus, $\beta_N(\zeta) \to 0$ and $e^{\beta_N(\zeta)} \to 1$ as $N \to +\infty$. Accordingly, letting $N \to +\infty$ in (49), and writing z for ζ, we have

$$\frac{\sin z}{z} = \lim_{N \to +\infty} \prod_{k=1}^{N} \left(1 - \frac{z^2}{k^2\pi^2}\right),$$

whence

$$\sin z = z \cdot \lim_{N \to +\infty} \prod_{k=1}^{N} \left(1 - \frac{z^2}{k^2 \pi^2}\right).$$

It will be clear that this result holds for *all* finite z, both sides vanishing for $z = 0, \pm\pi, \pm 2\pi \ldots$.

Definition. The infinite product

$$\prod_{k=1}^{+\infty} \{1 + f_k(z)\}$$

is said to be convergent (in the stricter sense) at the point z if there exists a positive integer m such that (i) $1 + f_k(z) \neq 0$ for $n > m$, and (ii)

$$\lim_{p \to +\infty} \prod_{k=m+1}^{m+p} \{1 + f_k(z)\}$$

exists finitely and is not zero; in this case, writing

$$\lim_{p \to +\infty} \prod_{k=m+1}^{m+p} \{1 + f_k(z)\} = \phi_m(z) \quad (\neq 0),$$

we say that

$$\prod_{k=1}^{+\infty} \{1 + f_k(z)\}$$

converges (at the point z) to

$$f(z) = \left[\prod_{k=1}^{m} \{1 + f_k(z)\}\right] \phi_m(z)$$

and write

$$\prod_{k=1}^{+\infty} \{1 + f_k(z)\} = f(z).$$

(It will be clear that $f(z)$ does not depend on m.) If the product

$$\prod_{k=1}^{+\infty} \{1 + f_k(z)\}$$

is convergent, in this sense, at each point z of a domain D, its value at the general point z in D being denoted by $f(z)$, we say that

$$\prod_{k=1}^{+\infty} \{1 + f_k(z)\}$$

converges in D to the function $f(z)$. It will be clear that, at each point z in D, we then have

$$f(z) = \lim_{N \to +\infty} \prod_{k=1}^{N} \{1 + f_k(z)\}. \tag{51}$$

Remark 1. It can be shown that

$$\lim_{k \to +\infty} f_k(z) = 0$$

at any point z at which

$$\prod_{k=1}^{+\infty} \{1 + f_k(z)\}$$

is convergent; and that, whenever

$$\sum_{k=1}^{+\infty} f_k(z)$$

is absolutely convergent, the product

$$\prod_{k=1}^{+\infty} \{1 + f_k(z)\}$$

is convergent and is unaltered in value when we derange the order of the factors in any manner. These facts explain why we denote the general factor in the product by $1 + f_k(z)$ and not by, say, $u_k(z)$.

Remark 2. If, at some point z, each of a finite number of the factors in the convergent product

$$\prod_{k=1}^{+\infty} \{1 + f_k(z)\}$$

vanishes, the product will converge to zero at this point. Any finite product vanishes if, and only if, at least one of its factors vanishes; the requirement $\phi_m(z) \neq 0$ in the above definition ensures that this property extends to convergent infinite products.

From the results obtained above it follows that

$$\sin z = z \prod_{k=1}^{+\infty} \left(1 - \frac{z^2}{k^2\pi^2}\right) \tag{52}$$

for *all* finite z. This expansion of $\sin z$ as an infinite product which is convergent at all points of the finite plane was first obtained (in a different way) by Euler.

Had we based our discussion on the series (43) instead of that in (44) we would have arrived at the expansion

$$\sin z = \prod_{k=-\infty}^{+\infty}{}' \left\{\left(1 - \frac{z}{k\pi}\right)e^{z/(k\pi)}\right\}; \tag{53}$$

here, the prime (') indicates that the factor corresponding to $k = 0$ is to be omitted. This expansion also holds for all finite z; the value of the product on the right is to be understood as the product of the values of the two convergent products

$$\prod_{k=1}^{+\infty} \left\{\left(1 - \frac{z}{k\pi}\right)e^{z/(k\pi)}\right\}$$

and

$$\prod_{k=1}^{+\infty} \left\{\left(1 + \frac{z}{k\pi}\right)e^{-z/(k\pi)}\right\}.$$

It will be seen that (52) follows immediately from (53).

The analogue of (53) in elementary algebra is the expansion of a polynomial (of degree $n \geqslant 1$) as a product of linear factors:

$$P(z) = A(z-a_1)(z-a_2)\ldots(z-a_n) = B \prod_{k=1}^{n} \left(1 - \frac{z}{a_k}\right),$$

23

for the points $a_k = k\pi$ are the zeros of the integral function $\sin z$. It can be shown that the products

$$\prod_{k=1}^{+\infty} \left(1 - \frac{z}{k\pi}\right)$$

and

$$\prod_{k=1}^{+\infty} \left(1 + \frac{z}{k\pi}\right)$$

are not convergent (in the sense of our definition) whenever $z \neq 0$; the additional factors $e^{z/(k\pi)}$ $(k = \pm 1, \pm 2, \ldots)$ in (53) are necessary to ensure convergence.

A similar result holds for a general integral function. Before stating this result we recall that any integral function $f(z)$ which is not identically zero can have at most a finite number of zeros in any bounded closed region R of the plane; in particular, we may take R defined by $n \leqslant |z| \leqslant n+1$; then, taking $n = 0, 1, 2, \ldots$ in succession, it follows readily that, even if the zeros a_k of $f(z)$ are infinite in number, they can be arranged in a sequence $\{a_k\}$ such that $|a_k| \leqslant |a_{k+1}|$ $(k = 1, 2, \ldots)$.

Weierstrass's theorem. Let the integral function $f(z)$ have a zero of order α_k $(\geqslant 1)$ at the point a_k $(k = 1, 2, \ldots)$ where

$$0 < |a_1| \leqslant |a_2| \leqslant \ldots \leqslant |a_k| \leqslant \ldots,$$

and let $f(z)$ have a zero of order n at $z = 0$. (We take $n = 0$ if $f(0) \neq 0$.) Then, if

$$h_k{}^p(z) = -\frac{z}{a_k} - \frac{z^2}{2a_k{}^2} - \ldots - \frac{z^p}{pa_k{}^p},$$

so that $h_k{}^p(z)$ is the sum of the first p terms in the Taylor expansion of $\ln[1-(z/a_k)]$ in powers of z, there exists a sequence $\{p_k\}$ of positive integers and a non-vanishing integral function $f_0(z)$ such that, for all finite z,

$$f(z) = f_0(z) \cdot z^n \prod_{k=1}^{+\infty} \left\{\left(1 - \frac{z}{a_k}\right) \exp[-h_k{}^{p_k}(z)]\right\}^{\alpha_k}. \tag{54}$$

The product on the right in (54) is convergent for all finite z and is known as *Weierstrass's expansion* of the integral function $f(z)$; it is the analogue of the familiar expansion of a polynomial as a product of linear factors.

Example. We consider an infinite sequence of point vortices, each having the same strength Γ, situated at the points $a_k = a_0 + kl$ (l real; $k = 0, \pm 1, \pm 2, \ldots$) so that they are spaced at a constant separation l along the line through a_0 parallel to the real axis. (This constitutes a vortex *chain* or *row*; see Fig. 121.)

Fig. 121

We first obtain the field due to the $2N + 1$ vortices corresponding to $-N \leqslant k \leqslant N$. The complex potential describing the corresponding flow is the sum of the potentials of the individual vortices:

$$w = \Phi_N(z)$$
$$= \frac{\Gamma}{2\pi i}\left\{\mathrm{Ln}\frac{\pi(z-a_0)}{l} + \sum_{k=1}^{N}\left[\mathrm{Ln}\left(\frac{z-a_k}{-kl}\right) + \mathrm{Ln}\left(\frac{z-a_{-k}}{kl}\right)\right]\right\}$$
$$(z \neq a_k; \; -N \leqslant k \leqslant N).$$

Here we have introduced a factor π/l associated with $(z-a_0)$ and factors $-1/(kl)$ associated with the arguments $(z-a_k)$ (*cf.* Art. 39); the effect of these factors is merely to change $\Phi_N(z)$ by an additive complex constant. Simple reduction gives

$$\Phi_N(z) = \frac{\Gamma}{2\pi i}\,\mathrm{Ln}\left\{\frac{\pi(z-a_0)}{l}\prod_{k=1}^{N}\left(1 - \frac{(z-a_0)^2}{k^2l^2}\right)\right\}.$$

The factors appearing in this product differ from the corresponding factors in (52) only in that z is now replaced by $\pi(z-a_0)/l$; hence, letting $N \to +\infty$ we see that the *complex potential of the infinite vortex chain* is given by

$$w = \Phi(z) = \frac{\Gamma}{2\pi i} \, \mathrm{Ln}\left\{\frac{\pi(z-a_0)}{l} \prod_{k=1}^{+\infty} \left(1 - \frac{(z-a_0)^2}{k^2 l^2}\right)\right\}$$

$$= \frac{\Gamma}{2\pi i} \, \mathrm{Ln}\left\{\sin \frac{\pi(z-a_0)}{l}\right\}. \tag{55}$$

A similar formula holds for the potential describing the field of an infinite system of like point-charges, each of strength $+q$, situated at the same points a_k:

$$w = F(z) = -2qi \cdot \mathrm{Ln}\left\{\frac{\pi(z-a_0)}{l} \prod_{k=1}^{+\infty} \left(1 - \frac{(z-a_0)^2}{k^2 l^2}\right)\right\}$$

$$= 2qi \cdot \mathrm{Ln}\left\{1 \Big/ \sin \frac{\pi(z-a_0)}{l}\right\}.$$

80. Euler's gamma function $\Gamma(z)$

We introduce the function $\Gamma(1+z)$ indirectly by defining what we later identify as its logarithmic derivative to be

$$\psi(1+z) = -C - \sum_{k=1}^{+\infty} \left(\frac{1}{z+k} - \frac{1}{k}\right). \tag{56}$$

Here, C is some constant whose value will be fixed later. The series (56) consists of the terms corresponding to negative values of k in the first expansion for $\pi \cot \pi z$ in (45). It is easily shown (*cf.* Art. 79) that this series is uniformly and absolutely convergent on the domain Δ formed from any finite open disc $|z| < A$ by removing all points of the form $z = -1, -2, -3, \ldots$ From this it can be shown that $\psi(1+z)$ is *meromorphic* in the finite plane, its only singularities in this plane being *first-order poles at the points* $z = -1, -2, -3, \ldots$ We let D denote any simply-connected sub-domain of Δ which contains $z = 0$; as D supports regular branches

$\ln[1 + (z/k)]$ of the logarithms of the functions $1 + (z/k)$, it follows from the uniform convergence of (56) on D that the function $\phi(z)$ defined in D by

$$\phi(z) = \int_0^z \psi(1+\zeta)\,\mathrm{d}\zeta$$
$$(L)$$

$$= -Cz - \sum_{k=1}^{+\infty} \left\{ \ln\left(1 + \frac{z}{k}\right) - \ln(1) - \frac{z}{k} \right\} \tag{57}$$

is regular in D and is a primitive of $\psi(1+z)$ in this domain; here, L is any path in D joining $\zeta = 0$ to the general point z in D (see Cor. 2, Theorem 5, Art. 49).

Euler's *gamma function* $\Gamma(1+z)$ is defined by

$$\frac{1}{\Gamma(1+z)} = \exp\{-\phi(z)\} = e^{Cz} \prod_{k=1}^{+\infty} \left\{ \left(1 + \frac{z}{k}\right) e^{-z/k} \right\}. \tag{58}$$

The function $1/\Gamma(1+z)$ so defined is clearly single-valued in the whole finite plane (convergence of the infinite product is clear since it comprises that part of Weierstrass's product for $\sin \pi z$ corresponding to negative values of k). The regularity of $1/\Gamma(1+z)$ has so far been established only in a domain such as D; regularity in the domain D_0 formed from the finite plane by removing the points $z = -1, -2, -3, \ldots$ follows from the facts that $1/\Gamma(1+z)$ is single-valued and that A can be taken arbitrarily large; it is then easily shown that $1/\Gamma(1+z)$ has *removable* singularities at

$$z = -1, -2, -3, \ldots$$

and that the function defined by the product in (58) is an integral function, its only zeros (each a simple zero) being the points $z = -k$ ($k = 1, 2, \ldots$). Thus, defining $\Gamma(1+z)$ in the finite plane by the relation (58), we see that $\Gamma(1+z)$ is *meromorphic* and *non-vanishing* in the finite plane, its only singularities in this plane being first-order poles at the points $z = -1, -2, -3, \ldots$ (For a direct definition of the gamma function as a product, along with the accompanying theory of such infinite products, see, e.g., Knopp, *Theory and Application of Infinite Series* (Blackie, 1928), Art. 57.)

By (58), $\Gamma(1) = 1$. As $\Gamma(2) \neq 0$ we can fix the value of C by requiring that $\Gamma(2)$ should also be equal to unity. Then, from (57),

$$0 = -C - \sum_{k=1}^{+\infty} \left\{ \ln\left(1 + \frac{1}{k}\right) - \frac{1}{k} \right\},$$

where we suppose the logarithms to be the ordinary *principal* values; thus,

$$C = \sum_{k=1}^{+\infty} \left\{ \frac{1}{k} - \ln\left(1 + \frac{1}{k}\right) \right\}$$

$$= \lim_{n \to +\infty} \left\{ \sum_{k=1}^{n} \frac{1}{k} - \ln\left(\frac{2}{1} \cdot \frac{3}{2} \cdots \frac{n+1}{n}\right) \right\}$$

$$= \lim_{n \to +\infty} \left\{ \sum_{k=1}^{n} \frac{1}{k} - \ln n \right\} - \lim_{n \to +\infty} \ln\left(1 + \frac{1}{n}\right)$$

$$= \lim_{n \to +\infty} \left\{ 1 + \frac{1}{2} + \ldots + \frac{1}{n} - \ln n \right\}. \tag{59}$$

The number C so defined is called *Euler's constant*

$$(C = 0 \cdot 5772157 \ldots);$$

the finite existence of the limit in (59) follows from our preceding analysis and is, indeed, a familiar result in elementary real analysis.

We now derive certain formulae concerning the Γ-function. Let D_1 be the domain of points ζ formed from the finite plane by removing the points $\zeta = 0, -1, -2, \ldots$; let z be a general point in D_1 and let D be any simply-connected sub-domain of D_1 containing $\zeta = 1, 2, z$. Then, in D, it follows from (56) that

$$\psi(1+\zeta) - \psi(\zeta) = \sum_{k=1}^{+\infty} \left\{ \frac{1}{\zeta+k-1} - \frac{1}{\zeta+k} \right\} = \frac{1}{\zeta}.$$

This domain supports regular branches $\ln \Gamma(1+\zeta)$, $\ln \Gamma(\zeta)$, $\ln \zeta$ of the logarithms of $\Gamma(1+\zeta)$, $\Gamma(\zeta)$ and ζ; thus, from (57) and (58), we have $\ln \Gamma(1+\zeta) - \ln \Gamma(\zeta) = \ln \zeta + \ln A$, where ζ is in D and A is some constant. This relation can be written

$$\Gamma(1+\zeta) = A\zeta \cdot \Gamma(\zeta).$$

Taking $\zeta = 1$ and using the fact that $\Gamma(1) = \Gamma(2) = 1$ we have $A = 1$, and it follows that

$$\Gamma(1+z) = z\Gamma(z) \qquad (z \neq 0, -1, -2, \ldots). \qquad (60)$$

This recurrence formula enables immediate calculation of the values of $\Gamma(z)$ in the strips

$$k < \operatorname{Re} z \leqslant k+1 \quad \text{and} \quad k-2 < \operatorname{Re} z \leqslant k-1$$

once we know its values in the strip $k-1 < \operatorname{Re} z \leqslant k$. Repeated application of (60) gives

$$\Gamma(z+2) = (z+1)\Gamma(z+1) = (z+1)z\Gamma(z),$$
$$\Gamma(z+3) = (z+2)\Gamma(z+2) = (z+2)(z+1)z\Gamma(z),$$

and so on; thus, for any positive integer n,

$$\Gamma(z+n) = (z+n-1)(z+n-2)\ldots z \,.\, \Gamma(z)$$
$$(z \neq 0, -1, -2 \ldots). \qquad (61)$$

Formula (61) enables us to find the values of $\Gamma(z)$ in the whole plane when we know its values in the strip $0 < \operatorname{Re} z \leqslant 1$.

In particular, for $z = 1$, (61) gives

$$\Gamma(1+n) = n! \,. \qquad (62)$$

Accordingly, $\Gamma(1+z)$ is the continuation, into the complex domain, of the familiar factorial function, $n!$, defined for non-negative integral values of n.

Formula (61) enables us to find the residues of $\Gamma(z)$ at its poles $z = -n$ ($n = 0, 1, \ldots$). We have ($z \neq 0, -1, -2, \ldots$)

$$\Gamma(z) = \frac{1}{z(z+1)\ldots(z+n)}\Gamma(z+n+1);$$

hence, by formula (41) of Art. 67,

$$\operatorname{res} \Gamma(-n) = \lim_{z \to -n} (z+n)\,\Gamma(z)$$

$$= \lim_{z \to -n} \left\{ \frac{1}{z(z+1)\ldots(z+n-1)}\Gamma(z+n+1) \right\}$$

$$= \frac{1}{-n(-n+1)\ldots(-1)}\Gamma(1),$$

so that

$$\operatorname{res} \Gamma(-n) = \frac{(-1)^n}{n!}. \tag{63}$$

Also, by (58),

$$\frac{1}{\Gamma(z)} = \frac{z}{\Gamma(1+z)} = z e^{Cz} \prod_{k=1}^{+\infty} \left\{ \left(1 + \frac{z}{k}\right) e^{-z/k} \right\}$$

and

$$\frac{1}{\Gamma(1-z)} = e^{-Cz} \prod_{k=1}^{+\infty} \left\{ \left(1 - \frac{z}{k}\right) e^{z/k} \right\}.$$

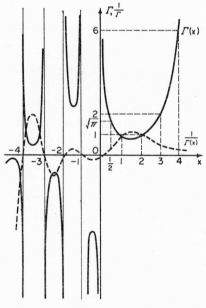

Fig. 122

Multiplying these products together we see that

$$\frac{1}{\Gamma(z)\Gamma(1-z)} = z \prod_{k=1}^{+\infty} \left(1 - \frac{z^2}{k^2}\right);$$

it is easily verified that the corresponding pairing of factors is permissible. Formula (52) shows that the right-hand side of the last equation is equal to $(1/\pi) \sin \pi z$. Thus,

$$\Gamma(z) \cdot \Gamma(1-z) = \frac{\pi}{\sin \pi z}. \tag{64}$$

This result enables us to reduce the evaluation of $\Gamma(z)$ in the strip $0 < \operatorname{Re} z \leqslant 1$ (and hence its evaluation in the whole plane—see above) to the calculation of its values in the strip $0 < \operatorname{Re} z \leqslant \frac{1}{2}$. In particular, taking $z = \frac{1}{2}$, (64) gives $\{\Gamma(\frac{1}{2})\}^2 = \pi$, whence

$$\Gamma(\tfrac{1}{2}) = \sqrt{\pi}. \tag{65}$$

We conclude this section by tabulating the values of $\Gamma(x)$ at steps of $0 \cdot 1$ along the real interval $1 < x < 2$:

x	$1 \cdot 1$	$1 \cdot 2$	$1 \cdot 3$	$1 \cdot 4$	$1 \cdot 5$	$1 \cdot 6$	$1 \cdot 7$	$1 \cdot 8$	$1 \cdot 9$
$\Gamma(x)$	$0 \cdot 9514$	$0 \cdot 9182$	$0 \cdot 8975$	$0 \cdot 8873$	$0 \cdot 8862$	$0 \cdot 8935$	$0 \cdot 9086$	$0 \cdot 9314$	$0 \cdot 9618$

The graphs of $\Gamma(x)$ and $1/\Gamma(x)$ for real x are shown in Fig. 122; the nature of these graphs will be clear from the properties of the Γ-function listed above. It may be remarked that the stationary points on the graph of $\Gamma(x)$ approach the negative real axis steadily as $x \to -\infty$. This behaviour is connected with the rapid decrease in the numerical value of res $\Gamma(-n)$ $(n = 0, 1, 2, \ldots)$ as $n \to +\infty$; for values of x in some deleted neighbourhood of the pole at $z = -n$ we have

$$\Gamma(x) = \frac{(-1)^n}{n!} \cdot \frac{1}{x+n} + c_0 + c_1(x+n) + \ldots,$$

and it will be clear that the coefficient in the principal part of this expansion decreases rapidly in magnitude as n increases.

81. Integral representations of the Γ-function

The integral

$$f(z) = \int\limits_{0}^{+\infty} e^{-t} t^{z-1} \, \mathrm{d}t \tag{66}$$

converges for any given z in the right half-plane $\operatorname{Re} z > 0$; here, t is a real variable, $z = x + iy$ is a complex parameter, and t^{z-1} is understood (see Art. 32) as $\exp\{(z-1) \ln t\}$. We have

$$|e^{-t}t^{z-1}| = e^{-t+(x-1)\ln t} = e^{-t}t^{x-1};$$

the factor e^{-t} ensures that

$$\int\limits_{1}^{+\infty} e^{-t}t^{z-1}\,\mathrm{d}t$$

converges for any given real x, and the factor t^{x-1} ensures convergence of

$$\int\limits_{0}^{1} e^{-t}t^{z-1}\,\mathrm{d}t$$

for $x > 0$.

We consider the sequence of integrals defined for $\mathrm{Re}\,z > 0$ by

$$f_n(z) = \int\limits_{0}^{n} \left(1 - \frac{t}{n}\right)^n t^{z-1}\,\mathrm{d}t;$$

as $[1-(t/n)]^n \to e^{-t}$ and the upper limit of integration tends to $+\infty$ as $n \to +\infty$, we would expect that

$$\lim_{n \to +\infty} f_n(z) = f(z) \qquad (\mathrm{Re}\,z > 0);$$

a strict proof of this result can be given but will be omitted here. We transform the expression for $f_n(z)$ by introducing a new variable $\tau = t/n$ and then integrating by parts:

$$f_n(z) = n^z \int\limits_{0}^{1} (1-\tau)^n \tau^{z-1}\,\mathrm{d}\tau$$

$$= n^z \int\limits_{\tau=0}^{1} (1-\tau)^n \cdot \mathrm{d}\left(\frac{1}{z}\tau^z\right)$$

$$= \left[\frac{n^z}{z}\tau^z(1-\tau)^n\right]_0^1 + \frac{n^{z+1}}{z} \int\limits_{0}^{1} (1-\tau)^{n-1}\tau^z\,\mathrm{d}\tau$$

$$= \frac{n^{z+1}}{z} \int\limits_{0}^{1} (1-\tau)^{n-1}\tau^z\,\mathrm{d}\tau.$$

Continued integration by parts, in which the degree of the term in $1-\tau$ is reduced by unity at each stage, then gives

$$f_n(z) = \frac{n^z(n!)}{z(z+1)\ldots(z+n-1)} \int_0^1 \tau^{z+n-1}\, d\tau$$

$$= \frac{n^z(n!)}{z(z+1)\ldots(z+n-1)(z+n)}$$

$$= \frac{\exp(z.\ln n)}{z\left(1+\dfrac{z}{1}\right)\left(1+\dfrac{z}{2}\right)\ldots\left(1+\dfrac{z}{n}\right)}.$$

Multiplying numerator and denominator by

$$\exp\left\{-z\sum_{k=1}^{n}(1/k)\right\},$$

we have

$$f_n(z) = \frac{\exp\left\{-z\left(1+\dfrac{1}{2}+\ldots+\dfrac{1}{n}-\ln n\right)\right\}}{z.\left(1+\dfrac{z}{1}\right)e^{-z/1}.\left(1+\dfrac{z}{2}\right)e^{-z/2}\ldots\left(1+\dfrac{z}{n}\right)e^{-z/n}}$$

$$= 1\left/\left[\left\{z\exp\left(z\left[1+\dfrac{1}{2}+\ldots+\dfrac{1}{n}-\ln n\right]\right)\right\}\prod_{k=1}^{n}\left\{\left(1+\dfrac{z}{k}\right).e^{-z/k}\right\}\right].\right.$$

Recalling formulae (59), (58) and (60), we thus have

$$f(z) = \lim_{n\to+\infty}f_n(z) = 1\left/\left[ze^{Cz}.\prod_{k=1}^{+\infty}\left\{\left(1+\dfrac{z}{k}\right)e^{-z/k}\right\}\right]\right.$$

$$= \frac{\Gamma(1+z)}{z} = \Gamma(z).$$

Accordingly, an *integral representation of the* Γ-*function in the right half-plane* is given by

$$\Gamma(z) = \int_0^{+\infty} e^{-t}t^{z-1}\,\mathrm{d}t \qquad (\mathrm{Re}\ z > 0). \tag{67}$$

We shall also consider the integral

$$F(z) = \int_C e^{-\zeta}\zeta^{z-1}\,\mathrm{d}\zeta,$$

where the contour C, shown in Fig. 123, consists of the edges (I and III) of a cut taken along the segment $[r, +\infty)$ of the positive real axis and the arc (II) of the circle $|\zeta| = r$. The factor ζ^{z-1} is to be

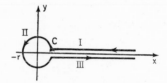

Fig. 123

understood as $\exp\{(z-1)\ln\zeta\}$, with $\ln\zeta = \ln|\zeta|+i\arg\zeta$, where $0 \leqslant \arg\zeta \leqslant 2\pi$: on the edge I, where $\zeta = t$ $(t > 0)$, we have

$$\zeta^{z-1} = \exp\{(z-1)\ln t\} = t^{z-1};$$

on the edge III we take $\zeta = te^{i2\pi}$ and

$$\zeta^{z-1} = \exp\{(z-1)(\ln t+i2\pi)\} = e^{i2\pi z} \cdot t^{z-1}.$$

Accordingly,

$$F(z) = \int_I + \oint_{II} + \int_{III}$$

$$= \int_{+\infty}^r e^{-t}t^{z-1}\,\mathrm{d}t + \oint_{II} e^{-\zeta}\zeta^{z-1}\,\mathrm{d}\zeta + e^{i2\pi z}\int_r^{+\infty} e^{-t}t^{z-1}\,\mathrm{d}t$$

$$= (e^{i2\pi z}-1)\int_r^{+\infty} e^{-t}t^{z-1}\,\mathrm{d}t + \oint_{II} e^{-\zeta}\zeta^{z-1}\,\mathrm{d}\zeta.$$

We suppose that z is given, with $\operatorname{Re} z > 0$; then, on the arc II, $\zeta = re^{i\phi}$ $(0 \leqslant \phi \leqslant 2\pi)$ and

$$\left| e^{-\zeta} \zeta^{z-1} \right| = e^{-r \cos \phi} \cdot e^{(x-1) \ln r - \phi y} = e^{-(r \cos \phi + y\phi)} \cdot r^{x-1};$$

accordingly, for $0 < r < 1$, $\left| e^{-\zeta} \zeta^{z-1} \right| < A r^{x-1}$, where A is a finite positive constant, and we have

$$\left| \oint_{II} \right| < A r^{x-1} \cdot 2\pi r = 2\pi A r^x,$$

so that

$$\oint_{II} \to 0 \text{ as } r \to +0.$$

Thus, letting $r \to +0$ and recalling (67), we have

$$F(z) = (e^{i2\pi z} - 1) \int_0^{+\infty} e^{-t} t^{z-1} \, \mathrm{d}t = (e^{i2\pi z} - 1) \Gamma(z),$$

and it follows that

$$\Gamma(z) = \frac{1}{e^{i2\pi z} - 1} \int_C e^{-\zeta} \zeta^{z-1} \, \mathrm{d}\zeta. \tag{68}$$

(As $e^{-\zeta} \zeta^{z-1}$ is regular in, and continuous on the closure of, the "exterior" domain defined by any such contour C, it is easily shown that

$$\int_C e^{-\zeta} \zeta^{z-1} \, \mathrm{d}\zeta$$

is independent of r.) The integral representation (68) was obtained for points z lying in the right half-plane. However, it can be shown that

$$g(z) = \int_C e^{-\zeta} \zeta^{z-1} \, \mathrm{d}\zeta$$

is regular for *all* finite z; that is, $g(z)$ is an integral function. As $e^{i2\pi z} - 1$ is an integral function whose zeros lie at the points $z = 0, \pm 1, \pm 2, \ldots$, it follows that the function $g(z)/(e^{i2\pi z} - 1)$ on the right in (68) is regular in the domain formed from the finite plane by removing the points $z = 0, \pm 1, \pm 2, \ldots$. It has been shown in the preceding article that the function $\Gamma(z)$ on the left in (68) is regular at all points of the finite plane other than the points $z = 0, -1, -2, \ldots$ The above derivation of (68) shows that $\Gamma(z)$ and $g(z)/(e^{i2\pi z} - 1)$ are identical in the right half-plane, the latter function being defined by continuity at $z = 1, 2, \ldots$; it then follows from the identity theorem (Art. 62) that these functions are identical throughout the whole of their common domain of regularity, so that the right side of (68) has removable singularities at $z = 1, 2, 3, \ldots$ Thus (68) gives *an integral representation of $\Gamma(z)$ which is valid in the domain of regularity* of $\Gamma(z)$. (It may be remarked that the limiting processes in the above derivation of (68) cannot be carried out for $\operatorname{Re} z \leqslant 0$.)

Formula (68) is of additional interest because it represents a meromorphic function $\Gamma(z)$ as the ratio of two integral functions (see Art. 71).

Replacing z by $1 - z$ in (68) and taking $-\zeta = |\zeta| e^{i\phi}(-\pi \leqslant \phi \leqslant \pi)$, we get

$$\Gamma(1 - z) = \frac{1}{e^{-i2\pi z} - 1} \int_C e^{-\zeta} \zeta^{-z} \, d\zeta$$

$$= \frac{e^{-i\pi z}}{e^{-i2\pi z} - 1} \int_C e^{-\zeta}(-\zeta)^{-z} \, d\zeta$$

$$= \frac{i}{2 \sin \pi z} \int_C e^{-\zeta}(-\zeta)^{-z} \, d\zeta.$$

We now replace the variable ζ by $-\zeta$, so that the contour C of Fig. 123 is replaced by the contour C_1 of Fig. 124; then, using

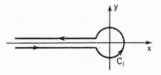

Fig. 124

formula (64) we obtain the following integral representation of the integral function $1/\Gamma(z)$:

$$\frac{1}{\Gamma(z)} = \frac{1}{2\pi i} \int_{C_1} e^{\zeta} \zeta^{-z} \, d\zeta. \tag{69}$$

The results expressed in (68) and (69) are usually called *Hankel's formulae*.

A more-detailed account of the theory of the Γ-function can be found in Macrobert, *Functions of a Complex Variable* (Macmillan, 2nd Edn., 1933.)

Exercises

1. Evaluate the following integrals:

(a) $\displaystyle\int_{-\infty}^{+\infty} \frac{dx}{1+x^4}$;　　(b) $\displaystyle\int_{0}^{2\pi} \frac{dx}{a+\cos x}$,　$(a>1)$;　　(c) $\displaystyle\int_{-\infty}^{+\infty} \frac{\cos ax \, . \, dx}{x^4+1}$;

(d) $\displaystyle\int_{0}^{+\infty} \left(\frac{\sin x}{x}\right)^2 dx$;　　　　　　　　　(e) $\displaystyle\int_{0}^{+\infty} \frac{\sin x \, . \, dx}{x(1+x^2+x^4)}$;

(f) $\displaystyle\int_{0}^{+\infty} \frac{x^{-a} \, dx}{1+2x\cos\lambda+x^2} \left(\begin{matrix} -1 < a < 1 \\ -\pi < \lambda < \pi \end{matrix}\right)$;　(g) $\displaystyle\int_{-1}^{1} \frac{dx}{\sqrt[3]{\{(1-x)(1+x)^2\}}}$;

(h) $\displaystyle\int_{0}^{+\infty} \frac{x^2 \ln x \, . \, dx}{(1+x^2)^2}$;　　　　　　　(i) $\displaystyle\int_{0}^{+\infty} \frac{(\ln x)^2 \, dx}{1+x^2}$.

2. Find the function $f(t)$ defined by

$$f(t) = \frac{1}{2\pi i} \int_{a-i\infty}^{a+i\infty} \frac{e^{zt}}{z^2} \, dz,$$

where t denotes a real variable and the integral is taken along the straight line $\operatorname{Re} z = \text{const.} = a$ $(a > 0)$.

3. Show that the equation $\lambda - z - e^{-z} = 0$ $(\lambda > 1)$ has a single root in the right half-plane $\operatorname{Re} z > 0$, and show that this root is real.

4. On the closed region $|z| \leqslant 1$, $f(z)$ is regular and $|f(z)| < 1$. Show that the equation $f(z) = z$ has a single root in this region. (This root is the "invariant point" of the mapping $w = f(z)$ of the disc $|z| < 1$.)

5. Expand each of the following functions as a series of simple fractions:

(a) $\tan z$,   (b) $\dfrac{1}{\sin z}$,   (c) $\dfrac{\pi}{\cos \pi z}$,   (d) $\dfrac{1}{e^z - 1}$.

6. Expand each of the following functions as an infinite product:

(a) $e^z - 1$,   (b) $\cos \pi z - \cos \pi z_0$,   (c) $\cosh z - \cos z$.

7. Find the complex potential of the field due to a system of (line) charges situated at the points $z_k = kd$ ($k = 0, \pm 1, \pm 2, \ldots$), the charges being equal in magnitude and alternating in sign.

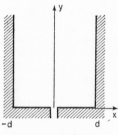

FIG. 125

8. Find the complex potential representing steady irrotational plane flow of an ideal fluid in the vessel whose cross-section is represented in Fig. 125. The "slit" at the bottom of the container is supposed narrow, and the flow (per unit length of the slit) out of the container is Q.

9. Express the Poisson integral

$$J = \int\limits_{0}^{+\infty} e^{-x^2}\, dx$$

in terms of the Γ-function, and hence evaluate this integral.

10. Prove that, in the strip $0 < \operatorname{Re} z < 1$,

$$\int\limits_{0}^{+\infty} t^{z-1} e^{-it}\, dt = \Gamma(z) \cdot e^{-i\pi z/2}.$$

Hence evaluate the following integrals for $n > 1$:

$$(a) \int_0^{+\infty} \cos(t^n)\, dt, \qquad (b) \int_0^{+\infty} \sin(t^n)\, dt, \qquad (c) \int_0^{+\infty} \frac{\sin(t^n)}{t^n}\, dt.$$

11. Prove that Euler's *beta-function*, defined by

$$B(p, q) = \int_0^1 t^{p-1}(1-t)^{q-1}\, dt, \qquad (\mathrm{Re}\, p > 0,\ \mathrm{Re}\, q > 0),$$

is expressed in terms of the Γ-function by the relation

$$B(p, q) = \frac{\Gamma(p) \cdot \Gamma(q)}{\Gamma(p+q)}.$$

12. Express the following integrals in terms of the Γ-function:

$$(a) \int_0^{\pi/2} \sin^{2p}\phi \, \cos^{2q}\phi \, d\phi,$$

$$(b) \int_0^{\pi/2} \tan^p\phi \cdot d\phi, \qquad (c) \int_0^1 \frac{dx}{\sqrt{(1-x^4)}},$$

$$(d) \int_0^{+\infty} \frac{x^m dx}{(a+bx^n)^p} \qquad (a > 0,\ b > 0,\ np > m+1).$$

CHAPTER VIII

MAPPING OF POLYGONAL DOMAINS

82. The symmetry principle

WE now establish a result which has important applications to the analytic continuation of conformal mapping functions. First we prove a general theorem on the analytic continuation of an arbitrary regular function; this theorem is called the *principle of continuous continuation*:

Let two non-overlapping domains D_1 and D_2, each bounded by simple closed curves, adjoin along a curve C which is a part of the boundary of each of these domains, and let the functions $f_1(z)$ and $f_2(z)$ be regular in D_1 and D_2 and continuous on $\overline{D}_1$ and $\overline{D}_2$, respectively (see Fig. 126). Then, if $f_1(z)$ and $f_2(z)$ are identically equal along C, each of the functions $f_1(z)$ and $f_2(z)$ is an analytic continuation (into the appropriate domain) *of the other.*

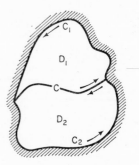

Let C_1 and C_2 denote those parts of the boundaries of D_1 and D_2, respectively, which have only the extremities of the curve C in common with each other (Fig. 126); on C_1+C_2+C we define a continuous function $\phi(\zeta)$ such that

$$\phi(\zeta) = \begin{cases} f_1(\zeta) \text{ on } C_1; \\ f_2(\zeta) \text{ on } C_2; \\ f_1(\zeta) = f_2(\zeta) \text{ on } C. \end{cases}$$

We now consider the integral

$$f(z) = \frac{1}{2\pi i} \oint_{C_1 + C_2} \frac{\phi(\zeta)\,d\zeta}{\zeta - z}; \tag{1}$$

this is an integral of Cauchy type and it follows from the results proved in Art. 52 that the function $f(z)$ so defined is regular in the domain Δ which is the interior of the region $\overline{D}_1 + \overline{D}_2$. Adding and subtracting the integral of the same function along the directed curve C, we see that, for points z in $D_1 + D_2$,

$$f(z) = \frac{1}{2\pi i} \oint_{C_1 + C} \frac{\phi(\zeta)\,d\zeta}{\zeta - z} + \frac{1}{2\pi i} \oint_{C_2 + C} \frac{\phi(\zeta)\,d\zeta}{\zeta - z}$$

$$= \frac{1}{2\pi i} \oint_{C_1 + C} \frac{f_1(\zeta)\,d\zeta}{\zeta - z} + \frac{1}{2\pi i} \oint_{C_2 + C} \frac{f_2(\zeta)\,d\zeta}{\zeta - z}, \tag{2}$$

since $\phi(\zeta) = f_1(\zeta)$ on $C_1 + C$ and $\phi(\zeta) = f_2(\zeta)$ on $C_2 + C$. Suppose z belongs to D_1: then, $f_2(\zeta)/(\zeta - z)$ is regular in D_2 and continuous on $\overline{D}_2$, and it follows from Cauchy's theorem (Art. 47) that the second integral on the right in (2) is equal to zero, so that

$$f(z) = \frac{1}{2\pi i} \oint_{C_1 + C} \frac{f_1(\zeta)\,d\zeta}{\zeta - z};$$

as we postulated that $f_1(z)$ is regular in D_1 and continuous on $\overline{D}_1$, it follows from Cauchy's integral formula (Art. 52) that, for all points z in D_1, $f(z) = f_1(z)$. In the same way we can show that, for all points z in D_2,

$$f(z) = \frac{1}{2\pi i} \oint_{C_2 + C} \frac{f_2(\zeta)\,d\zeta}{\zeta - z} = f_2(z).$$

This completes the proof of our theorem.

Remark 1. The above result is immediate when we are given that the functions $f_1(z)$ and $f_2(z)$ are regular, not only in the respective domains D_1 and D_2, but also at all points of C. In this case $f_1(z)$ and $f_2(z)$ are both regular in some domain D_0 containing C; as these functions are identically equal on C, it follows from the uniqueness theorem of Art. 62 that they are identically equal throughout D_0, so that $f_1(z)$ gives an analytic continuation of $f_2(z)$ into D_1 and $f_2(z)$ gives an analytic continuation of $f_1(z)$ into D_2.

Remark 2. In the above proof we have taken D_1 and D_2 to be bounded domains whose frontiers are rectifiable closed Jordan curves. The same result holds when D_1 and D_2 are *any* two non-overlapping domains, on the z-sphere, whose common boundary component C is a piecewise-smooth Jordan arc on this sphere (so that C *may* pass through $z = \infty$). The extremities ($z = a, b$, say) of any "interior" sub-arc C' of C can then be joined by smooth Jordan arcs C_1 and C_2 which, with C', cut off simply-connected *proper* sub-domains D_1' and D_2' of D_1 and D_2, respectively; here, all "interior" points on C_1 and C_2 belong to D_1 and D_2, respectively. We choose a finite point $z = c$ which is exterior to $\overline{D}_1' + \overline{D}_2'$. Then, under the bilinear mapping $w = 1/(z-c)$, D_1', D_2' are mapped on adjoining bounded domains Δ_1, Δ_2 of the finite w-plane, and it follows as before that $g_2(w) = f_2(w^{-1}+c)$ is an analytic continuation, into Δ_2, of the function $g_1(w) = f_1(w^{-1}+c)$ defined in Δ_1. The required result follows immediately.

An important consequence of the theorem just proved is the following:

The symmetry principle (Schwarz's reflection principle). Let one part C of the boundary of a domain D_1 of the extended z-plane be an arc of a circle or a segment of a straight line (this component C may be one edge of a cut—see Art. 23), *and let $w = f_1(z)$ be regular in D_1 and give a conformal mapping of D_1 onto the domain Δ_1 in such a way that the image Γ of C* (under continuous extension of $f_1(z)$ onto C from within D_1—see Art. 23) *is a part of the boundary of Δ_1 and is either a circular arc or a segment of a straight line. Then, there exists an analytic continuation of $w = f_1(z)$ into the domain D_2 which is obtained by inversion of D_1 with respect to the circle of which C is part* (D_2 is obtained by simple reflection of D_1 in C if C is a line-segment; *in all cases we say that D_2 and D_1 are symmetrical with respect to C*); *if this continuation be denoted by $f_2(z)$, the image of D_2 under the mapping $w = f_2(z)$ is the domain Δ_2 which is symmetrical to Δ_1 with respect to Γ and the function $f(z)$ defined by*

$$f(z) = \begin{cases} f_1(z) \text{ in } D_1 \\ f_2(z) \text{ in } D_2 \end{cases} \tag{2a}$$

*is regular in the domain D which is the interior of the set $D_1 + C + D_2$
and gives a conformal mapping of D onto the domain Δ which is the
interior of the set $\Delta_1 + \Gamma + \Delta_2$* (see Fig. 127). (Here, we suppose
$f(z)$ defined on C by continuity from within D_1 or D_2.)

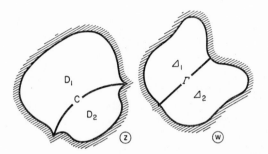

FIG. 127

To prove this we first carry out bilinear mappings

$$\zeta = \frac{az+b}{cz+d}, \qquad \omega = \frac{\alpha w + \beta}{\gamma w + \delta} \tag{3}$$

under which C and Γ are transformed into segments C^* and Γ^*,
respectively, of the real axes of the ζ and ω planes (Fig. 128), and
D_1 and Δ_1 are transformed into the respective domains D_1^* and Δ_1^*.

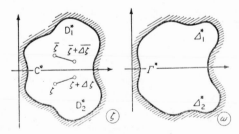

FIG. 128

Under these transformations the relation $w = f_1(z)$ becomes

$$\omega = g_1(\zeta),$$

a relation giving a conformal mapping of D_1^* onto Δ_1^*. Let D_2^*

be the domain symmetrical to D_1^* with respect to C^*; in D_2^* we consider the function

$$\omega = g_2(\zeta) = \overline{g_1(\bar{\zeta})}$$

and show that it is an analytic continuation of $g_1(\zeta)$ into this domain. It is clear that, on C^*, $g_1(\zeta) = g_2(\zeta)$; for, ζ and $g_1(\zeta)$ are then real, so that $\bar{\zeta} = \zeta$ and

$$\overline{g_1(\bar{\zeta})} = \overline{g_1(\zeta)} = g_1(\zeta).$$

We prove that $g_2(\zeta)$ is regular in D_2^* and then apply the preceding theorem. Let ζ, $\zeta + \Delta\zeta$ be distinct points of D_2^*; then,

$$\frac{g_2(\zeta + \Delta\zeta) - g_2(\zeta)}{\Delta\zeta} = \frac{\overline{g_1(\bar{\zeta} + \overline{\Delta\zeta})} - \overline{g_1(\bar{\zeta})}}{\Delta\zeta} = \overline{\left\{ \frac{g_1(\bar{\zeta} + \overline{\Delta\zeta}) - g_1(\bar{\zeta})}{\overline{\Delta\zeta}} \right\}},$$

where $\bar{\zeta}$ and $\bar{\zeta} + \overline{\Delta\zeta}$ are distinct points of D_1^*; accordingly, $g_2'(\zeta)$ exists and equals

$$\lim_{\overline{\Delta\zeta} \to 0} \overline{\left\{ \frac{g_1(\bar{\zeta} + \overline{\Delta\zeta}) - g_1(\bar{\zeta})}{\overline{\Delta\zeta}} \right\}} = \overline{g_1'(\bar{\zeta})},$$

since $g_1(\zeta)$ is regular at $\bar{\zeta}$. It follows that $g_2(\zeta)$ is regular in D_2^*; thus, the preceding theorem applies, so that $g_2(\zeta)$ is an analytic continuation of $g_1(\zeta)$ into D_2^*.

From the above construction it follows that $\omega = g_2(\zeta)$ gives a conformal mapping of D_2^* onto the domain Δ_2^* which is symmetrical to Δ_1^* with respect to Γ^*, so that the function defined by

$$\omega = g(\zeta) = \begin{cases} g_1(\zeta) \text{ in } D_1^*, \\ g_2(\zeta) \text{ in } D_2^* \end{cases}$$

gives a conformal mapping of the interior of $D_1^* + C^* + D_2^*$ onto the interior of $\Delta_1^* + \Gamma^* + \Delta_2^*$.

Under the transformations inverse to those in (3) the relations $\omega = g_1(\zeta)$ and $\omega = g_2(\zeta)$ become, respectively, $w = f_1(z)$ and $w = f_2(z)$; the function $w = f_2(z)$ is defined in the domain D_2 which is symmetrical to D_1 with respect to C, is regular in this domain, and gives a conformal mapping of D_2 onto the domain Δ_2 which is symmetrical to Δ_1 with respect to Γ. It is easily shown that $f_2(z)$ is continuous onto C from within D_2, and it follows readily that the function $f(z)$ defined by (2a) gives a conformal mapping of D on Δ. This completes the proof of the symmetry principle. It may be noted that if, in addition, the boundary of D_1 and the function $f_1(z)$ satisfy the requirements of the theorem at the beginning of this article, the function $f(z)$ will be given in $D_1 + D_2$ by the formula (2).

In the next article we illustrate the practical application of this principle with a series of examples.

Remark. The above principle of analytic continuation can be generalized as follows:

Let $w = f(z)$ give a regular, conformal mapping of a domain D onto a domain Δ, in such a way that the image (under continuous extension of $f(z)$ from within D) *of an analytic boundary-arc C of D is itself an analytic boundary-arc Γ of Δ; then, $f(z)$ can be continued analytically into a domain containing all points of the arc C, with the possible exception of the end-points of this arc.*

(An arc C is termed *analytic* if it can be represented by a continuous mapping $z = z(t)$ of a closed interval $\alpha \leqslant t \leqslant \beta$, where $z(t)$ can be expanded in a convergent power series

$$\sum_{k=0}^{+\infty} a_k (t - t_0)^k,$$

with $z'(t_0) = a_1 \neq 0$, in some neighbourhood $|t - t_0| < \epsilon$ of every interior point t_0 of $[\alpha, \beta]$.)

In particular, if the frontier of D, like the frontier of Δ, consists of a single analytic curve (so that *every* sub-arc is an analytic curve in the sense of the above definition) then $f(z)$ can be continued analytically into a domain containing $\overline{D}$.

83. Illustrative examples

Example 1. We seek a conformal mapping, onto a half-plane, of the domain exterior to a T-shaped cut (Fig. 129). To solve this problem we first make supplementary cuts EA and AB (shown dotted in Fig. 129) and find a mapping, onto a half-plane, of the domain, on the *right*, whose boundary is $AEDCBA$. (This domain is formed from the half-plane $\mathrm{Re}\, z > 0$ by removing the segment $(0, 1]$ of the real axis.) It is easily seen that this auxiliary problem is solved by the following sequence of mappings:

$$\zeta = z^2, \qquad \omega = \sqrt{(\zeta - 1)} = \sqrt{(z^2 - 1)};$$

the root is chosen so that $\omega = \sqrt{(z^2-1)}$ maps the domain bounded by $AEDCBA$ onto the right half-plane $\mathrm{Re}\,\omega > 0$. The linear boundary-segment EAB on the z-sphere, passing from $E(0)$ along the imaginary axis through $A(\infty)$ to $B(-2i)$, is thereby transformed into a linear boundary-segment EAB on the ω-sphere passing from $E(i)$ along the imaginary axis through $A(\infty)$ to $B(-i\sqrt{5})$. Thus, by the reflection principle, the analytic continuation of $\omega = \sqrt{(z^2-1)}$ across the boundary-segment EAB gives a conformal mapping, onto the left half-plane $\mathrm{Re}\,\omega < 0$, of the domain formed from the left half-plane $\mathrm{Re}\,z < 0$ by removing the segment $[-1, 0)$. Accordingly, a regular branch of $\omega = \sqrt{(z^2-1)}$

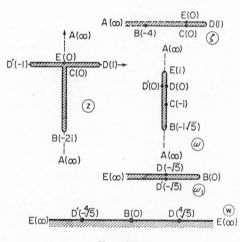

Fig. 129

exists in the *given* z-domain and maps the latter onto the ω-domain which is the exterior of the segment joining the points $\omega = -i\sqrt{5}$ and $\omega = i$; all points on the "auxiliary" segments EAB, other than the end-points E and B, are (interior) points of the appropriate domains; the T-shaped frontier of the z-domain is mapped onto the line segment BE in the ω-plane, this segment being the frontier of the ω-domain.

It remains to find a conformal mapping of this ω-domain onto the half-plane $\mathrm{Im}\,w > 0$. This problem also has an elementary solution. First,

$$\omega_1 = \frac{\omega + i\sqrt{5}}{\omega - i}$$

maps our ω-domain onto the exterior of a segment in the ω_1-plane joining the points $B(0)$, $E(\infty)$; as the point $D(0)$ in the ω-plane is mapped on the point $\omega_1 = -\sqrt{5}$, it follows that this segment is the negative real axis in the ω_1-plane. Finally, the function $w = \sqrt{(-\omega_1)}$, where we choose the regular branch whose value is $+i$ at $\omega_1 = 1$ maps our ω_1-domain onto Im $w > 0$. Accordingly, the function giving a conformal mapping, onto the half-plane Im $w > 0$, of the z-domain exterior to the given T-shaped cut is the appropriate regular branch of

$$w = \sqrt{\left\{ \frac{\omega + i\sqrt{5}}{i - \omega} \right\}} = \sqrt{\left\{ \frac{\sqrt{(z^2 - 1)} + i\sqrt{5}}{i - \sqrt{(z^2 - 1)}} \right\}}. \tag{4}$$

Example 2. We find a conformal mapping, onto the half-plane Im $w > 0$, of the z-domain formed from the strip

$$-\frac{\pi}{2} < \operatorname{Re} z < \frac{\pi}{2}$$

by taking cuts along the segments $[-\pi/2, -\pi/6]$, $[\pi/6, \pi/2]$ of the real axis.

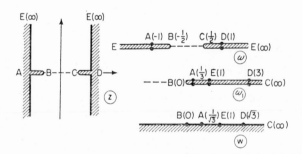

Fig. 130

We first make a supplementary cut (shown dotted in Fig. 130) along the segment $[-\pi/6, \pi/6]$ and then map the half-strip bordered by $EABCDE$ onto the half-plane Im $\omega > 0$. As shown in Example 2, Art. 33, the required mapping function is

$$\omega = \sin z.$$

Applying the symmetry principle to the segment BC, we see that the same function maps the lower half-strip

$$\left(-\frac{\pi}{2} < x < \frac{\pi}{2}, y < 0\right)$$

on the lower half-plane $\operatorname{Im}\omega < 0$, and maps the whole of the *given* z-domain onto the domain formed from the ω-plane by removing the rays EB and CE; the auxiliary barriers BC are "obliterated" in the process of analytic continuation, the remaining points on the real axis in the ω-plane (that is, the rays EB and CE) forming the frontier of our ω-domain.

It remains to map this ω-domain onto the half-plane $\operatorname{Im} w > 0$: the boundary-segment CEB on the ω-sphere is transformed into the positive real axis in the ω_1-plane by the mapping

$$\omega_1 = \frac{\omega+\frac{1}{2}}{\omega-\frac{1}{2}},$$

and the exterior of this semi-axis is then transformed into the half-plane $\operatorname{Im} w > 0$. Thus the required mapping is given by

$$w = \sqrt{\omega_1} = \sqrt{\left\{\frac{2\sin z+1}{2\sin z-1}\right\}}, \tag{5}$$

the root denoting the regular branch which assumes the value $+i$ at $z = 0$.

Example 3. We find a conformal mapping, onto the exterior of the unit circle, of the domain exterior to the "paddle wheel" shown in Fig. 131.

Auxiliary cuts (shown dotted) are made along the rays AB, EA; and the sectoral domain whose boundary (traversed positively) is $AEDCBA$ is mapped onto *another* such domain in the w-plane so that B and E are transformed into the "corner points" (that is, in such a way that the segments ED and CB are "gathered into" the circular arc forming part of the boundary of the w-domain). To begin, we apply the successive transformations

$$\zeta = z^8, \quad \omega = \frac{1}{2}\left(\zeta+\frac{1}{\zeta}\right);$$

the sectoral z-domain is thereby transformed into an ω-domain which is the exterior of the ray defined by $-1 \leqslant \omega \leqslant +\infty$, the images of B and E coinciding at the point $\omega = d = \frac{1}{2}(h^8 + h^{-8})$. Next, we find the linear transformation $\omega_1 = \alpha\omega + \beta$ which maps the segment $-1 \leqslant \omega \leqslant d$ onto the segment $-1 \leqslant \omega_1 \leqslant 1$: we have $-1 = -\alpha + \beta$, $1 = \alpha d + \beta$, whence $\alpha = 2/(1+d)$, $\beta = (1-d)/(1+d)$, and

$$\omega_1 = \frac{2\omega + 1 - d}{1 + d}.$$

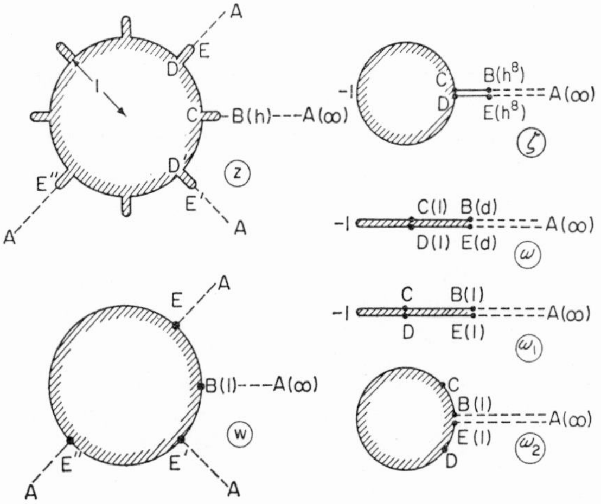

FIG. 131

We now transform the exterior of the segment $-1 \leqslant \omega_1 \leqslant 1$ onto the domain $|\omega_2| > 1$ exterior to the unit disc in the ω_2-plane; as shown in formula (12) of Art. 26, the required transformation is

$$\omega_2 = \omega_1 + \sqrt{(\omega_1^2 - 1)},$$

where we choose the regular branch such that $\omega_2 = 2 + \sqrt{3}$ when $\omega_1 = 2$; under this mapping, the edges of the cut along the segment $1 \leqslant \omega_1 \leqslant +\infty$ (shown dotted) map onto the corresponding edges of the cut along the segment $1 \leqslant \omega_2 \leqslant +\infty$. Finally, taking an appropriate eighth root, $w = \sqrt[8]{\omega_2}$, the ω_2-domain is mapped onto the sectoral w-domain defined by $|w| > 1$, $0 < \arg w < \pi/4$; the edges of the cut along the segment $1 \leqslant \omega_2 \leqslant +\infty$ (shown dotted) are mapped on the rays

$$\arg w = 0, \quad |w| > 1,$$

and

$$\arg w = \frac{\pi}{4}, \quad |w| > 1.$$

The resultant of this sequence of mappings is

$$
w = \sqrt[8]{\left\{ \frac{1}{1+d}\left[z^8 + z^{-8} + 1 - d + \sqrt{\{(z^8 + z^{-8} + 2)(z^8 + z^{-8} - 2d)\}} \right]\right\}}
$$

$$
= f(z) \text{ (say)}. \tag{6}
$$

From the symmetry principle it follows that $f(z)$ can be continued analytically across the auxiliary barrier AB; denoting this extension of the function by the same symbol $f(z)$, we see that $w = f(z)$ maps that portion of the exterior of the "paddle wheel" lying between the rays AE and $E'A$ onto the sectoral domain $|w| > 1$, $-\pi/4 < \arg w < \pi/4$; points z on AB for which $z > h$ thereby become interior points of the image domain in the w-plane. This function $f(z)$ can be continued across the auxiliary barrier $E'A$, and the resulting extension maps the z-domain whose boundary (traversed positively) is $AEDCBCD' \ldots E''A$ onto the domain $|w| > 1$, $-3\pi/4 < \arg w < \pi/4$. In turn, this extension can be continued across the auxiliary barrier $E''A$; in this way we obtain a function which maps the z-domain whose boundary (traversed positively) is $AEDCBCD' \ldots DEA$ onto the domain $|w| > 1$, $-7\pi/4 < \arg w < \pi/4$. A final application of the symmetry principle shows that this function can be continued across the auxiliary barrier AE. Thus the function given by (6) accomplishes the required mapping.

Remark. It is easily shown that, for $d = 1$, formula (6) reduces to $w = z$; this result becomes immediately obvious when it is realized that, in this case, the "paddle depth" is zero (that is, $h = 1$). For a small paddle depth ($h > 1$, $h \doteq 1$), $d = \frac{1}{2}(h^8 + h^{-8}) = 1 + \eta$, where η is a small positive number; making use of the approximation $\sqrt[n]{(1+\delta)} \doteq 1 + \delta/n$ (δ *small*) we then have

$$
w = \sqrt[8]{\left\{ \frac{1}{2+\eta}\left[z^8 + z^{-8} - \eta + \sqrt{\{(z^8 - z^{-8})^2 - 2\eta(z^8 + z^{-8} + 2)\}} \right]\right\}}
$$

$$
\doteq \sqrt[8]{\left\{ \frac{1}{2+\eta}\left[2z^8 - 2\eta\frac{z^8}{z^8-1} \right]\right\}}
$$

$$
\doteq z\left(1 - \frac{\eta}{16}\right)\left(1 - \frac{\eta}{8(z^8-1)}\right).
$$

Thus, neglecting terms in η^2, we arrive at the approximation

$$w = \left(1 - \frac{\eta}{16}\right)z - \frac{\eta z}{8(z^8 - 1)} \, . \tag{7}$$

When $|z|$ is large, the second term on the right in (7) can be neglected and we then have the simpler formula

$$w = \left(1 - \frac{\eta}{16}\right)z. \tag{8}$$

Formulae (7) and (8) give the "principal part" of the conformal mapping (6) as far as terms which are linear in the (small) parameter η.

The study of the behaviour of conformal mappings for small variations of certain parameters (in particular, for small variations of the domain being mapped) has been greatly aided by variational methods; major contributions along these lines are due to the Soviet mathematician M. A. Lavrent'ev (see Lavrent'ev, *Conformal Mappings* (Konformnyye otobrazheniya), Gostekhizdat, 1946; and Lavrent'ev and Shabat, *Methods of the Theory of Functions of a Complex Variable* (Metody teorii funktsii kompleksnogo peremennogo), Fizmatgiz, 1958).

Example 4. We find a conformal mapping, onto the upper half-plane $\operatorname{Im} w > 0$, of the domain formed from the half-plane $\operatorname{Im} z > 0$ by removing the segments defined by $0 < y \leqslant h$, $x = k\pi$ $(k = 0, \pm 1, \pm 2, \ldots)$. To solve this problem we make the supplementary cuts AB, EA (shown dotted in Fig. 132) and find a conformal mapping of the half-strip bordered by $ABCDEA$ onto a similar half-strip, in such a way that B and E are transformed into corner points of the boundary of the image domain. The function

$$\zeta = \cos z \tag{9}$$

maps our half-strip onto the upper half-plane $\operatorname{Im} \zeta > 0$: as $z = x$ traces the segment CD, $\zeta = \cos x$ traces the segment $[-1, 1]$ of the real axis; as $z = iy$ traces the ray DA, $\zeta = \cos iy = \cosh y$ traces the segment $[1, +\infty)$ of this axis; and as $z = -\pi + iy$ traces the ray AC, $\zeta = \cos(-\pi + iy) = -\cosh y$ traces the segment

$(-\infty, -1]$ of the same axis (see the *principle of correspondence of boundaries*, Art. 23). The points B, E map on the points

$$\zeta = \pm \cosh h;$$

these are in turn transformed into the points $\omega = \pm 1$ by

$$\omega = \frac{1}{\cosh h} \cdot \zeta.$$

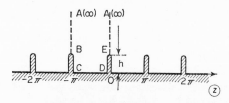

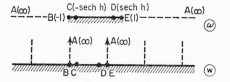

FIG. 132

Finally we use the mapping inverse to that in (9):

$$w = \text{arc cos } \omega.$$

Here, we choose the regular branch which assumes the value zero at $\omega = 1$ and the value $-\pi$ at $\omega = -1$; then, Im $\omega > 0$ is mapped on the half-strip $-\pi < \text{Re } w < 0$, Im $w > 0$, the points $B(-1)$, $E(1)$ being transformed into the points $B(-\pi)$, $E(0)$. The resultant mapping

$$w = \text{arc cos}\left(\frac{\cos z}{\cosh h}\right) \tag{10}$$

thus transforms the half-strip $-\pi < \text{Re } z < 0$, Im $z > 0$ onto the half-strip $-\pi < \text{Re } w < 0$, Im $w > 0$, the rays AB and EA becoming the rays $\text{Re } w = -\pi$, Im $w > 0$ and $\text{Re } w = 0$,

Im $w > 0$, and it will be clear from the symmetry principle that the mapping function (10) can be continued across the auxiliary barriers AB, EA. Repeated application of this principle shows that the analytic continuation of the function (10) into the *given* z-domain accomplishes the mapping of this domain onto Im $w > 0$.

Finally, we consider a case in which the symmetry principle is applied to the arc of a circle:

Example 5. As shown in Art. 26, the function

$$w = \frac{1}{2}\left(z + \frac{1}{z}\right) \tag{11}$$

gives a conformal mapping of $|z| > 1$ onto the w-domain exterior to the segment $[-1, 1]$ of the real axis, the domain D_z defined by $|z| > 1$, Im $z > 0$ being transformed into the half-plane Im $w > 0$.

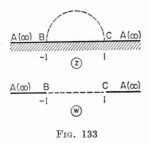

Fig. 133

The circular arc BC in Fig. 133 is part of the boundary of D_z and is transformed into the segment $[-1, 1]$. Applying the symmetry principle to the arc BC, we see that the analytic continuation of (11) into the domain D_z' which is symmetrical to D_z with respect to this arc will be such as to map D_z' onto Im $w < 0$. As D_z' is the domain $|z| < 1$, Im $z > 0$, it follows that the continuation of (11) into Im $z > 0$ maps this half-plane onto the domain formed from the w-plane by removing the segments $[-\infty, -1]$, $[1, +\infty]$ of the real axis.

84. The Schwarz–Christoffel integral

The Schwarz–Christoffel integral formula provides a mapping function which transforms the upper half-plane $\operatorname{Im} z > 0$ into a polygonal domain; that is, into a domain whose frontier consists of a finite number of line segments. Such transformations are of great use in many problems in applied mathematics.

To begin, we consider a bounded simply-connected domain D of the finite w-plane, its frontier being a closed polygon with n vertices, each at a finite point; we shall admit the possibility that a pair of adjacent sides of this polygon can lie along the adjacent edges of a cut, in accord with the definition of an "admissible" domain in Art. 23. Such a domain is called a polygonal domain; in the next article we extend the discussion to polygonal domains whose boundaries have one or more vertices at infinity.

By the fundamental existence theorem of Art. 23 there exists one, and only one, function $w = f(z)$ which is regular in $\operatorname{Im} z > 0$ and maps this half-plane one–one and *conformally* onto D in such a way that the continuous extension of $f(z)$ onto the x-axis from within the domain $\operatorname{Im} z > 0$ transforms three *given*, fixed points

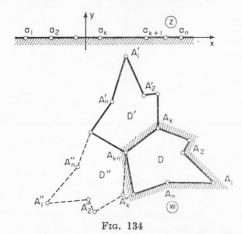

Fig. 134

$(a_1,\ a_2,\ a_3,$ say) of the x-axis into three prescribed points in the corresponding order (say, the vertices $A_1,\ A_2,\ A_3$; see Fig. 134) on the frontier of D. Let us first assume that $f(z)$ is known. Then, we know the points $a_k\ (k = 4, 5, \ldots, n)$ on the x-axis corresponding to the remaining vertices A_k; we shall suppose all the a_k finite, with $a_1 < a_2 < \ldots < a_n$, so that $A_1 A_2 \ldots A_n A_1$ represents a *positive* circuit about the domain D. We shall interpret a_{n+1} as a_1 and A_{n+1} as A_1.

The n points a_k on the real axis on the z-sphere divide this axis into n segments (a_k, a_{k+1}) $(k = 1, 2, \ldots, n)$. On the segment (a_k, a_{k+1}) the function $w = f(z)$ assumes values lying on the line segment $A_k A_{k+1}$; thus, by the symmetry principle, $f(z)$ can be continued across (a_k, a_{k+1}) into the lower half-plane $\text{Im } z < 0$; this continuation maps $\text{Im } z < 0$ conformally onto the polygonal domain D' obtained by reflecting D in the line $A_k A_{k+1}$. We denote by A_l' the point symmetrical to A_l with respect to $A_k A_{k+1}$. In turn, this continuation can itself be continued across another segment (a_m, a_{m+1}) into the upper half-plane $\text{Im } z > 0$; the continuation so obtained gives a conformal mapping of $\text{Im } z > 0$ onto the polygonal domain D'' obtained by reflecting D' in the side $A_m' A_{m+1}'$ of the boundary of D'.

Let us suppose that we have completed all possible sequences of continuations of the type described. The resulting infinitely-many-valued *complete* analytic function (see Art. 63) is denoted by $w = F(z)$; then, the required function $f(z)$ is one of the branches of $F(z)$ which is regular in the simply-connected domain $\text{Im } z > 0$.

We note that any two branches $w = f_1(z)$ and $w = f_2(z)$ of $F(z)$ which are regular in $\text{Im } z > 0$ are connected by a very simple relation. By construction, each of these branches can be obtained from the other by an *even* number of continuations across the segments (a_k, a_{k+1}); accordingly, they map $\text{Im } z > 0$ onto polygonal domains D_1 and D_2, each of which can be obtained from the other by an even number of reflections with respect to boundary sides. Each pair of reflections of the type described above is equivalent to the resultant of a rotation and a translation; thus, D_1 and D_2 can be obtained from one another by superposing a rotation and a translation, and it follows that, for $\text{Im } z > 0$,

$$f_2(z) = e^{i\alpha} f_1(z) + a, \tag{12}$$

where the real constant α characterizes the rotation and the complex constant a characterizes the translation. It will be clear that a similar relation holds between any two branches of $F(z)$ which are regular in the lower half-plane.

The function

$$\phi(z) = f''(z)/f'(z)$$

is regular in $\text{Im } z > 0$; for, $w = f(z)$ gives a *conformal* mapping of this half-plane, so that $f'(z)$ cannot vanish in $\text{Im } z > 0$. The function $\phi(z)$ is the same for every branch of $F(z)$ which is regular in $\text{Im } z > 0$; for, by (12),

$$f_2'(z) = e^{i\alpha}f_1'(z), \qquad f_2''(z) = e^{i\alpha}f_1''(z),$$

whence

$$\frac{f_2''(z)}{f_2'(z)} = \frac{f_1''(z)}{f_1'(z)}.$$

Denoting the complete analytic function generated by $\phi(z)$ by the same symbol, we see that $\phi(z)$ is single-valued and regular at all points of the z-sphere other than the points $z = a_k$ $(k = 1, 2, \ldots, n)$. (The regularity of $\phi(z)$ at points $z \neq a_k$ on the real axis, including the point $z = \infty$, and at points in $\text{Im } z < 0$ follows from the fact that each of these points belongs to some domain of the z-sphere in which $f(z)$ has a regular continuation with a non-vanishing derivative.) We now consider the behaviour of $\phi(z)$ in a neighbourhood of a point a_k. Let $\alpha_k\pi$ denote the interior angle of the polygon at A_k $(w = w_k)$; we have $0 < \alpha_k \leqslant 2$ $(k = 1, 2, \ldots, n)$. Under the auxiliary mapping

$$\omega = (w - w_k)^{1/\alpha_k} \tag{12'}$$

the angle at A_k "straightens out"; consequently, the compound function

$$\omega = \omega(z) = \{f(z) - w_k\}^{1/\alpha_k}$$

maps a certain closed "half-neighbourhood" of the point $z = a_k$ onto a corresponding "half-neighbourhood" of $\omega = 0$ (see Fig. 135). From the symmetry principle it follows that $\omega(z)$ has a continuation which is regular in a *complete* neighbourhood of a_k and can be represented in this neighbourhood by the Taylor series

$$\omega = \{f(z) - w_k\}^{1/\alpha_k} = c_1(z - a_k) + c_2(z - a_k)^2 + \ldots . \tag{13}$$

The constant term in the expansion (13) vanishes since $\omega(a_k) = 0$; however, $c_1 = \omega'(a_k) \neq 0$, since $\omega(z)$ gives a one–one mapping of some neighbourhood of a_k.

From (13), the many-valued function $f(z)$ is given in some neighbourhood of a_k by

$$f(z) = w_k + (z - a_k)^{\alpha_k}\{c_1 + c_2(z - a_k) + \ldots\}^{\alpha_k} \qquad (c_1 \neq 0)$$

$$= w_k + (z - a_k)^{\alpha_k}g(z), \text{ say.}$$

As $g(z)$ does not vanish at $z = a_k$, it follows from the results obtained in Art. 32 that there is a neighbourhood of a_k in which $g(z)$ can be represented by a Taylor expansion, so that

$$
\begin{aligned}
f(z) &= w_k + (z - a_k)^{\alpha_k}\{c_1' + c_2'(z - a_k) + \ldots\} \\
&= w_k + c_1'(z - a_k)^{\alpha_k} + c_2'(z - a_k)^{\alpha_k + 1} + \ldots \quad .
\end{aligned}
\tag{14}
$$

It follows that, in some deleted neighbourhood of a_k,

$$
\begin{aligned}
\phi(z) &= \frac{f''(z)}{f'(z)} = \frac{\alpha_k(\alpha_k - 1)c_1'(z - a_k)^{\alpha_k - 2} + \ldots}{\alpha_k c_1'(z - a_k)^{\alpha_k - 1} + (\alpha_k + 1)c_2'(z - a_k)^{\alpha_k} + \ldots} \\
\\
&= \frac{1}{z - a_k} \cdot \frac{\alpha_k(\alpha_k - 1)c_1' + (\alpha_k + 1)\alpha_k c_2'(z - a_k) + \ldots}{\alpha_k c_1' + (\alpha_k + 1)c_2'(z - a_k) + \ldots} \quad .
\end{aligned}
\tag{14$'$}
$$

Fɪɢ. 135

In this last expression the second factor represents a function which is regular at a_k and can hence be represented in a neighbourhood of this point by a series of the form

$$
(\alpha_k - 1) + c_1''(z - a_k) + c_2''(z - a_k)^2 + \ldots \quad ;
$$

here, the constant term $(\alpha_k - 1)$ is given by the value of this function at $z = a_k$. Thus, (14$'$) becomes

$$
\begin{aligned}
\phi(z) &= \frac{1}{z - a_k}\{(\alpha_k - 1) + c_1''(z - a_k) + c_2''(z - a_k)^2 + \ldots\} \\
\\
&= \frac{\alpha_k - 1}{z - a_k} + c_1'' + c_2''(z - a_k) + \ldots \quad .
\end{aligned}
\tag{15}
$$

Equation (15) gives the Laurent expansion of $\phi(z)$ in some deleted neighbourhood of a_k and it will be seen that, *at the point a_k, the function $\phi(z)$ has a first-order pole with residue $\alpha_k - 1$, where $\alpha_k \pi$ is the interior angle of the polygon at the vertex A_k.*

Thus, the function $\phi(z)$ is regular at all points of the z-sphere other than the points $z = a_k$ $(k = 1, 2, \ldots, n)$; at each of these singular points $\phi(z)$ has a first-order pole. Subtracting from $\phi(z)$ its principal parts at these poles, we obtain the function

$$\psi(z) = \phi(z) - \frac{\alpha_1 - 1}{z - a_1} - \frac{\alpha_2 - 1}{z - a_2} - \ldots - \frac{\alpha_n - 1}{z - a_n} ; \qquad (16)$$

defining $\psi(z)$ by continuity at the points $z = a_k$ we see that it is regular throughout the extended z-plane and is thus identically equal to a constant (see Liouville's theorem, Art. 69; and Art. 71). In order to evaluate this constant we note that, as $z = \infty$ is an "interior" point of the segment (a_n, a_1), the function $f(z)$ is regular at $z = \infty$ and hence can be represented in some neighbourhood of this point by a Laurent expansion of the form

$$f(z) = c_0 + \frac{c_{-p}}{z^p} + \frac{c_{-p-1}}{z^{p+1}} + \ldots, \quad (c_{-p} \neq 0), \qquad (17)$$

where p is some positive integer. Thus, in some neighbourhood of $z = \infty$ we have

$$\begin{aligned}
\phi(z) &= \frac{f''(z)}{f'(z)} = \frac{p(p+1)c_{-p}z^{-p-2} + (p+1)(p+2)c_{-p-1}z^{-p-3} + \ldots}{-\{pc_{-p}z^{-p-1} + (p+1)c_{-p-1}z^{-p-2} + \ldots\}} \\
&= -\frac{1}{z}\frac{p(p+1)c_{-p} + (p+1)(p+2)c_{-p-1}z^{-1} + \ldots}{\{pc_{-p} + (p+1)c_{-p-1}z^{-1} + \ldots\}} \\
&= -\frac{p+1}{z} + \frac{b_2}{z^2} + \frac{b_3}{z^3} + \ldots \quad \text{(say)},
\end{aligned}$$

and it follows that $\phi(\infty) = 0$. As each of the terms $(\alpha_k - 1)/(z - a_k)$ in (16) vanishes at $z = \infty$ it is immediately clear that $\psi(\infty) = 0$. Accordingly, $\psi(z) \equiv 0$ and (16) becomes

$$\phi(z) = \sum_{k=1}^{n} \{(\alpha_k - 1)/(z - a_k)\}.$$

We now let Δ denote any *simply-connected* domain of the finite z-plane which contains all points of the region Im $z \geq 0$ *other than* the points a_k: for example, we could suppose Δ formed from the domain $\operatorname{Im} z > -1$ by taking cuts along the segments $(a_k - i, a_k)$ $(k = 1, 2, \ldots, n)$. From the discussion leading to (12′) it will be clear that $f(z)$ has a continuation into Δ which is regular and has a non-vanishing derivative $f'(z)$ in this domain; accordingly, Δ supports a regular branch $\ln f'(z)$ of the logarithm of this derivative, so that, in Δ,

$$\frac{\mathrm{d}}{\mathrm{d}z} \ln f'(z) = \phi(z) = \frac{\alpha_1 - 1}{z - a_1} + \frac{\alpha_2 - 1}{z - a_2} + \ldots + \frac{\alpha_n - 1}{z - a_n}.$$

Integrating this relation along a path L lying in Δ and joining a fixed point z_0 to the general point z of this domain, we get

$$\ln f'(z) = (\alpha_1 - 1) \ln(z - a_1) + (\alpha_2 - 1) \ln(z - a_2) + \ldots$$
$$+ (\alpha_n - 1) \ln(z - a_n) + \ln C;$$

here, on the right, C is some constant and the logarithms may be taken to be the usual principal branches; this choice determines the particular regular branch of $\ln f'(z)$ to be taken in Δ. Taking exponentials, we see that the derivative of the required mapping function is given in Δ by

$$f'(z) = C(z - a_1)^{\alpha_1 - 1}(z - a_2)^{\alpha_2 - 1} \ldots (z - a_n)^{\alpha_n - 1}$$
$$(C = \text{const.}). \quad (18)$$

In turn, integrating this relation along any such path L in Δ, we obtain the *Schwarz–Christoffel integral formula*:

$$f(z) = C \int_{z_0}^{z} (z - a_1)^{\alpha_1 - 1}(z - a_2)^{\alpha_2 - 1} \ldots (z - a_n)^{\alpha_n - 1} \, \mathrm{d}z$$
$$\quad (L)$$

$$= C \int (z - a_1)^{\alpha_1 - 1}(z - a_2)^{\alpha_2 - 1} \ldots (z - a_n)^{\alpha_n - 1} \, \mathrm{d}z + C_1, \quad (19)$$

where C_1 is another constant and $\int$ denotes an indefinite integral in Δ (see Art. 49). We recall that, in this formula, the a_k denote the points of the x-axis which correspond with the vertices A_k of the polygon, the interior angle at A_k being $\alpha_k \pi$ $(k = 1, 2, \ldots, n)$. It is easily verified in any given case that the mapping of $\operatorname{Im} z > 0$ given by (19) is, indeed, one–one.

For the reader acquainted with the discussion of Dirichlet's problem in Chap. V we shall now give a simpler derivation of the

Schwarz–Christoffel formula. We consider the imaginary part of a suitable regular branch of the logarithm of $f'(z)$, where $w = f(z)$ gives the desired conformal mapping of the half-plane $\operatorname{Im} z > 0$ onto the given polygonal domain D:

$$V(z) = \operatorname{Im}\{\ln f'(z)\}.$$

This function is harmonic in $\operatorname{Im} z > 0$ and at each point of this half-plane represents the corresponding angle of rotation in our mapping; it follows that, on every segment (a_k, a_{k+1}) of the x-axis (corresponding to a side $A_k A_{k+1}$ of the polygon), $V(z)$ assumes a constant value given by the angle, in the w-plane, between the vector

$$\overrightarrow{A_k A_{k+1}}$$

and the positive real axis. It is easily seen that the required function $V(z)$ is given by the solution (66) of the Dirichlet problem of Example 1, Art. 57:

$$V(z) = v_n + \frac{v_0 - v_1}{\pi} \arg(z - a_1) + \ldots + \frac{v_{n-1} - v_n}{\pi} \arg(z - a_n);$$

here, $v_0 = v_n$ is the value of V on the segments $(-\infty, a_1)$ and $(a_n, +\infty)$, and v_k is the value of V on the segment (a_k, a_{k+1}) $(k = 1, 2, \ldots, n-1)$. From the above it is clear that $v_k - v_{k-1}$ is equal to the difference of the angles at which the segments $A_{k-1}A_k$ and $A_k A_{k+1}$ are inclined to the real axis of the w-plane: we have $v_k - v_{k-1} = (1 - \alpha_k)\pi$, where $\alpha_k \pi$ is the interior angle of the polygon at A_k, so that

$$V(z) = \operatorname{Im}\{\ln f'(z)\} = c_2 + (\alpha_1 - 1)\arg(z - a_1) + \ldots$$
$$+ (\alpha_n - 1)\arg(z - a_n),$$

where $c_2 = v_0 = v_n$ is some constant. As

$$\arg(z - a_k) = \operatorname{Im}\{\ln(z - a_k)\},$$

we can easily construct the corresponding analytic function

$$\ln f'(z) = (c_1 + ic_2) + (\alpha_1 - 1)\ln(z - a_1) + \ldots + (\alpha_n - 1)\ln(z - a_n);$$

then, taking exponentials and integrating, as before, we obtain the Schwarz–Christoffel formula (19).

The formula (19) was obtained on the assumption that we knew the points $a_1, a_2, \ldots, a_n$ on the real axis corresponding to the vertices of the polygon. In practice, however, the vertices A_k are given and the points $z = a_k$ are unknown. By the existence theorem for conformal mappings, three of these points a_k (say, a_1, a_2, a_3) can be chosen arbitrarily, in the appropriate left-to-right order; the remaining points $a_4, a_5, \ldots, a_n$ and the constants C and C_1 are determined by this choice and the given conditions of the problem; the difficulties involved in their evaluation present the main problem in applying the Schwarz–Christoffel formula.

Later, in Art. 86, we illustrate the methods used to determine C, C_1 and the a_k by a series of examples. The theoretical possibility of solving this problem for a given polygon will be clear from the method used to derive formula (19): for, supposing the polygonal domain D specified and the points a_1, a_2, a_3 selected, we can assert, on the basis of the fundamental theorem of Art. 23, that there exists a *unique* one–one conformal mapping $z = \phi(w)$ of D, onto $\text{Im } z > 0$, in which the vertices A_1, A_2, A_3 map on the respective points a_1, a_2, a_3. We denote the images of the remaining vertices of the polygon by $a_4, a_5, \ldots, a_n$, and let $w = f(z)$ be the function inverse to $z = \phi(w)$. As shown above, the function $w = f(z)$ is given by formula (19), where the a_k are the points just mentioned and C and C_1 are certain constants. Thus, given the polygonal domain D and the three points a_1, a_2, a_3, the remaining points $a_4, \ldots, a_n$ and the constants C, C_1 are determined uniquely. We note that, by (19), a change in the values of C and C_1 is equivalent to a linear transformation of w; accordingly, these constants are determined uniquely by the shape, linear dimensions, position and orientation of D.

85. Degenerate cases

In Art. 84 we postulated that all the points a_k were finite. We now let one of these points (a_n, say) be at infinity and reduce this case to that discussed above by carrying out a suitable linear transformation

$$\zeta = a_n' - \frac{1}{z-a}.$$

Here, a_n' denotes any given finite real number, and a is a finite real constant which differs from each of the a_k; under this transformation the points $a_1, a_2, \ldots, a_n \ (= \infty)$ are mapped on the respective *finite* points $a_1', a_2', \ldots, a_n'$ on the real axis in the ζ-plane, the correct left-to-right order being preserved, so that Im $z > 0$ is mapped onto Im $\zeta > 0$. For simplicity we shall assume that none of the a_k vanish, so that we may take $a = 0$; then, our linear transformation becomes

$$\zeta = a_n' - \frac{1}{z}. \tag{20}$$

With an obvious notation, the function $w = g(\zeta)$ giving the appropriate mapping of Im $\zeta > 0$ onto D is given by the formula

$$w = C' \int_{\zeta_0 \atop (L')}^{\zeta} (\zeta - a_1')^{\alpha_1 - 1} (\zeta - a_2')^{\alpha_2 - 1} \ldots (\zeta - a_n')^{\alpha_n - 1} \,d\zeta.$$

Under the substitution (20) this formula becomes

$$w = C' \int_{z_0 \atop (L)}^{z} \left(a_n' - a_1' - \frac{1}{z} \right)^{\alpha_1 - 1} \left(a_n' - a_2' - \frac{1}{z} \right)^{\alpha_2 - 1} \ldots \left(-\frac{1}{z} \right)^{\alpha_n - 1} \frac{1}{z^2} \,dz.$$

Using an elementary result concerning the sum of the internal angles of an n-gon, we have $\alpha_1 + \alpha_2 + \ldots + \alpha_n = n - 2$, whence

$$w = C' \int_{z_0 \atop (L)}^{z} \{ (a_n' - a_1')z - 1 \}^{\alpha_1 - 1} \{ (a_n' - a_2')z - 1 \}^{\alpha_2 - 1} \ldots$$

$$\ldots \{ (a_n' - a_{n-1}')z - 1 \}^{\alpha_{n-1} - 1} \frac{dz}{z^{\alpha_1 + \ldots + \alpha_n - n + 2}}$$

$$= C \int_{z_0 \atop (L)}^{z} (z - a_1)^{\alpha_1 - 1} (z - a_2)^{\alpha_2 - 1} \ldots (z - a_{n-1})^{\alpha_{n-1} - 1} \,dz$$

$$= C \int (z - a_1)^{\alpha_1 - 1} (z - a_2)^{\alpha_2 - 1} \ldots (z - a_{n-1})^{\alpha_{n-1} - 1} \,dz + C_1. \tag{21}$$

Here, L denotes a path joining z_0 to z in a *simply-connected* domain Δ which contains all points of the region Im $z \geqslant 0$ *other than* the points $a_1, a_2, \ldots, a_{n-1}$ appearing in the integrand; and $\int$ denotes an indefinite integral in Δ.

Thus, *if one of the vertices of the polygon is to be mapped onto the point at infinity in the z-plane, the corresponding factor does not appear in the integrand in the Schwarz–Christoffel formula.* In practice, this fact is used to simplify the calculations involved (see below, and Art. 86).

The case in which one or more of the vertices of the boundary of D lies at $w = \infty$ was excluded in the preceding article. We now examine this case as it is of great practical importance. Before proceeding we remark that, given any polygonal domain whose boundary has vertices at $w = \infty$, it is instructive to *display this domain on the w-sphere*; in this way it is easy to grasp the significance of the interior angle at a vertex at infinity. (For example, taking the half-strip $0 < \mathrm{Re}\, w < 1$, $\mathrm{Im}\, w > 0$, we see that the interior angle at $w = \infty$ is zero; for the *exterior* of this half-strip the corresponding angle is 2π; and for the sector $0 < \arg w < \frac{1}{4}\pi$ the angle at $w = \infty$ is $\frac{1}{4}\pi$.)

We consider a polygon ($n \geqslant 3$) with a single vertex A_p at $w = \infty$, the corresponding interior angle being $\beta\pi$ ($0 \leqslant \beta \leqslant 2$), and the corresponding sides being l and l'. To begin, we suppose $\beta \neq 0$; and that, if $\beta = 1$ or $\beta = 2$, the arms l, l' do *not* lie along *distinct* parallel lines. Then, these arms, when produced, pass through a common finite point w_0. We choose axes so that $w_0 = 0$; then, for $k = p$, the auxiliary mapping (12′) is replaced by

$$\omega = (1/w)^{1/\beta} = \{1/f(z)\}^{1/\beta};$$

proceeding as in Art. 84 we easily show that, in some deleted neighbourhood of $z = a_p$, the required function $f(z)$ can be represented in the form

$$f(z) = (z - a_p)^{-\beta}\{c_1{}'' + c_2{}''(z - a_p) + \ldots\}, \qquad (c_1{}'' \neq 0),$$

and it follows that $\phi(z) = f''(z)/f'(z)$ has a simple pole at $z = a_p$ with residue $-(\beta + 1)$; thus, the required mapping is given by (19), *provided the coefficient* α_p *is taken equal to* $-\beta$. The same result holds when $\beta = 1$ or $\beta = 2$ and the arms l, l' lie along *distinct* (parallel) lines; these cases are difficult to prove and require consideration of more complicated auxiliary mappings: e.g., with $\beta = 1$, we may consider the auxiliary mapping which is the inverse of a transformation of the form $w = C(\omega^{-1} + \ln \omega) + K.$(*)

~~required mapping is given by the formula (19),~~ *~~provided the coeffi-~~*
~~cient~~ α_p ~~is taken equal to~~ $-\beta$.

The same rule covers the case $\beta = 0$. As this case is important
in practice (see Art. 86) we sketch the derivation of the Schwarz-
Christoffel formula when the polygon has a single vertex A_p at
$w = \infty$, the corresponding interior angle being *zero*. It will suffice
to show that the function $\phi(z) = f''(z)/f'(z)$ has a first-order pole
at $z = a_p$ with residue -1. We suppose the parallel rays $A_{p-1}A_p$
and $A_{p+1}A_p$ to be at distance h apart and to be inclined at angle
γ to the positive u-axis (see Fig. 136). The auxiliary transformation

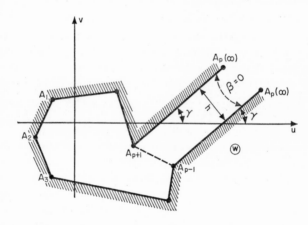

FIG. 136

$\omega = \exp[-(\pi/h)we^{-i\gamma}]$ gives a simple conformal mapping of the
interior of the "triangle" $A_{p-1}A_pA_{p+1}$ on an open "half-neighbourhood" of $\omega = 0$ (*cf.* Fig. 135), the vertex A_p corresponding with
the point $\omega = 0$. Using the symmetry principle, as in Art. 84, we
see that the compound function

$$\omega = \omega(z) = \exp[-(\pi/h)e^{-i\gamma}f(z)]$$

has a continuation which is regular and univalent in a *complete*
neighbourhood of the (finite) point a_p and can be represented in this
neighbourhood by the Taylor series

$$\omega(z) = c_1(z-a_p)+c_2(z-a_p)^2+ \ldots \quad (c_1 \neq 0).$$

Thus, in some deleted neighbourhood of $z = a_p$, the many-valued
function $f(z)$ is given by

$$f(z) = -(h/\pi)e^{i\gamma}\{\ln(z-a_p)+g(z)\},$$

where $g(z) = \ln\{c_1+c_2(z-a_p)+ \ldots\}$ is regular at $z = a_p$. Accordingly, there is a deleted neighbourhood of $z = a_p$ in which

$$\phi(z) = f''(z)/f'(z) = \{-(z-a_p)^{-2} + g''(z)\}/\{(z-a_p)^{-1} + g'(z)\}$$
$$= -(z-a_p)^{-1}\{1 - (z-a_p)^2 g''(z)\}/\{1 + (z-a_p)g'(z)\},$$

and it follows immediately that $\phi(z)$ has a first-order pole at $z = a_p$ with residue -1 $(= -\beta - 1$, since $\beta = 0)$.

The above arguments can be applied to cases in which *several* of the vertices of the given polygon coincide at $w = \infty$. Thus, to sum up, *the Schwarz-Christoffel formula* (19) *applies, without formal change, to polygons in which one or more of the vertices coincides with the point at infinity, provided we adopt the convention that, at any such vertex* (A_p, *say), the corresponding angle index* α_p *is to be taken equal to* $-\beta$, *where* $\beta\pi$ *is the interior angle obtained at* A_p *when the given polygonal domain is displayed on the w-sphere. It* should also be noted that *the rule expressed immediately after equation* (21) *holds even when the vertex concerned lies at* $w = \infty$.

An interesting discussion of integrals of the type (19) is given by Saks and Zygmund (*Analytic Functions*, Warsaw, 1952). Further developments and references, concerning mappings onto the interior and exterior of a circle, are given by Nehari (*Conformal Mapping*, Ch. V, McGraw-Hill, 1952) and by Jeffreys and Jeffreys (*Mathematical Physics*, Ch. 13, Cambridge, 1950). It may be remarked that an excellent modern account of the general theory of conformal mapping (and, indeed, of a wide field of function theory) is given by Hille (*Analytic Function Theory*, Ginn): elementary theory is covered in Vol. I (1959), advanced theory in Vol. II (1962).

86. Illustrative examples

In applying the formulae (19) and (21) of the preceding articles we shall make no explicit mention of the path L or the domain Δ. It may be remarked that the initial point z_0 on the paths L can be taken to coincide with one of the points a_k appearing in the integrand (all other points on L lying in Δ) provided the corresponding index $\alpha_k - 1$ exceeds -1 (that is, provided $\alpha_k > 0$); it will be clear that this condition is satisfied whenever the vertex A_k lies in the finite w-plane.

We begin with two elementary examples; these do not lead to fresh results and have been chosen merely to illustrate the method.

Example 1. The boundary of the half-strip $-\pi/2 < \operatorname{Re} w < \pi/2$, $\operatorname{Im} w > 0$ is a "triangle" with vertices $A_1(-\pi/2)$, $A_2(\pi/2)$, $A_3(\infty)$, the corresponding angles being given by $\alpha_1 = \frac{1}{2}$, $\alpha_2 = \frac{1}{2}$, $\alpha_3 = 0$. (Here, as for all triangles, $\alpha_1 + \alpha_2 + \alpha_3 = 1$.) These facts, along with the corresponding points a_k, are tabulated below. (As there are three points a_k they can be chosen arbitrarily on the x-axis, in the correct left-to-right order.)

A_k	α_k	a_k
$-\frac{\pi}{2}$	$\frac{1}{2}$	-1
$\frac{\pi}{2}$	$\frac{1}{2}$	1
∞	0	∞

The Schwarz–Christoffel integral assumes the form

$$w = C \int_0^z (z+1)^{-1/2}(z-1)^{-1/2}\,\mathrm{d}z + C_1$$

$$= C' \int_0^z \frac{\mathrm{d}z}{\sqrt{(1-z^2)}} + C_1 = C' \arcsin z + C_1.$$

As a_1, a_2 correspond with the respective points A_1, A_2, we have

$$-\frac{\pi}{2} = -C'\frac{\pi}{2} + C_1, \qquad \frac{\pi}{2} = C'\frac{\pi}{2} + C_1,$$

whence $C_1 = 0$, $C' = 1$. Accordingly, the function mapping the half-plane $\operatorname{Im} z > 0$ on the given half-strip is

$$w = \arcsin z. \tag{22}$$

The inverse mapping $z = \sin w$ was obtained by elementary means in Art. 31.

Example 2. The domain formed from the half-plane $v > 0$ by removing the segment defined by $0 < v \leqslant h$, $u = 0$ ($w = u + iv$) is bounded by a "quadrilateral". The data specifying this figure, along with the points a_k corresponding to the vertices, are displayed in the table. Three of the a_k can be chosen arbitrarily (in left-to-right order); the fourth is denoted temporarily by ξ. At the vertex $A_1(\infty)$ the interior angle is π since the rays A_2A_1, A_4A_1 are adjoining arcs of the same great circle (the real axis) on the w-sphere; accordingly, we take $\alpha_1 = -1$; then, as for all quadrilaterals, we have $\Sigma \alpha_k = 2$:

A_k	α_k	a_k
∞	-1	∞
0	$\frac{1}{2}$	-1
ih	2	0
0	$\frac{1}{2}$	ξ

To determine $a_4 = \xi$ we apply the symmetry principle: the required mapping can be obtained as the result of a continuation, across the positive y-axis, of a mapping of the second quadrant of the z-plane onto the second quadrant of the w-plane such as to satisfy the correspondences $w = \infty \leftrightarrow z = \infty$, $w = ih \leftrightarrow z = 0$; accordingly, as will be clear from the table, ξ must be symmetrical to the point a_2 with respect to the y-axis, so that $a_4 = \xi = 1$. Thus, the Schwarz–Christoffel formula becomes

$$w = C \int (z+1)^{-1/2} z(z-1)^{-1/2} \, dz$$

$$= C \int \frac{z \, dz}{\sqrt{(z^2-1)}} = C\sqrt{(z^2-1)} + C_1.$$

To determine C and C_1 we use the correspondence of the points A_2, A_3 with the respective points a_2, a_3:

$$0 = 0 + C_1, \qquad ih = iC + C_1.$$

Thus, $C_1 = 0$, $C = h$, and the required mapping (cf. Art. 27) is

$$w = h\sqrt{(z^2-1)}. \tag{23}$$

We now consider a problem whose solution would present considerable difficulties without the aid of the Schwarz–Christoffel formula.

Example 3. The given w-domain is shown in Fig. 137, its boundary being a quadrilateral with three vertices at infinity. The associated data and the points a_k corresponding to the vertices are displayed in the accompanying table; three of the a_k are chosen arbitrarily (in the appropriate left-to-right order), the fourth is denoted by ξ. As is easily seen by displaying the given domain on the w-sphere, each interior angle at the vertices at infinity is zero; then, as for all quadrilaterals, $\Sigma\alpha_k = 2$.

A_k	α_k	a_k
∞	0	∞
∞	0	-1
0	2	ξ
∞	0	1

The corresponding Schwarz–Christoffel integral is

$$w = C \int (z+1)^{-1}(z-\xi)(z-1)^{-1}\,\mathrm{d}z = C \int \frac{z-\xi}{z^2-1}\,\mathrm{d}z$$

$$= C\left\{\frac{1+\xi}{2}\ln(z+1) + \frac{1-\xi}{2}\ln(z-1)\right\} + C_1, \qquad (23')$$

and contains three unknown constants C, C_1 and ξ. To find ξ we reason as follows. We consider a small semi-circular indentation C_r about the point a_2; this semi-circle is given by $|z+1| = r$, $y \geqslant 0$,

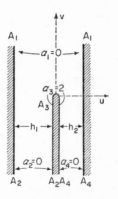

Fig. 137

where r is *small*. As z traverses C_r in the *clockwise* sense the image point w moves from the ray A_1A_2 to the ray A_2A_3; thus, the corresponding increment in w is of the form

$$\Delta w = h_1 + i \cdot \eta(r),$$

where $\eta(r)$ is *real*. It is easily shown that, when r is small, the image of C_r under (23′) differs little from a line segment which connects points on A_1A_2 and A_2A_3 and is perpendicular to each of these rays; from this it follows that $\eta(r) \to 0$ as $r \to +0$. The same result can be established by considering the increment in the function (23′) as z traces C_r: the contribution from the term $\ln(z-1)$ becomes vanishingly small as $r \to +0$ since $\ln(z-1)$ has a continuation which is regular, and hence continuous, in a neighbourhood of $z = -1$; also, on C_r, $\ln(z+1) = \ln r + i\phi$ $(0 \leqslant \phi \leqslant \pi)$, so that the corresponding increment in $\ln(z+1)$ is $-\pi i$; accordingly,

$$\Delta w = -C\frac{1+\xi}{2}\pi i + \delta(r),$$

where $\delta(r) \to 0$ as $r \to +0$. Comparing the two expressions for Δw and letting $r \to +0$, we have

$$-C\frac{1+\xi}{2}\pi i = h_1.$$

Similarly, by considering the increment in w when z traverses a small upper semi-circular indentation about the point $a_4 = 1$, we can show that

$$-C\frac{1-\xi}{2}\pi i = h_2.$$

These relations determine the constants C, ξ:

$$C = i\frac{h_1+h_2}{\pi}, \qquad \xi = \frac{h_1-h_2}{h_1+h_2};$$

thus, the required mapping function is of the form

$$w = \frac{i}{\pi}\{h_1\ln(z+1) + h_2\ln(z-1)\} + C_1. \tag{24}$$

The constant C_1 is determined by the correspondence of the point $a_3 = \xi$ with the vertex A_3 $(w = 0)$:

$$C_1 = h_2 - \frac{i}{\pi}\ln\{h_1{}^{h_1}h_2{}^{h_2}(2/H)^H\},$$

where $H = h_1 + h_2$.

Example 4. The w-domain shown in Fig. 138 is bounded by a quadrilateral with two vertices (A_1, A_2) at $w = \infty$. We make an auxiliary cut $A_1 A_2$ (shown dotted) along the axis of symmetry $(v = -h, -\infty \leqslant u \leqslant +\infty)$ of this domain and find a mapping of the upper half onto Im $\zeta > 0$. This upper half is bounded by a triangle $A_1 A_2 A_3$ and it is easily seen that the data determining the mapping are as shown in the following table:

A_k	α_k	a_k
∞	0	1
∞	$-1/2$	∞
0	$3/2$	0

Here, the a_k are chosen arbitrarily, in left-to-right order; and the α_k corresponding to the vertices at infinity are given by the rule

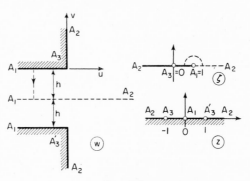

FIG. 138

of Art. 85, so that $\Sigma \alpha_k = 1$. The function giving a simple (one–one) conformal mapping of Im $\zeta > 0$ onto this triangular domain is of the form

$$w = C \int\limits_0^\zeta (\zeta - 1)^{-1} \zeta^{1/2} \, d\zeta + C_1.$$

As $\zeta = 0$ corresponds with $w = 0$, we have $C_1 = 0$ and

$$w = C \int_0^\zeta \frac{\sqrt{\zeta}}{\zeta - 1} d\zeta. \tag{25}$$

To find C we use the fact that the numerator $\sqrt{\zeta}$ in the integrand is continuous at $\zeta = 1$: thus, in taking this integral in the clockwise sense along the semi-circular indentation C_r defined by $|\zeta - 1| = r$, Im $\zeta \geqslant 0$, where r is small, the factor $\sqrt{\zeta}$ can be represented approximately by the value unity; in this way we can show that the *corresponding* increment in w is given by

$$\Delta w = C \int_{C_r} \frac{d\zeta}{\zeta - 1} + \delta(r) = C(-i\pi) + \delta(r), \tag{26}$$

where $\delta(r)$ is a complex function of r which tends to zero as $r \to +0$. As ζ traverses the semi-circle C_r in the clockwise sense, the image point w passes from the ray $A_3 A_1$ to the straight line $A_1 A_2$ along a path which, when r is small, differs little from a line segment perpendicular to $A_3 A_1$ and $A_1 A_2$; from this it can be shown (see Fig. 138) that $\Delta w = -ih + \eta(r)$, where $\eta(r) \to 0$ as $r \to +0$. Comparing this expression with (26), and letting $r \to +0$, we have

$$-hi = -\pi Ci,$$

whence $C = h/\pi$. Accordingly, (25) becomes

$$w = \frac{h}{\pi} \int_0^\zeta \frac{(\sqrt{\zeta}) d\zeta}{\zeta - 1} = \frac{h}{\pi} \left[2\sqrt{\zeta} + \ln \frac{(\sqrt{\zeta}) - 1}{(\sqrt{\zeta}) + 1} \right]_0^\zeta$$

$$= \frac{2h}{\pi} \sqrt{\zeta} + \frac{h}{\pi} \ln \frac{(\sqrt{\zeta}) - 1}{(\sqrt{\zeta}) + 1} - hi. \tag{27}$$

Under this mapping, the auxiliary cut $A_1 A_2$ (shown dotted) in the w-plane corresponds with the upper edge of the cut $[1, +\infty]$ along the real axis in the ζ-plane. Thus, by the symmetry principle, the continuation of the function (27) into the domain Δ formed from the ζ-plane by taking a cut along the segment $[-\infty, 1]$ of the real axis is such as to give a conformal mapping of Δ onto the whole of the *given* w-domain shown in Fig. 138. A suitable regular

26

branch of $z = i\sqrt{(\zeta-1)}$ maps Δ onto $\operatorname{Im} z > 0$; accordingly, substituting $\zeta = 1-z^2$ in (27), we obtain the function mapping the half-plane $\operatorname{Im} z > 0$ onto the *given* w-domain:

$$
\begin{aligned}
w &= \frac{2h}{\pi}\sqrt{(1-z^2)} + \frac{h}{\pi}\ln\frac{-1+\sqrt{(1-z^2)}}{1+\sqrt{(1-z^2)}} - hi \\
&= \frac{2h}{\pi}\left\{\sqrt{(1-z^2)} + \ln\frac{z}{1+\sqrt{(1-z^2)}}\right\}.
\end{aligned}
\tag{28}
$$

87. Determination of the field at the edges of a condenser. Rogowski's condenser

The field of a plane condenser is effectively uniform over any interior region which is remote from the edges. In the neighbourhood of the edges this is no longer the case and special methods are necessary for the calculation of the field. To simplify these calculations we consider the condenser as formed from two half-planes situated one above the other. The section of the condenser by a plane perpendicular to the edges in question is shown in Fig. 139. We suppose the plates maintained at potentials $\pm V$. Our problem belongs to Type I of the problems discussed in Art. 40; its solution is obtained when we have found a conformal mapping, onto the strip $-V < \operatorname{Im} w < V$, of the z-domain shown in Fig. 139.

We seek the inverse mapping $z = z(w)$. To begin, we make an auxiliary cut A_3A_1 (shown dotted in Fig. 139) along the axis of symmetry (the x-axis) of the given z-domain, and find the mapping of the auxiliary half-plane $\operatorname{Im} \omega > 0$ onto the resulting "triangular" domain with boundary $A_1A_2A_3A_1$. The data for this triangle and the points a_k corresponding to its vertices are set out in the following table:

A_k	α_k	a_k
∞	-1	∞
z_2	2	-1
∞	0	0

The points a_k are chosen arbitrarily, in left-to-right order, and the x-coordinate of z_2 is left unspecified for the time being. The function mapping Im $\omega > 0$ onto this triangular domain is given by

$$z = C \int (\omega+1)\omega^{-1} \, d\omega = C \int \left(1 + \frac{1}{\omega}\right) d\omega$$

$$= C(\omega + \ln \omega) + C_1. \tag{29}$$

To find C we consider the increment in z when ω traces a semi-circular indentation C_r, about $\omega = 0$, in the clockwise sense; here, C_r is defined by $|\omega| = r$, Im $\omega \geqslant 0$, where r is *small*. The image point z moves from the ray $A_2 A_3$, onto the ray $A_3 A_1$, along a path

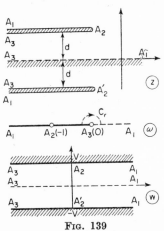

FIG. 139

which differs little from a line-segment perpendicular to both these rays; accordingly, the increment in z is $\Delta z = -id + \eta(r)$, where $2d$ is the plate separation and $\eta(r) \to 0$ as $r \to +0$. On the other hand, by (29), it follows readily that

$$\Delta z = C \cdot \Delta(i \arg \omega) + \delta(r) = -iC\pi + \delta(r),$$

where $\delta(r) \to 0$ as $r \to +0$. Thus, $-id = -iC\pi$, whence $C = d/\pi$ and (29) becomes

$$z = \frac{d}{\pi}(\omega + \ln \omega) + C_1.$$

A change in the constant C_1 is equivalent to a parallel displace-ment of the condenser in the z-plane (that is, to a change of the coordinate axes in this plane). Taking $C_1 = 0$, we have

$$z = \frac{d}{\pi}(\omega + \ln \omega); \tag{30}$$

as $\omega > 0$ on the ray A_3A_1 in the ω-plane it is easily verified from (30) that the ray A_3A_1 in the z-plane coincides with the x-axis, as is required. The position of the edge through A_2 is determined by substituting $\omega = -1$ in (30):

$$z_2 = \frac{d}{\pi}\{-1+\ln(-1)\} = -\frac{d}{\pi}+id.$$

The position of the condenser is thus determined completely.

We now consider a further auxiliary mapping, in which Im $\omega > 0$ is transformed into the strip $0 < \text{Im } w < V$ and the positive semi-axis A_3A_1 in the ω-plane (shown dotted) is transformed into the complete real axis of the w-plane; the required mapping is given by $w = (V/\pi) \ln \omega$, whence

$$\omega = e^{\pi w / V}.$$

Substituting for ω in (30) we obtain the function mapping the strip $0 < \text{Im } w < V$ onto the upper half of the field-domain of the condenser:

$$z = \frac{d}{\pi}\left(e^{\pi w / V} + \frac{\pi w}{V}\right). \tag{31}$$

From the symmetry principle it follows that the continuation of the function (31) into the strip $-V < \text{Im } w < V$ maps this strip onto the complete field-domain of the condenser. Thus, (31) gives the inverse $z = z(w)$ of the complex potential $w = w(z)$ representing the field. (It is not possible to solve (31) for w in terms of elementary functions.)

Figure 140 shows the equipotentials and lines of force for the field. Under the mapping $\omega = e^{\pi w/V}$, the lines Im $w = $ const. and Re $w = $ const. become the rays arg $\omega = $ const. and the circles $|\omega| = $ const. Putting $z = x+iy$ and $\omega = \rho e^{i\psi}$ in (30) and separating real and imaginary parts we obtain the equations

$$\left. \begin{array}{l} x = \dfrac{d}{\pi}\,(\rho \cos\psi+\ln\rho), \\[2mm] y = \dfrac{d}{\pi}\,(\rho \sin\psi+\psi); \end{array} \right\} \tag{32}$$

for $\psi = $ const., these are the parametric equations, in terms of the parameter ρ, of the equipotential lines; for $\rho = $ const. they are the parametric equations, in terms of the parameter ψ, of the lines of force. The lines given by $\operatorname{Im} w = \pm V$ (that is, by $\psi = \pm \pi$) clearly represent the plates of the condenser: $y = \pm d$ and $x = (d/\pi)(\ln \rho - \rho)$, where ρ ranges from 0 to $+\infty$, so that x increases from $-\infty$ to $-d/\pi$ and then decreases to $-\infty$.

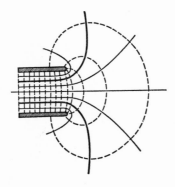

FIG. 140

By formula (39) of Art. 38, the intensity at a field point z is given by

$$\mathbf{E} = -i\overline{\left(\frac{dw}{dz}\right)} = -i\bigg/\left\{\overline{\left(\frac{dz}{dw}\right)}\right\}$$

$$= -i\frac{V}{d} \cdot \frac{1}{(1+e^{\pi\bar{w}/V})} = -\frac{iV}{(1+\bar{\omega})d} . \qquad (33)$$

For points z well inside the condenser (that is, for $z = -X + iy$, where $-d < y < d$ and X is a large positive number) the corresponding values of ω are close to $\omega = 0$, so that the intensity of the field is

$$\mathbf{E} \doteqdot -i\frac{V}{d};$$

thus the field is effectively uniform over any region well inside the condenser. As z approaches the edge represented by A_2, then $\omega \to -1$, so that $\bar{\omega} \to -1$, and it follows that $|\mathbf{E}| \to +\infty$.

The magnitude of the field intensity is given by $E = |dw/dz|$. We consider the variation of this quantity E along the equipotential lines. As the derivative,

$$dw/dz = \lim_{\Delta z \to 0} (\Delta w/\Delta z),$$

of a regular function $w = w(z)$ is independent of the manner in which $\Delta z \to 0$, we may suppose this derivative evaluated by letting $z + \Delta z$ approach the field point z along a line of force; then, if $w = u + iv$, we have $|\Delta w| = |\Delta v|$, since u is constant along a line of force. Also, to the first order, $|\Delta z| = |\Delta s|$, where s denotes the arc-length along the line of force. Transferring to the plane of the auxiliary variable $\omega = \rho e^{i\psi}$, we have $v = V\psi/\pi$, whence

$$dv = (V/\pi)\, d\psi,$$

and (putting $\rho = $ const. in the equations (32))

$$|ds| = \sqrt{\{(dx)^2 + (dy)^2\}} = \frac{d}{\pi} \{\sqrt{(\rho^2 + 2\rho \cos\psi + 1)}\} |d\psi|.$$

Thus,

$$E = \left| \frac{dv}{ds} \right| = \frac{V}{d} \cdot \frac{1}{\sqrt{(\rho^2 + 2\rho \cos\psi + 1)}}.$$

In order to find the maximum value of E along an equipotential line, it suffices to find the minimum of $\rho^2 + 2\rho \cos\psi + 1$ when ψ is constant and ρ varies; a necessary condition for such a minimum is $2\rho + 2 \cos\psi = 0$. As $\rho \geqslant 0$, this condition cannot be satisfied for values of ψ in the range $-\pi/2 < \psi < \pi/2$; along any equipotential line corresponding to a value of ψ in this range, the quantity E varies monotonically, having neither a maximum nor a minimum.

For $\psi = \pm \pi/2$, E increases steadily and tends to the finite limiting value V/d as $\rho \to +0$ (that is, as the field point z approaches A_3). The equations of these equipotential lines are obtained from (32): $x = (d/\pi) \ln \rho$ and $y = \pm (d/\pi)(\rho + \pi/2)$, whence

$$y = \pm \left(\frac{d}{2} + \frac{d}{\pi} e^{\pi x/d} \right).$$

The equipotential lines $\psi = \pm \pi/2$ are represented by the bold lines in Fig. 140. If we construct a condenser whose plates have the form of these lines, the magnitude of the field intensity at a

point on the "interior" surfaces of these plates is given in terms of
the parameter ρ by

$$E = \frac{V}{d} \cdot \frac{1}{\sqrt{(1+\rho^2)}}, \tag{34}$$

and it will be clear that E will then decrease as the point concerned
approaches the "edges". Such a condenser was designed and constructed by *Rogowski*; condensers of this form have useful applications in the testing of insulating materials.

88. The field of angular electrodes

The intersection of the electrodes with the z-plane is shown in
Fig. 141. We suppose these electrodes to be at potentials $\pm V$.
For calculation of the field it suffices to find the conformal mapping
of the polygonal field-domain onto the strip $-V < \operatorname{Im} w < V$.
To begin, we construct the mapping of the upper half of the field-
domain (that is, of the domain bounded by the "triangle" $A_1 A_2 A_3 A_1$)
onto the auxiliary half-plane $\operatorname{Im} \zeta > 0$. The data for this triangle,
along with the points $\zeta = a_k$ corresponding to its vertices, are
tabulated below:

A_k	α_k	a_k
∞	$1-\alpha-\beta$	∞
0	α	0
d	β	1

The corresponding Schwarz–Christoffel integral has the form

$$z = C \int\limits_0^\zeta \zeta^{\alpha-1}(\zeta-1)^{\beta-1}\,\mathrm{d}\zeta = C' \int\limits_0^\zeta \zeta^{\alpha-1}(1-\zeta)^{\beta-1}\,\mathrm{d}\zeta; \tag{35}$$

it will be clear from the correspondence of the points $\zeta = 0$ and
$z = 0$ that the additive constant C_1 vanishes. To find C' we use
the fact that $\zeta = 1$ maps on the point $z = d$, where d (see Fig. 141)
is the distance between the vertices of the electrodes:

$$d = C' \int\limits_0^1 \zeta^{\alpha-1}(1-\zeta)^{\beta-1}\,\mathrm{d}\zeta.$$

This integral can be expressed in terms of the beta function (see Exercise 11, Chap. VII):

$$\int\limits_0^1 \zeta^{\alpha-1}(1-\zeta)^{\beta-1}\,d\zeta = B(\alpha, \beta) = \frac{\Gamma(\alpha) \cdot \Gamma(\beta)}{\Gamma(\alpha+\beta)},$$

whence $C' = \{\Gamma(\alpha+\beta)\}d/\{\Gamma(\alpha) \cdot \Gamma(\beta)\}$, and (35) becomes

$$z = d \cdot \frac{\Gamma(\alpha+\beta)}{\Gamma(\alpha) \cdot \Gamma(\beta)} \int\limits_0^{\zeta} \zeta^{\alpha-1}(1-\zeta)^{\beta-1}\,d\zeta. \tag{36}$$

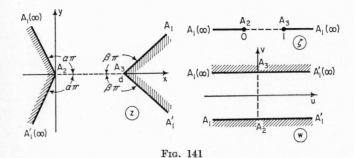

FIG. 141

It is left to the reader to verify that the function

$$w = \frac{2Vi}{\pi}\text{arc}\sin(2\zeta-1) \tag{37}$$

gives a simple conformal mapping of Im $\zeta > 0$ onto the half-strip $-V < \text{Im } w < V$, $\text{Re } w < 0$, in which the segment $[0, 1]$ of the real axis in the ζ-plane is transformed into the segment $[-iV, iV]$ of the imaginary axis in the w-plane. (This result can be obtained from formula (22) of Art. 86 with the aid of a supplementary linear transformation.)

Eliminating ζ between (36) and (37) we obtain a function $w = w(z)$ mapping the upper half of the given field-domain onto the left-hand half-strip defined by $-V < \text{Im } w < V$, $\text{Re } w < 0$; under this transformation the segment $[0, d]$ of the x-axis is mapped on the segment $[-iV, iV]$ of the v-axis. From the symmetry principle it follows that the same function $w = w(z)$ maps the whole of the given field-domain onto the strip $-V < \operatorname{Im} w < V$, in such a way that the electrode $A_1 A_2 A_1'$ maps on $\operatorname{Im} w = -V$ and the electrode $A_1' A_3 A_1$ maps on $\operatorname{Im} w = V$. Accordingly, $w = w(z)$ gives the complex potential of this field.

We shall now find an expression for the magnitude of the field strength at a point in the neighbourhood of the vertex A_2 ($z = 0$): writing $B = B(\alpha, \beta)$, we have

$$E = \left| \frac{dw}{dz} \right| = \left| \frac{dw}{d\zeta} \right| / \left| \frac{dz}{d\zeta} \right| = \frac{2VB}{\pi d} \left| \frac{\zeta^{1-\alpha}(1-\zeta)^{1-\beta}}{\sqrt{\{\zeta(1-\zeta)\}}} \right|$$

$$\doteqdot \frac{2VB}{\pi d} |\zeta|^{\frac{1}{2}-\alpha},$$

since $1 - \zeta \doteqdot 1$ for values of ζ near $\zeta = 0$. From (36) it follows that, for field points z near A_2 ($z = 0$),

$$|z| \doteqdot \left| (d/B) \int_0^\zeta \zeta^{\alpha-1} \, d\zeta \right| = \left| \frac{d}{\alpha B} \zeta^\alpha \right|;$$

accordingly, the above approximation becomes

$$E \doteqdot \frac{2V}{\pi} (B/d)^{1/(2\alpha)} (\alpha |z|)^{(1-2\alpha)/(2\alpha)}$$

$$= AVd^{-1/(2\alpha)} |z|^{(1-2\alpha)/(2\alpha)}, \tag{38}$$

where A is some constant depending on α and β.

Let us now suppose that we wish to test a dielectric material by subjecting a body made of this material to an electric field of given strength E_0. We suppose the test body to be *small* and placed at a given field point z_0 near the vertex A_2; the inter-electrode distance d is kept constant and the potential difference $2V$ is increased until the field at z_0 has the given magnitude E_0. Let the required potential difference be denoted by $2V_0$.

From (38) we see that, for given values of E_0, z_0, α, β, the relation connecting the test voltage with the distance between the electrodes is of the form

$$2V_0 \doteqdot cd^{1/(2\alpha)} \qquad (|z_0| \ll d), \tag{39}$$

where c is a constant.

For parallel flat plates (Fig. 142a) we have $\alpha = \frac{1}{2}$, so that (39) becomes $2V_0 \doteqdot cd$; thus, in this case, the required voltage is directly proportional to the distance between the plates. If the adjacent electrode is bent in a right angle (Fig. 142b) we have $\alpha = \frac{3}{4}$, so that $2V_0 \doteqdot cd^{2/3}$. Finally, if the electrodes are flat plates placed at right angles, we have $\alpha = 1$ and $2V_0 \doteqdot c\sqrt{d}$.

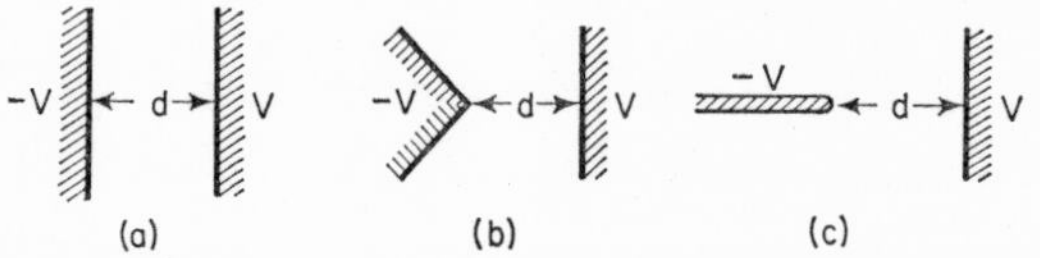

FIG. 142

89. The mapping of rectangular domains. Introduction to elliptic integrals

We consider the mapping of the half-plane $\operatorname{Im} w > 0$ onto the z-domain bounded by a rectangle with sides of lengths ω_1 and ω_2. The data specifying this rectangle, along with the corresponding points $w = a_k$, are given in the following table:

A_k	$\frac{1}{2}\omega_1$	$\frac{1}{2}\omega_1 + i\omega_2$	$-\frac{1}{2}\omega_1 + i\omega_2$	$-\frac{1}{2}\omega_1$
α_k	$\frac{1}{2}$	$\frac{1}{2}$	$\frac{1}{2}$	$\frac{1}{2}$
a_k	1	κ	a_3	a_4

Here, κ, a_3 and a_4 are real constants subject to further definition; obviously we require that a circuit of the real axis in the closed w-plane according to the sequence 1, κ, a_3, a_4, 1 should be such as to keep the domain $\operatorname{Im} w > 0$ on the *left*; thus we suppose that $\kappa > 1$. As only *one* of the four points a_k has been specified, we may stipulate that the points $w = 0$ and $w = \infty$ shall be mapped onto the respective points $z = 0$ and $z = i\omega_2$. Then, by the symmetry principle, it follows that our mapping function can be considered as the continuation, into $\operatorname{Im} w > 0$, across the positive v-axis, of the function $z = z(w)$ which gives a conformal mapping of the first quadrant of the w-plane onto the right-hand half of the given rectangular z-domain. Accordingly, $a_3 = -\kappa$ and $a_4 = -1$, so that the function giving the required mapping is of the form

$$z = C' \int_0^w \frac{dw}{\sqrt{\{(w^2-1)(w^2-\kappa^2)\}}} + C_1.$$

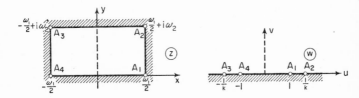

Fɪɢ. 143

As $w = 0$ maps on $z = 0$, we have $C_1 = 0$; accordingly,

$$z = C \int_0^w \frac{dw}{\sqrt{\{(1-w^2)(1-k^2w^2)\}}} \quad , \tag{40}$$

where C and $k = 1/\kappa$ $(0 < k < 1)$ are certain constants. The integral (40) cannot be expressed in terms of a finite number of elementary functions and is called an *elliptic integral of the first kind*.

To find C and k we make use of the correspondence between A_1, A_2 and the respective points $a_1 = 1$ and $a_2 = 1/k$: thus,

$$\frac{\omega_1}{2} = C \int_0^1 \frac{dw}{\sqrt{\{(1-w^2)(1-k^2w^2)\}}}; \tag{41}$$

and

$$\frac{\omega_1}{2} + i\omega_2 = C \int_0^1 \frac{dw}{\sqrt{\{(1-w^2)(1-k^2w^2)\}}}$$

$$+ C \int_1^{1/k} \frac{dw}{\sqrt{\{(1-w^2)(1-k^2w^2)\}}},$$

whence, by (41),

$$\omega_2 = \frac{C}{i} \int_1^{1/k} \frac{dw}{\sqrt{\{(1-w^2)(1-k^2w^2)\}}}$$

$$= C \int_1^{1/k} \frac{dw}{\sqrt{\{(w^2-1)(1-k^2w^2)\}}} . \qquad (42)$$

On dividing (42) by (41) the constant C cancels out and we obtain a relation between k and ω_2/ω_1. Thus, k depends only on the ratio of the lengths of the sides of the rectangle. The constant C depends on the size of the rectangle; it will be clear from (41) that C is real and positive.

Under the transformation $t = \sin \psi$, the elliptic integral

$$\int_0^{\sin\phi} \frac{dt}{\sqrt{\{(1-t^2)(1-k^2t^2)\}}}$$

assumes the form

$$F(\alpha, \phi) = \int_0^{\phi} \frac{d\psi}{\sqrt{(1-k^2\sin^2\psi)}}; \qquad (43)$$

here, α is defined by $k = \sin \alpha$. Detailed numerical tables exist for this function $F(\alpha, \phi)$. (See, e.g., Jahnke and Emde, *Funktionentafeln*, pub. Teubner; repr. as *Tables of Functions*, by Dover.) The parameter ϕ is called the *amplitude* of the integral (43). When $\phi = \pi/2$ the integral (43) is called a *complete elliptic integral* and is denoted by

$$K = F(\alpha,\pi/2) = \int_0^{\pi/2} \frac{d\psi}{\sqrt{(1-k^2\sin^2\psi)}}$$

$$= \int_0^1 \frac{dt}{\sqrt{\{(1-t^2)(1-k^2t^2)\}}}. \qquad (44)$$

The following table is an extract from a table of complete elliptic integrals given by Jahnke and Emde:

α	6°	7°	8°	9°	10°	11°
K	1·5751	1·5767	1·5785	1·5805	1·5828	1·5854

The quantity $k = \sin \alpha$ is called the *modulus* of the elliptic integral; we call the quantity k' defined by $k' = \sqrt{(1-k^2)} = \cos \alpha$ the *complementary modulus*, and call the integral

$$K' = \int_0^{\pi/2} \frac{\mathrm{d}\phi}{\sqrt{(1-k'^2\sin^2\phi)}} = \int_0^1 \frac{\mathrm{d}t}{\sqrt{\{(1-t^2)(1-k'^2t^2)\}}}$$

the *complementary complete elliptic integral*. Making the substitution $\tau = 1/\sqrt{(1-k'^2t^2)}$, we have

$$K' = \int_1^{1/k} \frac{\mathrm{d}\tau}{\sqrt{\{(\tau^2-1)(1-k^2\tau^2)\}}} . \tag{45}$$

With this notation, the formulae (41) and (42) giving the value of the constant C in equation (40) become $\omega_1 = 2CK$, $\omega_2 = CK'$, so that

$$\frac{K'}{K} = 2\frac{\omega_2}{\omega_1} . \tag{46}$$

The quantity $e^{-\pi K'/K}$ is usually denoted by q; we then have

$$\ln q = -\pi \frac{K'}{K} .$$

Tables exist which give the common logarithm of q (denoted by $\log q$) as a function of α (see Jahnke and Emde, *loc. cit.*). We give an extract from these tables:

α	6°	7°	8°	9°	10°	11°
$\log q$	$\bar{4}$·8367	$\bar{4}$·9709	$\bar{3}$·0872	$\bar{3}$·1899	$\bar{3}$·2819	$\bar{3}$·3651

Given the side lengths ω_1, ω_2, we can calculate K'/K from (46); this ratio determines the value of $\log q$ and we can then use the tables to find the value, first of α and then of K. Knowing K and ω_1 we can find C by using the formula $\omega_1 = 2CK$.

As an example, consider the mapping of $\operatorname{Im} w > 0$ onto a square domain, of side-length unity, situated as in Fig. 143. We have $\omega_1 = \omega_2 = 1$, whence $K'/K = 2$, $\ln q = -2\pi \doteqdot -6\cdot283$, so that

$$\log q \doteqdot -6\cdot283 \log e \doteqdot -6\cdot283 \times 0\cdot4343 \doteqdot -2\cdot729 = \bar{3}\cdot271.$$

Using the second table we find $\alpha \doteqdot 10°$; then, from the first table, $K \doteqdot 1\cdot583$. Thus, $C = \omega_1/2K \doteqdot 0\cdot316$, $k = \sin \alpha \doteqdot 0\cdot174$, and $k^2 \doteqdot 0\cdot03$. Accordingly, the required conformal mapping is given approximately by

$$z = (0\cdot316) \int_0^w \frac{dw}{\sqrt{\{(1-w^2)(1-0\cdot03w^2)\}}}. \tag{47}$$

90. Introduction to Jacobian elliptic functions

The function $w = w(z)$ inverse to that defined by the elliptic integral

$$z = \int_0^w \frac{dw}{\sqrt{\{(1-w^2)(1-k^2w^2)\}}} \qquad (0 < k < 1) \tag{48}$$

is denoted by $w = \operatorname{sn}(z, k)$, or simply by $\operatorname{sn} z$, and is called the *Jacobian elliptic function* sn *with modulus* k. (We have seen in the preceding article that the integral (48) can be written

$$z = \int_0^\phi \frac{d\psi}{\sqrt{(1-k^2 \sin^2\psi)}},$$

where ϕ is the amplitude of z and $w = \operatorname{sn} z = \sin \phi$. Accordingly, $\operatorname{sn} z$ is sometimes called the *sine of the amplitude*; similarly, the functions $\operatorname{cn} z$ and $\operatorname{dn} z$, introduced later, are called the *cosine of the amplitude* and the *delta of the amplitude*.)

As shown by (40) the function

$$w = \operatorname{sn}\left(\frac{z}{C}, k\right) = \operatorname{sn}\frac{z}{C} \tag{49}$$

gives a simple conformal mapping, onto Im $w > 0$, of the rectangular domain shown in Fig. 143, the constants C and k $(0 < k < 1)$
being determined by the side lengths ω_1 and ω_2, as indicated above,
from the formulae $\omega_1 = 2CK$, $\omega_2 = CK'$, $K'/K = 2\omega_2/\omega_1$. We
shall suppose the dimensions of this rectangle to be such that
$C = 1$. Let the sides be denoted by I, II, III, IV. Then, with the
notation of Fig. 144, it follows from the symmetry principle that
the continuation of $w = \operatorname{sn} z$ across I into the rectangular domain
(2) will map *this* domain onto the lower half-plane Im $w < 0$.
Continuing this function in turn across the side corresponding to
II we obtain a function which maps the rectangular domain (3)
onto the upper half-plane Im $w > 0$; and so on. We use the same
symbol $w = \operatorname{sn} z$ to denote all the continuations (into rectangular
domains) obtained in this way. (The rectangular domains shown
shaded in Fig. 144 are mapped onto Im $w > 0$; those not shaded
are mapped onto Im $w\ < 0$.)

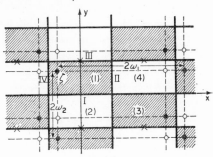

Fig. 144

In this way the function $w = \operatorname{sn} z$, defined originally in the
rectangular domain (1), can be continued into a z-domain D formed
from the finite plane by omitting a set S of *isolated* points. (To
begin, we might think of S as consisting of the *lattice points* in
Fig. 144, these corresponding to the *vertices* of the rectangles,
together with the points marked X). It is easily seen that, if z makes
one complete circuit of any simple closed path in D, the correspond-
ing variation in $\operatorname{sn} z$ is *zero*: any two regular branches of this function
in, say, the domain (1) will map this domain conformally onto
Im $w > 0$, *each with the same normalization*; thus, by the uniqueness
theorem of Art. 23, these branches will be identical in (1). Accord-
ingly, the function $\operatorname{sn} z$ is single-valued in D. As $\operatorname{sn} z$ is bounded
in some deleted neighbourhood of every lattice point it follows

readily that sn z has a *removable singularity* at each such point. We suppose sn z defined by continuity at these points; then, the set S of exceptional points consists merely of the points marked X. As $w = $ sn z maps (1) onto Im $w > 0$ in such a way that $z = i\omega_2$ (the mid-point of the boundary III) is transformed into $w = \infty$, it follows readily that sn z has a *pole* at each of the points marked X. Thus, sn z is *meromorphic* in the finite plane.

Let ζ (marked by a black dot in Fig. 144) be an arbitrary point, inside or on the boundary of (1), at which sn z is regular; black dots denote points at which sn z assumes the value sn ζ and open dots denote points at which sn $z = \overline{\text{sn } \zeta}$. From a consideration of this figure it follows that, if k_1 and k_2 are any given integers, then, in the domain D,

$$\text{sn}(z + 2k_1\omega_1 + 2k_2 i\omega_2) \equiv \text{sn } z. \tag{50}$$

We express this property by saying that sn z is *doubly periodic*, having the two *periods* $T_1 = 2\omega_1$ and $T_2 = 2i\omega_2$. This property of double periodicity enables us to deduce the properties of sn z in the finite plane from a study of its behaviour in any rectangular region with sides, of lengths $2\omega_1$ and $2\omega_2$ respectively, parallel to the x and y axes.

From the above discussion it also follows that sn $0 = 0$ and that sn z is an *odd* function:

$$\text{sn}(-z) \equiv -\text{sn } z. \tag{51}$$

An enumeration of the properties of sn z and sin z indicates a certain similarity between these functions. We may note that, by (48), z becomes arc sin w as k tends to $+0$; thus, we identify sn$(z, 0)$ with the function sin z.

Other Jacobian elliptic functions of importance are those defined by the relations

$$\text{cn } z = \sqrt{(1 - \text{sn}^2 z)}, \qquad \text{dn } z = \sqrt{(1 - k^2 \text{sn}^2 z)}. \tag{52}$$

These functions have similar properties. As $k \to +0$, cn z degenerates into the familiar function cos z and dn z becomes identically equal to unity.

We shall now indicate certain relations connecting the Jacobian elliptic functions. From (48), using the rule for differentiating an inverse function, we have

$$\frac{d}{dz} \text{sn } z = \sqrt{\{(1 - \text{sn}^2 z)(1 - k^2 \text{sn}^2 z)\}} = \text{cn } z \,.\, \text{dn } z. \tag{53}$$

Also, differentiating (52), we have

$$\left.\begin{aligned}
\frac{d}{dz}\operatorname{cn}z &= -\frac{\operatorname{sn}z}{\operatorname{cn}z}\operatorname{cn}z\,.\,\operatorname{dn}z = -\operatorname{sn}z\,.\,\operatorname{dn}z, \\[2mm]
\frac{d}{dz}\operatorname{dn}z &= -\frac{k^2\operatorname{sn}z}{\operatorname{dn}z}\operatorname{cn}z\,.\,\operatorname{dn}z = -k^2\operatorname{sn}z\,.\,\operatorname{cn}z.
\end{aligned}\right\} \quad (54)$$

We note that, for $k = 0$, (53) and the first relation in (54) reduce to the familiar results for the derivatives of $\sin z$ and $\cos z$.

It can be shown (see references at the end of this article) that the Jacobian elliptic functions obey the following *addition formulae*:

$$\left.\begin{aligned}
\operatorname{sn}(z+w) &= \frac{\operatorname{sn}z\,\operatorname{cn}w\,\operatorname{dn}w+\operatorname{sn}w\,\operatorname{cn}z\,\operatorname{dn}z}{1-k^2\operatorname{sn}^2z\,\operatorname{sn}^2w}, \\[2mm]
\operatorname{cn}(z+w) &= \frac{\operatorname{cn}z\,\operatorname{cn}w-\operatorname{sn}z\,\operatorname{sn}w\,\operatorname{dn}z\,\operatorname{dn}w}{1-k^2\operatorname{sn}^2z\,\operatorname{sn}^2w}, \\[2mm]
\operatorname{dn}(z+w) &= \frac{\operatorname{dn}z\,\operatorname{dn}w-k^2\operatorname{sn}z\,\operatorname{sn}w\,\operatorname{cn}z\,\operatorname{cn}w}{1-k^2\operatorname{sn}^2z\,\operatorname{sn}^2w}.
\end{aligned}\right\} \quad (55)$$

These results recall the familiar addition formulae of elementary trigonometry; it may be noted that, for $k = 0$, the first two relations reduce to the formulae $\sin(z+w) = \sin z\cos w+\cos z\sin w$ and $\cos(z+w) = \cos z\cos w-\sin z\sin w$.

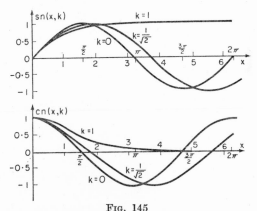

Fig. 145

In conclusion we graph $\operatorname{sn}(x, k)$ and $\operatorname{cn}(x, k)$ (see Fig. 145), as functions of the real variable x, for $k = 0, 1/\sqrt{2}, 1$.

More-detailed accounts of elliptic integrals and functions can be found in the following references: N. I. Akhiyezer, *Elements of the*

27

Theory of Elliptic Functions (Elementy teorii ellipticheskikh funktsii), Gostekhizdat, 1948 (includes solution of problems of interest in applied mathematics); Macrobert, *Functions of a Complex Variable*, Macmillan, 1933; Whittaker and Watson, *Modern Analysis*, Cambridge, 1927; Appell and Lacour, *Fonctions Elliptiques*, Gauthier-Villars, 1922; Hancock, *Elliptic Integrals*, Wiley, 1917; Jeffreys and Jeffreys, *Mathematical Physics*, Cambridge, 1950; Nehari, *Conformal Mapping* (Chap. VI), McGraw-Hill, 1952; Hille, *Analytic Function Theory* (Chap. 13, Vol. II), Ginn, 1962.

Exercises

1. Using the symmetry principle, find conformal mappings, onto the upper half-plane Im $w > 0$, of the z-domains shown in Fig. 146.

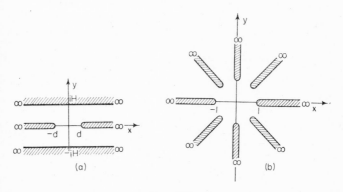

Fig. 146

2. Show that the function mapping the unit disc $|z| < 1$ on the polygonal w-domain of Art. 84 is of the form

$$w = C \int\limits_{0}^{z} (z-a_1)^{\alpha_1-1}(z-a_2)^{\alpha_2-1} \ldots (z-a_n)^{\alpha_n-1} \, dz + C',$$

where the (interior) angles of the polygon are denoted by $\pi\alpha_k$ ($k = 1, 2, \ldots, n$), the a_k are the points on $|z| = 1$ corresponding to the vertices, and C and C' are certain constants.

3. Show that the function mapping the unit disc $|z| < 1$ onto the exterior domain defined by a closed Jordan polygon in the w-plane is given by

$$w = C \int_{z_0}^{z} e^{\lambda z} \, (z-a_1)^{\alpha_1-1} (z-a_2)^{\alpha_2-1} \ldots (z-a_n)^{\alpha_n-1} \, z^{-2} dz + C',$$

where $z_0 \neq 0$ and

$$\lambda = \sum_{k=1}^{n} (1-\beta_k)/a_k;$$

here, the *interior* angles of the polygon are denoted by $\pi \beta_k$, and $\alpha_k = 2 - \beta_k \ (k = 1, 2, \ldots, n)$; the a_k are the points on $|z| = 1$ corresponding to the vertices, and C and C' are certain constants. It is supposed that $z = 0$ maps on $w = \infty$.

4. Find a conformal mapping, onto the upper half-plane Im $w > 0$, of each of the following domains:

(a) the "interior" domain bounded by the parabola $y^2 = 2px$;

(b) the "interior" domain bounded by the right-hand branch of the hyperbola $(x/a)^2 - (y/b)^2 = 1$;

(c) the interior domain bounded by the ellipse $(x/a)^2 + (y/b)^2 = 1$.

5. In each of the following cases find a conformal mapping, onto $|w| > 1$, of the domain formed from the extended z-plane by taking cuts as prescribed:

(a) the cut is x-shaped, being formed by the pair of segments $[-e^{i\pi/4}, e^{i\pi/4}]$ and $[-e^{-i\pi/4}, e^{-i\pi/4}]$;

(b) the cut is ψ-shaped, being formed by the segment $[0, -2i]$ and the lower semi-circle $|z| = 1$, Im $z \leqslant 0$;

(c) the cut is star-shaped, being formed from the segments $[-i, i], [1+i, -1-i], [-1+i, 1-i]$.

6. Find a conformal mapping, onto the unit disc $|w| < 1$, of the domain formed from $|z| < 1$ by deleting the segments $[-i, \frac{1}{2}i]$, $[-\frac{1}{2}, \frac{1}{2}]$.

7. Find a conformal mapping, onto the upper half-plane Im $w > 0$, of each of the polygonal z-domains shown in Fig. 147.

8. Show that the elliptic integral of the second kind, given by

$$E(z, k) = \int_{0}^{z} \sqrt{\left\{ \frac{1-k^2 z^2}{1-z^2} \right\}} \, dz \qquad (0 < k < 1),$$

defines a function which gives a conformal mapping, onto the domain shown in Fig. 148, of a domain formed from the z-plane by deleting the rays defined by $y = 0$, $|x| \geqslant 1$.

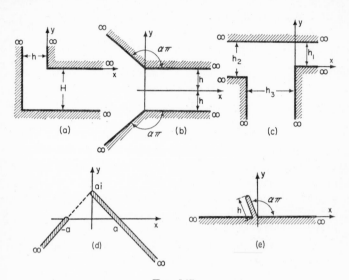

FIG. 147

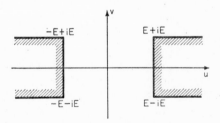

FIG. 148

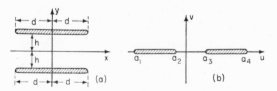

FIG. 149

9. Find a conformal mapping of the (doubly-connected) z-domain of Fig. 149a onto the (doubly-connected) w-domain of Fig. 149b. Determine the constants a_k.

10. Let the domain D be formed from the z-plane by deleting the infinite number of segments defined by

$$-a \leqslant x \leqslant a, \ y = kh \quad (h > 0, \ k = 0, \ \pm 1, \ \pm 2, \ldots).$$

Find (a) a one–one mapping of D onto a domain formed from the w-plane by deleting an infinite number of segments of the real axis; and (b) a single-valued (though not one–one) mapping of D onto the domain $|w| > 1$.

ANSWERS AND HINTS FOR SOLUTION OF EXERCISES

Introduction

1. $2e^{i\pi/3}$; $(2\sin\frac{1}{2}\alpha)e^{i(\pi-\alpha)/2}$.

2. Drawn consecutively, the vectors representing z_1, z_2, z_3 form an equilateral triangle.

3. $z_4' = -z_1+z_2+z_3$, $z_4'' = z_1-z_2+z_3$, $z_4''' = z_1+z_2-z_3$.

4. $z_c = (m_1z_1+m_2z_2+ \ldots +m_nz_n)/(m_1+m_2+ \ldots +m_n)$.

5. Enumerating the vertices in anticlockwise order,

$$z_k = z_0+(z_1-z_0)(e^{i2k\pi/n}-1)/(e^{i2\pi/n}-1)$$

$$= z_0+(z_1-z_0)e^{i(k-1)\pi/n}\left(\sin\frac{k\pi}{n}\right)\bigg/\sin\frac{\pi}{n} \quad (k = 1, 2, \ldots, n).$$

6. Transform to Cartesian coordinates, or use the relation $|z_1+z_2|^2 = (z_1+z_2)(\bar{z}_1+\bar{z}_2)$. For a parallelogram, the sum of the squares of the diagonals equals the sum of the squares of the four sides.

7. $\cos 4\phi = \cos^4\phi - 6\cos^2\phi \cdot \sin^2\phi + \sin^4\phi$.

8. $\pm(2+i)$; $\quad 2e^{i(2k+1)\pi/6} \quad (k = 0, 1, \ldots, 5)$;

$(\sqrt[6]{2}) \cdot e^{i(8k+3)\pi/12} \quad (k = 0, 1, 2)$.

9. $1+i, 1+2i$; $i\pm 2$.

10. $z_1 = 1-i, z_2 = i$; $z_1 = \lambda(1-i), z_2 = \lambda(1+i)$, where λ is an arbitrary complex number.

11. (a) The perpendicular bisector of the segment joining the points a and b. (b) A straight line ($a \neq 0$). (c) The interior domain bounded by a trapezium, together with the two (open) segments forming the pair of parallel sides. (d) For $\alpha > |b-a|$, an ellipse with foci at a, b; for $\alpha = |b-a|$, the segment joining the points a, b; the empty set for $\alpha < |b-a|$. (e) The "interior" domain bounded by the parabola $y^2 = 1-2x$. (f) The domain formed from the left half-plane $\operatorname{Re} z < 0$ by omitting all points of the closed disc $x^2+y^2+2x-1 \leqslant 0$.

12. (a) $x/(x^2+y^2) = \alpha$—the family of circles touching the y-axis at the origin.

(b) $2y/(x^2+y^2-1) = \tan\alpha$—the family of all circular arcs joining the points ± 1.

(c) $(x-1)^2+y^2 = \alpha^2\{(x+1)^2+y^2\}$—the family of coaxal circles having ± 1 as limit points (including the y-axis).

(d) For given positive α the locus is that of a point moving so that the product of its distances from the points ± 1 is a constant (lemniscates with foci at ± 1). For $\alpha < 1$ the locus consists of two ovals, each enclosing one of the points ± 1; for $\alpha = 1$ we obtain the familiar lemniscate of Bernoulli; for $\alpha > 1$ the locus is a single closed curve (see Fig. 67).

(e) $z^2+2az+b = (z-z_1)(z-z_2)$ where z_1, z_2 are the roots of $z^2+2az+b = 0$. In general we obtain a family of lemniscates with foci at z_1 and z_2.

13. Put $x = \frac{1}{2}(z+\bar{z})$, $y = (z-\bar{z})/(2i)$: we obtain

$$z\bar{z}+(1+\tfrac{1}{2}i)z+(1-\tfrac{1}{2}i)\bar{z} = 1, \qquad z^2+\bar{z}^2 = 2.$$

14. The inverse $\zeta = \xi+i\eta$ of $z = x+iy$ with respect to the unit circle is given by $\xi = x/(x^2+y^2)$, $\eta = y/(x^2+y^2)$. For the circle $|z| = r$ the corresponding formulae are

$$\xi = r^2x/(x^2+y^2), \qquad \eta = r^2y/(x^2+y^2).$$

15. (a) $\gamma(\xi^2+\eta^2)+\alpha\xi+\beta\eta = 0$, a circle passing through the origin; for $\gamma = 0$ this becomes the given straight line $\alpha\xi+\beta\eta = 0$.

(b) $\alpha+\beta\xi+\gamma\eta+\delta(\xi^2+\eta^2) = 0$, a circle; for $\delta = 0$ this becomes a straight line.

(c) $\xi^2-\eta^2 = (\xi^2+\eta^2)^2$, i.e.

$$\{(\xi-2^{-1/2})^2+\eta^2\}\{(\xi+2^{-1/2})^2+\eta^2\} = \tfrac{1}{4},$$

a lemniscate of Bernoulli with foci at $(\pm 2^{-1/2}, 0)$.

(d) $\eta^2 = 2p\xi(\xi^2+\eta^2)$, or $\eta^2 = 2p\xi^3/(1-2p\xi)$, a cissoid.

Chapter 1

1. The stereographic image $Z(\xi, \eta, \zeta)$ of $z = x+iy$ is given by $\xi = 4R^2x/(4R^2+r^2)$, $\eta = 4R^2y/(4R^2+r^2)$, $\zeta = 2Rr^2/(4R^2+r^2)$, where $r = |z| = \sqrt{(x^2+y^2)}$, R is the radius of the sphere, the axes of ξ and η coincide with the axes of x and y, and the ζ-axis lies along the vertical diameter of the sphere.

2. (a) No. (b) Yes.

3. $2/(2-i)$.

4. (a) $x = (\alpha+\beta)\cos t$, $y = (\alpha-\beta)\sin t$—an ellipse with semi-axes $|\alpha+\beta|$, $|\alpha-\beta|$.

(b) $r = e^{\alpha\phi/\beta}$, where $a = \alpha+i\beta$, $z = re^{i\phi}$— a logarithmic spiral.

5. $\dot{z} = {}^{r}e^{i\phi}+r\dot{\phi}ie^{i\phi}$,

$$\ddot{z} = (\ddot{r}-r\dot{\phi}^2)e^{i\phi}+\left\{\frac{1}{r}\frac{d}{dt}(r^2\dot{\phi})\right\}ie^{i\phi};$$

the coefficients of $e^{i\phi}$ and $ie^{i\phi}$ give the required quantities.

6. The complex velocity vector is $\mathbf{v} = (dw/dz)\,.\,(dz/dt) = izf'(z)$.

7. The extended form of Ohm's Law gives

$$\left(R+\frac{1}{i\omega C}\right)\mathscr{I} = \mathscr{E}.$$

The steady-state current is $I = \mathrm{Im}\,\mathscr{I}$ where $\mathscr{I} = I_0 e^{i(\omega t+\alpha+\delta)}$,

$$I_0 = E_0\bigg/\sqrt{\left\{R^2+\frac{1}{\omega^2 C^2}\right\}}, \quad \tan\delta = \frac{1}{\omega RC}.$$

8. $w = \sin 2\phi$—the segment defined by $-1 \leqslant w \leqslant 1$.

9. Prove that parallel lines in the z-plane map onto parallel lines in the w-plane.

10. The parabolas $v^2 = 4\alpha^2(u+\alpha^2)$ and $v^2 = 4\beta^2(\beta^2-u)$, with the omission of the vertices.

11. (a) Circles $u^2+v^2 = u/\alpha$, $u^2+v^2 = -v/\beta$, touching the co-ordinate axes at the origin.

(b) The circles $u^2+v^2-2v\cot\alpha = 1$.

(c) The ellipses $u = \frac{1}{2}(r+r^{-1})\cos\phi$, $v = \frac{1}{2}(r-r^{-1})\sin\phi$, and the hyperbolas $(u/\cos\alpha)^2-(v/\sin\alpha)^2 = 1$; the foci of all the curves are at the points ± 1.

(d) The lemniscate $\rho = \sqrt{(2\cos 2\theta)}$, $(w = \rho e^{i\theta})$.

12. The finite w-plane with the omission of the positive real axis and the origin; $u = r^3\cos 3\phi = \alpha$, $v = r^3\sin 3\phi = \beta$, $(z = re^{i\phi})$.

13. $f(z) = 1$ between the parabolas $y = x^2$ and $y = 2x^2$, $f(z) = 0$ at all other points of the plane.

14. $w = \tan\phi$; continuous at all points of the finite plane other than those lying on the y-axis.

15 and 16. Use the Cauchy–Riemann relations.

17. (a) Regular for $z \neq \infty$. (b) Regular for $z \neq 0$. (c) Not regular anywhere, as the function is many-valued for $0 < |z| < +\infty$. (Regular *branches* can be separated in a suitably cut plane.) (d) Not regular anywhere, although differentiable at $z = 0$.

Chapter 2

1. $\mathrm{d}u + i\,\mathrm{d}v = \left(\dfrac{\partial u}{\partial x} + i\dfrac{\partial v}{\partial x}\right)\mathrm{d}x + \left(\dfrac{\partial u}{\partial y} + i\dfrac{\partial v}{\partial y}\right)\mathrm{d}y;$

if $\mathrm{d}u + i\,\mathrm{d}v = A(\mathrm{d}x + i\,\mathrm{d}y)$ then

$$A = \frac{\partial u}{\partial x} + i\frac{\partial v}{\partial x} = \frac{1}{i}\left(\frac{\partial u}{\partial y} + i\frac{\partial v}{\partial y}\right),$$

and the Cauchy–Riemann relations follow. The converse is verified directly.

2. $L = \displaystyle\int_{C} |f'(z)|\,\mathrm{d}s, \qquad S = \displaystyle\iint_{(D)} |f'(z)|^2\,\mathrm{d}x\mathrm{d}y.$

3. $\left(\dfrac{\mathrm{d}w}{\mathrm{d}z}\right)_{z=-1} = -1, \qquad \left(\dfrac{\mathrm{d}w}{\mathrm{d}z}\right)_{z=i} = -\dfrac{i}{2}.$

Magnification coefficients are 1 and $\frac{1}{2}$, and the angles are π and $-\frac{1}{2}\pi$, respectively.

4. $S = 8/3$, $L = 2\ln(1+\sqrt{2}) + 2(1+\sqrt{2})$.

5. The length of a single loop of the lemniscate is

$$L = 2\sqrt{2}\int_{0}^{\pi/4} \mathrm{d}\theta/\sqrt{(\cos 2\theta)} = 2\sqrt{2}\int_{0}^{1} \mathrm{d}t/\sqrt{(1-t^4)}.$$

The last integral is an elliptic integral (see Art. 89).

6. The condition for the orthogonality of the gradients gives $v_y/u_x = -v_x/u_y = \lambda$ (say). From the second condition, $\lambda = \pm 1$. For $\lambda = -1$, angles are reversed in sense; for $\lambda = 1$ the mapping is *directly* conformal.

7. $w + 1 = 2i(z-i)$, or $w = 2iz + 1$;

$$|\mathrm{d}w - \Delta w| = |\mathrm{d}z|^2 < 1/100 \text{ for } |\mathrm{d}z| < 1/10.$$

8. A half-strip from which we remove a closed semi-circular region having as diameter the finite segment which is one of the three lines forming the boundary of this half-strip.

9. The (open) fourth quadrant, with the omission of all points belonging to the closed disc $|z-\frac{1}{2}| \leqslant \frac{1}{2}$.

10. The abscissae of points which are inverse with respect to each of the given circles are $\alpha = -\frac{1}{4}, \beta = -4$. Take $w = (4z+1)/(z+4)$; $R = 2$.

11. $(w-1)/(w+1) = a(z-1)/(z+1)$, where a is an arbitrary complex constant.

12. $w = i(1-z)/(1+z)$.

13. $w = 1/(1-z)$.

14. $w = 2i(z-i)/(z+i)$; $R = 2$.

15. θ is the argument of the point, of the circle $|w| = 1$, into which the point $z = \infty$ is transformed. The family of straight lines Im $z = $ const. corresponds with the pencil of circles touching $|w| = 1$ at the point $w = e^{i\theta}$; the straight lines Re $z = $ const. corresponds with the pencil of circles cutting $|w| = 1$ orthogonally at the same point $w = e^{i\theta}$.

16. $w = (a_2-a_3)(z-a_1)/\{(a_2-a_1)(z-a_3)\}$.

17. a, b, c, d are real and $ad-bc > 0$.

Chapter 3

1. $\sin(x+iy) = \sin x \cosh y + i \cos x \sinh y$,

$\cos(x+iy) = \cos x \cosh y - i \sin x \sinh y$,

$$\tan(x+iy) = \frac{2 \sin z \cos \bar{z}}{2 \cos z \cos \bar{z}} = \frac{\sin 2x + i \sinh 2y}{\cos 2x + \cosh 2y}.$$

4. When z makes a positive circuit of a circle enclosing the points 0 and 1, the argument of the expression under the root sign increases by 6π, so that any continuous branch of the root returns to its original value; the required branch equals $(\sqrt[6]{2})e^{-i5\pi/12}$ at $z = i$.

5. $(\ln 3) + i\pi$.

6. A suitable regular branch of $\omega = z + \sqrt{(z^2-1)}$ maps the given domain D onto the upper half-plane Im $\omega > 0$.

7. $w_1 = \exp\{-e(1+i\pi)\}$, $w_2 = \exp\{-e(1-i\pi)\}$.

8. The circles $|z| = $ const., and the rays arg $z = $ const.

9. If $f(z_1) = f(z_2)$ then either $z_1 = z_2$ or $z_1+z_2+2 = 0$; in the latter case $|z_2| \geqslant 2-|z_1|$, so that *both* points cannot lie in the disc $|z| < 1$.

10. The domain formed from the finite w-plane by omitting the ays $(-\infty < u \leqslant -1, v = 0), (1 \leqslant u < +\infty, v = 0)$.

11. (a) The right half-plane $\operatorname{Re} w > 0$, with the exclusion of the ray $(1 \leqslant u < +\infty, v = 0)$.

(b) The disc $|w| < 1$; the family of all circular arcs through the points $w = \pm i$ ("meridians", $x = \alpha$); the family of coaxal circles having $w = \pm i$ as limit points ("parallels", $y = \beta$). (It is convenient to consider the successive mappings

$$\zeta = e^{i2z}, \qquad w = -i(\zeta - 1)/(\zeta + 1).)$$

(c) The finite w-plane with the exclusion of the rays

$$(-\infty < u \leqslant -1, \qquad v = \pm \pi).$$

(d) The disc defined by $(u-1)^2 + v^2 < 1$.

(e) The domain formed from the disc $|w| < 1$ by removing all points inside and on the parabola $v^2 = 4u$. Circles $|w| = \rho$ correspond with the lemniscates $(x^2 + y^2)\{(4-x)^2 + y^2\} = 16\rho^2$; rays $\arg w = \theta$ correspond with hyperbolas.

12. (a) The finite plane with the omission of the rays

$$-\infty < u \leqslant 0, \qquad v = k\pi \qquad (k = 0, \pm 1, \pm 2, \ldots).$$

(b) The upper half-plane $\operatorname{Im} w > 0$ with the omission of the segments $u = k\pi$ $(k = 0, \pm 1, \pm 2, \ldots), 0 < v \leqslant |\alpha|$.

13. (a) $\zeta = z^{\pi/\alpha}$ maps the sector on a semicircular domain which is mapped on $\operatorname{Im} \omega > 0$ by $\omega = \{(\zeta + 1)/(\zeta - 1)\}^2$; it remains to use formula (23) of Chap. II.

(b) $w = (1/\pi) \ln\{i(1+z)/(1-z)\}$.

(c) $\zeta = \frac{1}{3}z$ maps the given ellipse on an ellipse with foci $\zeta = \pm 1$; $\zeta = \frac{1}{2}(\omega + \omega^{-1})$ maps $|\omega| > 3$ on the exterior of this second ellipse. Putting $\omega = 3w$ we obtain the composite mapping

$$w = \{z + \sqrt{(z^2 - 9)}\}/9$$

where we choose the branch which is regular in the given z-domain and has the value $\frac{1}{3}(2 + \sqrt{3})$ at $z = 6$.

(d) Suppose $p > 0$. The exterior of the parabola

$$\eta^2 = 4\alpha^2(\xi + \alpha^2) \qquad (\alpha > 0)$$

is mapped on the half-plane $\operatorname{Im} \omega > \alpha$ by $\omega = \sqrt{\zeta}$ (we choose the regular branch whose value at $\zeta = -2\alpha^2$ is $i\alpha\sqrt{2}$). Take

$\alpha = \sqrt{(p/2)}$; the boundary becomes $\eta^2 = 2p(\xi + \tfrac{1}{2}p)$; taking

$$\zeta = z - \tfrac{1}{2}p$$

this becomes $y^2 = 2px$. It remains to put $w = \omega - i\sqrt{(p/2)}$. The resultant mapping is $w = \sqrt{(z - \tfrac{1}{2}p)} - i\sqrt{(\tfrac{1}{2}p)}$ (the root denoting the regular branch such that $w = 0$ at $z = 0$).

(e) Make use of the properties of the mapping $z = \tfrac{1}{2}(\zeta + \zeta^{-1})$.

(f) The spirals intersect the rays $\arg z = $ const. at constant angles; $\zeta = \ln z$, where $\ln$ denotes a branch which is regular in the given domain D, maps these rays onto parallel straight lines, so that (by conformality) D is mapped on a certain strip. The further transformations are obvious.

14. (a) $\zeta = (\pi/2)z$, $s = e^{\zeta}$, $t = s^2$, $Z = \tfrac{1}{2}(t + t^{-1})$; we obtain the finite Z-plane with the omission of the rays $(Y = 0, X \leqslant \cosh \pi)$, $(Y = 0, X \geqslant \cosh 2\pi)$. Finally, we get

$$w = \sqrt{\{(Z - \cosh 2\pi)/(Z - \cosh \pi)\}}.$$

(b) $= \zeta \ (\pi/2)z$, $s = e^{\zeta}$, $t = (s-i)/(s+i)$, $\omega = t^2$; continue as in (a).

(c) $\zeta = 1/z$ transforms the domain into a vertical strip with a horizontal cut; continue as in Example 4, Art. 33.

(d) $\zeta = 1/z$ maps the domain onto the strip $-1 < \xi < 1$ with the cut $(\xi = 0, \eta \geqslant \tfrac{1}{2})$; continue as in Example 3, Art. 33.

(e) $\zeta = \tfrac{1}{2}(z + z^{-1})$ maps the domain on the exterior of a cut of the form $(\eta = 0, -d \leqslant \xi \leqslant d)$, and then apply $\omega = \zeta/d$. A mapping inverse to the first mapping then transforms the ω-domain into the exterior of the unit circle. The remaining steps will be clear.

(f) $\zeta = (1+z)/(1-z)$, $s = \zeta^{4/5}$, $t = (1-s)/(1+s)$; we get the upper half-plane $\operatorname{Im} t > 0$ with the omission of a segment of the imaginary axis; continue as in Example 1, Art. 27.

(g) $\zeta = iz/3$ (rotation and contraction); $\zeta = \tfrac{1}{2}(s + s^{-1})$, i.e. $s = \zeta + \sqrt{(\zeta^2 - 1)}$ (choose branch equal to 3 at $\zeta = 5/3$); $t = s/3$; $\omega = \tfrac{1}{2}(t + t^{-1})$—we obtain the exterior of the cut joining $\omega = -1$ and $\omega = (50 - 4\sqrt{91})/9$. The continuation is obvious.

(h) $\zeta = \sqrt{z}$ maps the given domain onto the half-strip $0 < \eta < 1$, $\xi > -2$ (choose regular branch equal to $e^{i\pi/4}$ at $z = i$); continue as in Example 2, Art. 33.

(i) The points $z = \pm 1$ are inverse points with respect to the circle $(x - \sqrt{2})^2 + y^2 = 1$. Take $\zeta = (z+1)/(z-1)$, $s = \zeta^2$; continue as in (b).

(*j*) The hyperbolic boundary arcs have foci at $z = \pm 1$ (eccentricity $= \sqrt{2}$). Take $z = \frac{1}{2}(\zeta + \zeta^{-1})$, i.e. $\zeta = z + \sqrt{(z^2 - 1)}$, choosing the branch which equals i at $z = 0$ and $2i$ at $z = 3i/4$; $s = \zeta^4$; $t = \frac{1}{2}(s + s^{-1})$; we obtain the finite t-plane cut along the real axis from $t = -\infty$ to $t = \frac{1}{2}(2^4 + 2^{-4})$. The continuation will be clear.

Chapter 4

1. $cr^2 = -\sin 2\phi$, $kr^2 = \cos 2\phi$ (c, k constants; $z = re^{i\phi}$); $\mathbf{E} = E_x + iE_y = -i\overline{(f'(z))} = 2i/(\bar{z})^3$.

2. $w = \ln(\sinh \pi z) + c$, $|\sinh \pi z| = \text{const.}$

3. $V = \phi\{(x^2 + y^2)/(2x)\}$, where ϕ is an arbitrary differentiable real function; $E_1 : E_2 = 1 : 2$.

5. Hyperbolas with foci at $z = \pm a$; fourth-degree curves

$$y = C \sqrt{\left\{1 + \frac{H^2}{x^2 + C^2}\right\}}$$

(see Fig. 75).

6. A charge $2q$ at $z = 0$ and four charges, each $-q$, at the points $z = \pm e^{i\pi/4}$, $\pm e^{-i\pi/4}$.

8. $\sigma = V_0/\{2\pi^2 \sqrt{(1 + x^2)}\}$.

9. $w = 4\pi i\, \mathrm{Ln}\{(z + i\sqrt{3})/(z - i\sqrt{3})\}$; at the point $z = 2i + e^{i\phi}$ the charge density is $\sigma = (\sqrt{3})/(2 + \sin \phi)$.

10. $w = (i/\ln 2)\, \mathrm{Ln}\{(z + 4)/(4z + 1)\}$ ($V = 0$ on inner cylinder, $V = -1$ on outer); on inner, greatest and least charge densities are $25a$ and $9a$, where $a = 1/(60\pi \ln 2)$; corresponding densities on outer are $-2a$ and $-18a$.

11. $w = u + iv = 100i\left\{1 - \dfrac{\mathrm{Ln}[z + \sqrt{(z^2 - 1)}]}{\ln(2 + \sqrt{3})}\right\}.$

(Choose branch of $\sqrt{(z^2 - 1)}$ equal to $i\sqrt{2}$ at $z = i$.)

12. Take $\zeta = (\pi/\alpha)\ln(z/a)$, $s = \cosh \zeta$, $t = (1 + s)/(1 - s)$. Then,

$$w = u + iv = i - \frac{1}{\pi}\ln t$$

$$= -\frac{1}{\pi}\ln\left\{\left[\cosh\left(\frac{\pi}{\alpha}\ln\frac{z}{a}\right) + 1\right]\Big/\left[\cosh\left(\frac{\pi}{\alpha}\ln\frac{z}{a}\right) - 1\right]\right\}$$

$$= +\frac{2}{\pi}\ln\left[\tanh\left(\frac{\pi}{2\alpha}\ln\frac{z}{a}\right)\right];$$

at $z = re^{i\phi}$ $(r > a, 0 < \phi < \alpha)$,

$$\tan\frac{\pi v}{2} = \left[\sin\frac{\pi\phi}{\alpha}\right] \bigg/ \left[\sinh\left(\frac{\pi}{\alpha}\ln\frac{r}{a}\right)\right].$$

Alternatively, take $\zeta = (z/a)^{\pi/\alpha}$, $s = \frac{1}{2}(\zeta + \zeta^{-1})$, $t = (1+s)/(1-s)$; we get the equivalent result

$$w = (2/\pi)\ln\{[(z/a)^{\pi/\alpha} - 1]/[(z/a)^{\pi/\alpha} + 1]\}.$$

13. $w = \phi + i\psi = (Q/\pi)\ln\{z + \sqrt{(z^2+1)}\}$ (choose branch such that $\sqrt{(z^2+1)} = 1$ at $z = 0$).

14. $w = \phi + i\psi = (Q/2\pi)\,\mathrm{Ln}(1 + 4z^{-4})$; streamlines are given by $\sin 4\theta = c(r^4 + 4\cos 4\theta)$, where $z = re^{i\theta}$.

15. $\zeta = -\frac{1}{2}(z + z^{-1})$ maps domain on upper half-plane $\mathrm{Im}\,\zeta > 0$. By inspection, required complex potential is

$$w = U + iV = a\ln(\zeta - 1) + b\ln\zeta + c\ln(\zeta + 1),$$

where $\pi a = V_0$, $\pi b = -2V_0$, $\pi c = V_0$. Thus

$$w = (2V_0/\pi)\ln\{(1 - z^2)/(1 + z^2)\}.$$

16. Take $\zeta = z^3$. Then

$$w = \phi + i\psi = \frac{Q}{2\pi}\ln\{(\zeta - a^3 i)(\zeta + a^3 i)\} = \frac{Q}{2\pi}\ln(z^6 + a^6).$$

Chapter 5

1. (a) i; (b) $2i$; (c) $2i$.
2. $4\pi i$.
3. $i(\sinh 1 - \cosh 1)$.
4. (a) $e(2 - e^{-i}) - 1$; (b) $1 + e^{-i}(e - 2)$.
5. The length of the path L.
6. $1/(2i)$.
7. $\pi i/\sqrt{2}$.
8. $\frac{1}{2}\pi(\pi i - 1)$.
9. Suppose $f(z) \neq 0$ in D: then, $|f(z)|$ and $|1/f(z)|$ attain their maxima on $\overline{D}$ at points on the frontier of D; this would imply that $f(z)$ is constant on $\overline{D}$—contradiction. The lemniscate with n foci is defined by the equation $|P_n(z)| = \mathrm{const.}$, where $P_n(z)$ is a polynomial of degree n.
11. $a + c = 0$.

13. Put $x = \frac{1}{2}(z+\bar{z})$, $y = (z-\bar{z})/(2i)$; then,

$$u = \{\sin(z+\bar{z})\}/\{\cos(z-\bar{z}) - \cos(z+\bar{z})\} = \frac{1}{2}(\cot z + \cot \bar{z}),$$

whence $f(z) = \cot z + iC$ (C real); the normalization gives $C = 0$.

14. By Poisson's formula, $(r < 1)$,

$$u(re^{i\phi}) = \frac{1}{2\pi} \int\limits_{\alpha}^{\beta} \frac{(1-r^2)\, d\psi}{1 - 2r\cos(\psi - \phi) + r^2}$$

$$= \frac{1}{\pi}\left\{\arctan\left(\frac{1+r}{1-r}\tan\frac{\beta - \phi}{2}\right) - \arctan\left(\frac{1+r}{1-r}\tan\frac{\alpha - \phi}{2}\right)\right\}.$$

17. Use formula (61).

Chapter 6

1. (a) The half-plane $\operatorname{Re} z > 1$. (b) As in Art. 64 we write the series in the form

$$\sum_{n=-\infty}^{+\infty} c_n e^{inz};$$

in general, the domain of convergence in the plane of $\zeta = e^{iz}$ is an annulus, and in the z-plane a horizontal strip.

2. (a) $+\infty$; (b) $\varlimsup_{n \to +\infty} |n^{\ln n}|^{1/n} = \varlimsup_{n \to +\infty} e^{(\ln n)^2/n} = 1$.

Radius of convergence is 1.

3. (a) $(\sqrt[3]{i})\left(1 + \frac{z-i}{i}\right)^{1/3} = (\sqrt[3]{i})\left\{1 + \left(\frac{z-i}{3i}\right) - \frac{1 \cdot 2}{2!}\left(\frac{z-i}{3i}\right)^2\right.$

$$\left. + \frac{1 \cdot 2 \cdot 5}{3!}\left(\frac{z-i}{3i}\right)^3 - \frac{1 \cdot 2 \cdot 5 \cdot 8}{4!}\left(\frac{z-i}{3i}\right)^4 + \dots \right\},$$

where $\sqrt[3]{i}$ assumes in turn the three possible values $e^{i\pi/6}$, $e^{i5\pi/6}$, $e^{-i\pi/2}$ $(= -i)$.

(b) $\operatorname{Ln}(i + z - i) = i\left(\frac{\pi}{2} + 2k\pi\right) + \left(\frac{z-i}{i}\right) - \frac{1}{2}\left(\frac{z-i}{i}\right)^2$

$$+ \frac{1}{3}\left(\frac{z-i}{i}\right)^3 - \frac{1}{4}\left(\frac{z-i}{i}\right)^4 + \dots,$$

where $k = 0, \pm 1, \pm 2, \dots$.

4. $f(z) = \exp\{(1/z)\ln(1+z)\} = \exp(1+\zeta)$, where

$$\zeta = -\frac{z}{2} + \frac{z^2}{3} - \frac{z^3}{4} + \cdots \qquad (|z| < 1).$$

Thus, $f(z) = e(1 + \zeta + \frac{1}{2}\zeta^2 + \cdots) = e[1 - \frac{1}{2}z + (11/24)z^2 - \cdots]$.

5. Clearly, $f(z)$ has a singularity at $z = 1$; also,

$$f(z) = z^2 + \sum_{n=1}^{+\infty} (z^2)^{2^n} = z^2 + f(z^2),$$

so that f has singularities at the points given by $z^2 = 1$; similarly, $f(z) = z + z^4 + f(z^4)$, so that there are singularities at the points given by $z^4 = 1$; and so on.

6. (a) Two single-valued; (b) one two-valued;

$$(c) \qquad \cos\sqrt{z} = 1 - \frac{z}{2!} + \frac{z^2}{4!} - \cdots :$$

one single-valued; (d) two single-valued; (e) one single-valued; (f) infinitely many single-valued; (g) one infinitely many-valued.

7. Put $t = \cos\phi$ and express $f(z)$ in partial fractions:

$$f(z) = -1 + \frac{1}{1 - \frac{1}{2}ze^{-i\phi}} + \frac{1}{1 - \frac{1}{2}ze^{i\phi}}.$$

Thus, for $|z| < 1$,

$$f(z) = 1 + \sum_{n=1}^{+\infty} \frac{\cos n\phi}{2^{n-1}} z^n = \sum_{n=0}^{+\infty} \frac{\cos n\phi}{2^{n-1}} z^n,$$

whence $T_n(\cos\phi) = (1/2^{n-1})\cos n\phi$.

8. *Hint.* Put $z = e^{it}$ and find the Laurent expansion of the resulting function.

$$(a) \sum_{n=1}^{+\infty} a^n \sin nt; \qquad (b) -2 \sum_{n=1}^{+\infty} \frac{a^n}{n} \cos nt.$$

9. (a) $1 - z - \dfrac{z^2}{2!} + \dfrac{z^3}{3!} + \dfrac{z^4}{4!} - \cdots, \qquad (|z| < +\infty).$

(b) $\pm z\left(1 - \dfrac{1}{z}\right)^{1/2}\left(1 - \dfrac{2}{z}\right)^{1/2} = \pm z\left(1 + \dfrac{a_1}{z} + \dfrac{a_2}{z^2} + \cdots\right),$

the series on the right being obtained by multiplying the (absolutely convergent) binomial expansions, valid for $2 < |z| < +\infty$.

(c) The function does not admit a Laurent expansion in any deleted neighbourhood of $z = \infty$ as regular branches cannot be separated in such a neighbourhood.

(d) The expansion of the general regular branch in

$$\max(|a|, |b|) < |z| < +\infty$$

is

$$i2\pi k + \left\{ \frac{b-a}{z} + \frac{b^2 - a^2}{2z^2} + \frac{b^3 - a^3}{3z^3} + \ldots \right\}$$

$$(k = 0, \pm 1, \pm 2, \ldots).$$

10. $J_n(t) = \displaystyle\sum_{k=0}^{+\infty} \frac{(-1)^k}{k!(n+k)!} \left(\frac{t}{2}\right)^{n+2k}.$

This is obtained by multiplying the (absolutely convergent) power series expansions of $\exp(\frac{1}{2}tz)$ and $\exp(-\frac{1}{2}t/z)$. From the formula for the coefficients of a Laurent expansion we have

$$J_n(t) = \frac{1}{2\pi i} \oint_C \frac{1}{z^{n+1}} \exp\left\{\frac{t}{2}\left(z - \frac{1}{z}\right)\right\} \mathrm{d}z$$

where C is any circle $|z| = r$. Take $r = 1$, putting $z = e^{i\theta}$; thus,

$$J_n(t) = \frac{1}{2\pi i} \int_0^{2\pi} e^{it\sin\theta} \cdot e^{-in\theta} \cdot i \, \mathrm{d}\theta = \frac{1}{2\pi} \int_0^{2\pi} \cos(n\theta - t\sin\theta) \, \mathrm{d}\theta.$$

(The substitution $\phi = 2\pi - \theta$ shows immediately that

$$\int_0^{2\pi} \sin(n\theta - t\sin\theta) \, \mathrm{d}\theta = 0.)$$

11. $z = 1$ is a singular point (isolated essential singularity) of $f(z)$.

12. The first function, along with its derivatives of all orders, vanishes and is *continuous* at $x = 0$; the second has $z = 0$ as its (only) singular point (isolated essential singularity).

14. (a) An isolated essential singularity at $z = 1$, and a first-order pole at each of the points $z = i2k\pi$ $(k = 0, \pm 1, \pm 2, \ldots)$;

28

$z = \infty$ is a non-isolated singularity, being a limit point of poles. (b) A first-order pole at each of the points $z = k\pi - (\pi/4)$ ($k = 0, \pm 1, \pm 2, \ldots$); $z = \infty$ is a non-isolated singularity. (c) A first-order pole at each of the points

$$z = i(2k+1)\pi \qquad (k = 0, \pm 1, \pm 2, \ldots)$$

and a non-isolated singularity at $z = \infty$. (d) An isolated essential singularity at $z = \infty$.

15. We require that the integrand have zero residue at $z = 0$: thus, $a = -2$ (Cauchy's residue theorem).

16. (a) $(1/\cos z)_{z = k\pi} = (-1)^k$.

(b) $z_k = e^{i(2k+1)\pi/n}$, $\quad \operatorname{res} f(z_k) = z_k^{2n}/(n z_k^{n-1}) = -z_k/n$;

at $z = \infty$, the residue is 0 for $n \neq 1$ and is -1 for $n = 1$.

(c) $\operatorname{res} f(-1) = (-1)^{n-1} \cdot {}^{2n}C_{n-1}$, $\quad \operatorname{res} f(\infty) = (-1)^n \cdot {}^{2n}C_{n-1}$.

(d) $\operatorname{res} f(\infty) = 0$. $\qquad$ (e) $\operatorname{res} f(\infty) = 0$.

(f) $\operatorname{res} f(-1) = e^{-1}$,

$$\operatorname{res} f(\infty) = -\left(1 - \frac{1}{1!} + \frac{1}{2!} - \frac{1}{3!} + \ldots\right) = -e^{-1}.$$

(g) $\operatorname{res} f(\infty) = (b-a) + \dfrac{b^2 - a^2}{1! \, 2} + \dfrac{b^3 - a^3}{2! \, 3} + \ldots = e^b - e^a$.

17. See Art. 48:

$$\Gamma + iQ = \oint_{c^+} \Phi'(z) \, dz = 2\pi i\left(\frac{-i}{2}\right) = \pi.$$

18. C is $|z| = n + \frac{1}{2}$. Then,

$$Q = \frac{1}{4\pi} \operatorname{Re}\left\{\oint_{c^+} F'(z) \, dz\right\} = (2n+1)q.$$

Chapter 7

1. (a) $(\pi\sqrt{2})/2$; (b) $2\pi/\sqrt{(a^2 - 1)}$; (c) Suppose $a > 0$: we get

$$\left(\frac{\pi}{\sqrt{2}}\right) e^{-a/\sqrt{2}}\left(\cos\frac{a}{\sqrt{2}} + \sin\frac{a}{\sqrt{2}}\right).$$

(d) $\pi/2$. (e) $(\pi/2) - (\pi/6)e^{-(\sqrt{3})/2}[3 \cos\frac{1}{2} + (\sqrt{3}) \sin\frac{1}{2}]$.

(f) $(\pi \sin a\lambda)/(\sin a\pi . \sin \lambda)$.   (g) $2\pi/\sqrt{3}$.   (h) $\pi/4$.   (i) $\pi^3/8$
(integrate $(\ln z)^3/(z^2+1)$ around path consisting of circles

$$|z| = R, \quad |z| = r \quad (0 < r < 1 < R)$$

together with a cut along the negative real axis between $-R$ and $-r$).

2. $f(t) = 0$ for $t < 0$, $f(t) = t$ for $t \geqslant 0$.

5. (a) $\tan z = \cot z - 2\cot 2z = 2z \displaystyle\sum_{k=1}^{+\infty} \dfrac{1}{\frac{1}{4}(2k-1)^2\pi^2 - z^2}$.

(b) $\dfrac{1}{\sin z} = \cot z + \tan\dfrac{z}{2} = \dfrac{1}{z} + 2z \displaystyle\sum_{k=1}^{+\infty} \dfrac{(-1)^k}{z^2 - k^2\pi^2}$.

(c) Replace z by $(\pi/2) - \pi z$ in (b):

$$\frac{\pi}{\cos \pi z} = \frac{(-1)}{z - \frac{1}{2}} + \sum_{k=1}^{+\infty} \frac{(-1)^k(1-2z)}{(z-k-\frac{1}{2})(z+k-\frac{1}{2})}$$

$$= 4 \sum_{k=1}^{+\infty} \frac{(-1)^k(2k-1)}{4z^2 - (2k-1)^2}.$$

(d) $\dfrac{1}{e^z - 1} = -\dfrac{1}{2} + \dfrac{i}{2}\cot\dfrac{iz}{2}$

$$= -\frac{1}{2} + \frac{1}{z} + 2z \sum_{k=1}^{+\infty} \frac{1}{z^2 + 4k^2\pi^2}.$$

6. (a) $e^z - 1 = 2ie^{z/2}\sin\dfrac{z}{2i} = e^{z/2}z \displaystyle\prod_{k=1}^{+\infty}\left(1 + \dfrac{z^2}{4\pi^2k^2}\right)$

(b) $\cos \pi z - \cos \pi z_0 = -2\sin\dfrac{\pi(z+z_0)}{2} . \sin\dfrac{\pi(z-z_0)}{2}$

$$= -\tfrac{1}{2}\pi^2(z^2 - z_0^2) \prod_{k=1}^{+\infty}\left\{\left(1 - \frac{(z+z_0)^2}{4k^2}\right)\left(1 - \frac{(z-z_0)^2}{4k^2}\right)\right\}.$$

(c) $\cosh z - \cos z = 2 \sin \dfrac{ze^{i\pi/4}}{\sqrt{2}} \cdot \sin \dfrac{ze^{-i\pi/4}}{\sqrt{2}}$

$$= z^2 \prod_{k=1}^{+\infty} \left(1 + \frac{z^4}{4k^4}\right).$$

7. Use the infinite-product expansions for $\sin z$ and

$$\cos z = \sin(\tfrac{1}{2}\pi - z)$$

to show that

$$w = U + iV = 2qi \operatorname{Ln}\left(\cot \frac{\pi z}{2d}\right) + C.$$

8. Assume the "exit space" to be a similar inverted vessel: then, $\zeta = \sin(\tfrac{1}{2}\pi z/d)$ maps the flow domain on the union of $\operatorname{Im} \zeta > 0$, $\operatorname{Im} \zeta < 0$, and a *small* neighbourhood of $\zeta = 0$; the corresponding flow in $\operatorname{Im} \zeta > 0$ is that due to a line source of strength $-2Q$ at $\zeta = 0$ (i.e. the "slot" is replaced by a *sink*); thus, the required complex potential is

$$w = \phi + i\psi = (-2Q\ln \zeta)/(2\pi) = (-Q/\pi) \ln \sin(\tfrac{1}{2}\pi z/d).$$

(*Note.* For a narrow exit channel with walls parallel to the y-axis it can be shown by the methods of the next chapter that the complex potential for the flow in the vessel tends to

$$w = (-Q/\pi) \ln \sin(\tfrac{1}{2}\pi z/d)$$

as the width of this channel becomes vanishingly small.)

9. Put $x = \sqrt{t}$. Then,

$$J = \tfrac{1}{2} \int_{0}^{+\infty} e^{-t} t^{-1/2} \, dt = \tfrac{1}{2}\Gamma(\tfrac{1}{2}) = \tfrac{1}{2}\sqrt{\pi}.$$

10. Integrate $f(\zeta) = \zeta^{z-1} e^{-\zeta}$ around the boundary of the quadrantal domain $|\zeta| < R$, $0 < \arg \zeta < \pi/2$, and let $R \to +\infty$.

(a) $\dfrac{1}{n}\Gamma\left(\dfrac{1}{n}\right) \cdot \cos\left(\dfrac{\pi}{2n}\right)$;   (b) $\dfrac{1}{n}\Gamma\left(\dfrac{1}{n}\right) \cdot \sin\left(\dfrac{\pi}{2n}\right)$;

(c) $\dfrac{1}{n-1}\Gamma\left(\dfrac{1}{n}\right) \cdot \cos\left(\dfrac{\pi}{2n}\right)$.

11. Put $t = \tau/(1+\tau)$ in the integral defining $B(p, q)$: we get

$$B(p, q) = \int\limits_{0}^{+\infty} \frac{\tau^{p-1}}{(1+\tau)^{p+q}} \, d\tau \quad (*).$$

In the integral

$$\Gamma(p+q) = \int\limits_{0}^{+\infty} t^{p+q-1} e^{-t} \, dt$$

introduce a new variable σ defined by $t = (1+\tau)\sigma$, where τ is now regarded as a constant; we get

$$\frac{1}{(1+\tau)^{p+q}} = \frac{1}{\Gamma(p+q)} \int\limits_{0}^{+\infty} \sigma^{p+q-1} e^{-(1+\tau)\sigma} \, d\sigma.$$

Substitute this result in (*) and change the order of integration:

$$B(p, q) = \frac{1}{\Gamma(p+q)} \int\limits_{0}^{+\infty} \tau^{p-1} \, d\tau \int\limits_{0}^{+\infty} \sigma^{p+q-1} e^{-(1+\tau)\sigma} \, d\sigma$$

$$= \frac{1}{\Gamma(p+q)} \int\limits_{0}^{+\infty} \sigma^{q-1} e^{-\sigma} \, d\sigma \times \int\limits_{0}^{+\infty} (\tau\sigma)^{p-1} e^{-(\tau\sigma)} \, d(\tau\sigma)$$

$$= \Gamma(p) \cdot \Gamma(q)/\Gamma(p+q).$$

12. (a) Put $t = \sin^2\phi$; we get

$$\tfrac{1}{2}B(p+\tfrac{1}{2}, q+\tfrac{1}{2}) = \tfrac{1}{2}\Gamma(p+\tfrac{1}{2}) \cdot \Gamma(q+\tfrac{1}{2})/\Gamma(p+q+1)$$
$$(\operatorname{Re} p > -\tfrac{1}{2}, \operatorname{Re} q > -\tfrac{1}{2}).$$

(b) Use (a) and formula (64):

$$\pi \Big/ \Big\{2 \sin \frac{(p+1)\pi}{2}\Big\}.$$

(c) Put $x^2 = \sin\phi$ and use (a) and (64):

$$\tfrac{1}{4}B(\tfrac{1}{4}, \tfrac{1}{2}) = \{\Gamma(\tfrac{1}{4})\}^2/\{4\sqrt{(2\pi)}\}.$$

(d) Substitute $bx^n = a\tan^2\theta$, i.e. $x = (a/b)^{1/n}\tan^{2/n}\theta$, and use (a):

$$\left(\frac{a}{b}\right)^{(n+1)/n}\frac{1}{na^p}B\left(\frac{m+1}{n},\,p-\frac{m+1}{n}\right)$$

$$= \left(\frac{a}{b}\right)^{(n+1)/n}\frac{1}{na^p}\Gamma\left(\frac{m+1}{n}\right)\Gamma\left(p-\frac{m+1}{n}\right)\Big/\Gamma(p).$$

Chapter 8

1. (a) $\zeta = e^{\pi z/H}$ maps the upper half of the given domain D onto $\operatorname{Im}\zeta > 0$, the auxiliary cut $[-d, d]$ mapping on the segment $[e^{-\pi d/H}, e^{\pi d/H}]$. By the symmetry principle, the same function maps D on the domain formed from the ζ-plane by omitting the segments $[-\infty, e^{-\pi d/H}]$, $[e^{\pi d/H}, +\infty]$ of the ξ-axis. It remains to apply the mappings

$$\omega = \left(\zeta - \cosh\frac{\pi d}{H}\right)\Big/\sinh\frac{\pi d}{H}, \quad w = \omega + \sqrt{(\omega^2 - 1)};$$

or, better,

$$\omega = (\zeta - e^{\pi d/H})/(\zeta - e^{-\pi d/H}), \quad w = \sqrt{\omega}$$

(where $\omega = -1 \leftrightarrow w = i$).

(b) Isolate the domain $-\pi/4 < \arg z < 0$ by auxiliary cuts of unit length. Under the successive mappings $\zeta = 1/z$, $s = \zeta^4$, $t = s + \sqrt{(s^2 - 1)}$ (where $s = i \leftrightarrow t = i(1 + \sqrt{2})$), $w = \sqrt[4]{t}$ (where $t = 16i \leftrightarrow w = 2e^{i\pi/8}$), this sectoral domain is mapped on

$$0 < \arg w < \pi/4, \quad |w| > 1,$$

the auxiliary cuts corresponding with the boundary rays $w = r$, $w = re^{i\pi/4}$ ($1 \leqslant r \leqslant +\infty$). By the symmetry principle it follows that the resultant mapping function transforms the *given* domain into $|w| > 1$; the completion will be clear. [We have

$$w = (1/z)\sqrt[4]{\{1 + \sqrt{(1 - z^8)}\}} \text{ or } z = (w\sqrt[4]{2})/\sqrt[4]{(1 + w^8)}.]$$

2 and 3. See Nehari, *Conformal Mapping*, Chap. V; note that, in this reference, tne expression for λ at the top of page 194 *should* read $\Sigma\,(\mu_\nu/a_\nu)$, *not* $\Sigma\,(\mu_\nu/\alpha_\nu)$. Associated results are given by Jeffreys and Jeffreys (*Mathematical Physics*, Ch. 13).

4. (a) As shown in Exercise 13(d), Chap. 3, $\zeta = \sqrt{(z - \frac{1}{2}p)}$ maps the parabola on the line $\operatorname{Im}\zeta = \sqrt{(p/2)}$. (We suppose $p > 0$ and choose the branch which is regular in $\operatorname{Im}z > 0$ and equals $e^{i3\pi/8}\sqrt{(p/2)}$ at $z = ip/2$.) This function gives a one–one mapping of the *upper half* of the given z-domain onto the half-strip $\xi > 0$,

$0 < \eta < \sqrt{(p/2)}$; this half-strip is then mapped on the half-plane Im $\omega > 0$. An auxiliary cut $[0, +\infty]$ in the z-plane is thereby mapped on some segment of the real axis in the ω-plane. The continuation of the resultant mapping function into the *given* z-domain thus transforms this domain into a suitably-cut ω-plane. The remaining steps will be clear.

(*b*) Take $a, b > 0$. $Z = z/\sqrt{(a^2+b^2)}$ maps the hyperbola on one with foci at $Z = \pm 1$. Then $Z = \frac{1}{2}(\zeta + \zeta^{-1})$, i.e.

$$\zeta = Z + \sqrt{(Z^2 - 1)}$$

(where $Z = i \leftrightarrow \zeta = (1+\sqrt{2})i$), maps the *upper half* of the enclosed Z-domain onto a domain $|\zeta| > 1$, $0 < \arg \zeta < \alpha$, where $0 < \alpha < \frac{1}{2}\pi$ and $\tan \alpha = b/a$. The remaining steps will be clear.

(*c*) Take $a > b > 0$. $Z = z/\sqrt{(a^2-b^2)}$ maps the ellipse on one with foci at $Z = \pm 1$. The *upper half* of the enclosed Z-domain is then mapped on the semi-annulus $1 < |\zeta| < (a+b)/\sqrt{(a^2-b^2)}$, $0 < \arg \zeta < \pi$ by $Z = \frac{1}{2}(\zeta + \zeta^{-1})$, i.e. by $\zeta = Z + \sqrt{(Z^2-1)}$ (where $Z = i \leftrightarrow \zeta = i(1+\sqrt{2})$); $\omega = \ln \zeta$ maps this domain onto a rectangular domain, and it follows from the symmetry principle that the continuation of the compound mapping function into the *whole* of the given z-domain transforms this domain into a certain rectangular domain in the ω-plane. Use is then made of the elliptic function sn.

5. (*a*) Take auxiliary cuts along the bisector $y = x$ and use $\zeta = z^2$. The remaining steps will be clear.

(*b*) Take auxiliary cuts along the bisector $x = 0$ and apply $\zeta = (z-i)/(z+i)$ to the left half of the given z-domain. The remaining steps will be clear.

(*c*) Take auxiliary cuts along the bisector $x = 0$ and apply $\zeta = z^2$ to the right half of the given domain. Bisect the resulting domain by taking an auxiliary cut along the positive ξ-axis. The remaining steps will be clear.

6. Bisect the given domain by an auxiliary barrier along the segment $[\frac{1}{2}i, i]$. Then, under the sequence of mappings $\zeta = z^2$, $s = (\zeta - \frac{1}{4})/(1 - \frac{1}{4}\zeta)$, $t = \sqrt{s}$ (where $s = \frac{1}{2} \leftrightarrow t = 1/\sqrt{2}$),

$$\omega = \frac{1}{2}(t + t^{-1}),$$

the right-hand half of the given domain is mapped on the right half-plane Re $\omega > 0$, the auxiliary barrier being mapped on a segment of the imaginary axis. The remaining steps will be clear.

7. (a) Take $z = +\infty, 0, i(+\infty), -(h+iH) \leftrightarrow w = -a, 0, 1, \infty$, respectively. Then,

$$z = A \int_0^w \frac{\sqrt{w}}{(w-1)(w+a)}\,dw,$$

where $h = iA\pi/(1+a)$ and $-iH = +\pi A(\sqrt{a})/(1+a)$—i.e. $a = H^2/h^2$ and $A = (H^2+h^2)/(i\pi h)$.

(b) Take auxiliary cut along negative x-axis. Then, with

$$z = -\infty, +\infty, ih \leftrightarrow \zeta = \infty, -1, 0,$$

the *upper* half of the given domain is mapped onto Im $\zeta > 0$ by

$$z = A \int_0^\zeta \zeta^{1-\alpha}(\zeta+1)^{-1}\,d\zeta + B,$$

where $B = ih$, and $-ih = A(e^{i\pi})^{1-\alpha}i\pi$, i.e. $A = (h/\pi)e^{i\pi\alpha}$. The auxiliary cut corresponds with an infinite segment of the ξ-axis. Use the reflection principle; the remaining steps will be clear.

(c) Take

$$z = -\infty, -h_3-i(h_2-h_1), i(-\infty), 0, +\infty \leftrightarrow w = a, \infty, -b, 0, 1,$$

respectively. Then,

$$z = A \int_0^w (\sqrt{w})(w-a)^{-1}(w+b)^{-1}(w-1)^{-1}\,dw,$$

where

$$h_1 = A\pi/\{(a-1)(b+1)\}, \qquad h_2 = (\pi A\sqrt{a})/\{(a+b)(a-1)\},$$
$$h_3 = (\pi A\sqrt{b})/\{(a+b)(b+1)\}.$$

(d) The vertices $z = -a, \infty, ia, \infty$ (corresponding to a *positive* circuit) are mapped on the respective points $w = 0, k, 1, \infty$ $(0 < k < 1)$, the corresponding interior angles being $2\pi, \frac{1}{2}\pi, 2\pi, \frac{3}{2}\pi$. Then,

$$z = A \int_{(L)}^w \mkern-18mu {}_0\, w(w-k)^{-3/2}(w-1)\,dw - a.$$

For $w = u > 1$, the angle of rotation in the mapping is

$$\arg(dz/dw) = -\pi/4;$$

hence, $A = re^{-i\pi/4}$ $(r > 0)$. To find r and k, use the fact that $z = ia$ for $w = 1$: let L consist of the *upper* half C of the circle $|w-k| = k$ and the line segment K joining $w = 2k$ to $w = k$; we get

$$\int_{(L)}^{1} = \frac{8}{3}k^{3/2} + ik^{1/2}\left(4 - \frac{16k}{3}\right) + (1-k)^{1/2}\left(\frac{16k}{3} - \frac{4}{3}\right) - \frac{8}{3}k^{3/2} = p+iq$$

(say). As $a(i+1) = re^{-i\pi/4}$ $(p+iq)$, it follows that $k = \frac{1}{4}$, and $r = 3a/(2\sqrt{2})$.

(e) Vertices $z = \infty$, 0, $he^{ia\pi}$, 0 (*positive* circuit) map on the respective points $w = \infty$. $-a$, -1, 0 $(a > 1)$; the corresponding interior angles are π, $\pi(1-\alpha)$, 2π, $\pi\alpha$. Then,

$$z = A \int_{0}^{w} (w+a)^{-\alpha}(w+1)w^{\alpha-1}\,dw\ .$$

For $w = u > 0$, $\arg(dz/dw) = 0$; hence $A = r$ (> 0). Also, $z = he^{ia\pi}$ for $w = -1$; putting $w = \rho e^{i\pi}$ we see that r is given by

$$h = r \int_{0}^{1} \frac{(1-\rho)\,d\rho}{(a-\rho)^{\alpha}\rho^{1-\alpha}}\ .$$

9. First make auxiliary cut (I) along y-axis; *then* make auxiliary cut (II) along positive x-axis. Denote given domain by D and the respective sub-domains in $\operatorname{Re} z > 0$ and in the first quadrant by D_1 and D_2. Consider D_2: let $z = \infty$, ih, $d+ih$, ih, 0 (*positive* circuit) map on $\zeta = \infty$, $-b$, $-a$, -1, 0, respectively $(b > a > 1)$; the corresponding interior angles are $\frac{1}{2}\pi$, $\frac{1}{2}\pi$, 2π, $\frac{1}{2}\pi$, $\frac{1}{2}\pi$, whence

$$z = A \int_{0}^{\zeta} (\zeta+b)^{-1/2}(\zeta+a)(\zeta+1)^{-1/2}\zeta^{-1/2}\,d\zeta.$$

For $\zeta = \xi > 0$, $\arg(dz/d\zeta) = 0$; thus, $A = r > 0$. The points $z = ih$, $d+ih$, ih correspond with $\zeta = -1$, $-a$, $-b$; thus, putting

$\zeta = \rho e^{i\pi}$ $(\rho > 0)$, we get the following three equations determining r, a, b:

$$h = r \int_0^1 \{(a-\rho)/\sqrt{[(b-\rho)(1-\rho)\rho]}\} \, d\rho,$$

$$d = r \int_1^a \{(a-\rho)/\sqrt{[(b-\rho)(\rho-1)\rho]}\} \, d\rho,$$

$$d = r \int_a^b \{(\rho-a)/\sqrt{[(b-\rho)(\rho-1)\rho]}\} \, d\rho.$$

The cut II maps on the positive ξ-axis. Use the reflection principle to show that the continuation of the mapping function maps the ζ-plane, cut along the negative real axis, onto D_1. Take $\omega = \sqrt{\zeta}$ and make a second application of the reflection principle. The final step is trivial: $w = i\omega$. We get $a_1 = -\sqrt{b}$, $a_2 = -\sqrt{a}$, $a_3 = \sqrt{a}$, $a_4 = \sqrt{b}$.

10. (a) Take auxiliary cuts, first along the y-axis and then along the rays $(y = h, \ a \leqslant x \leqslant +\infty)$, $(y = 0, \ a \leqslant x \leqslant +\infty)$. Make use of the method of Example 4, Art. 83, and the symmetry principle.

(b) Use $\zeta = e^{2\pi z/h}$ to map the strip $0 < y < h \ (-\infty < x < +\infty)$ onto the ζ-plane with a cut along the positive real axis; the given segments correspond with the segments $[e^{-2\pi a/h}, \ e^{2\pi a/h}]$ of the upper and lower edges of this cut. Use $\omega = A\zeta + B$ to map these segments on the upper and lower edges of the cut between $\omega = -1$ and $\omega = +1$ $(A = \operatorname{cosech}(2\pi a/h)$, $B = -\coth(2\pi a/h))$. Then, using $\omega = \frac{1}{2}(w + w^{-1})$ (i.e. $w = \omega + \sqrt{(\omega^2 - 1)}$, where

$$\omega = i \leftrightarrow w = i(1 + \sqrt{2})),$$

and applying the symmetry principle, we get the required many-sheeted mapping.

INDEX